Instructor's Solutions Manual

Cheryl V. Roberts
Laurel Technical Services

Intermediate Algebra

THIRD EDITION

John Tobey   Jeffrey Slater

PRENTICE HALL, Upper Saddle River, NJ 07458

Senior Editor: Karin Wagner
Production Editor: Bob Walters
Supplement Cover Designer: Liz Nemeth
Special Projects Manager: Barbara A. Murray
Supplement Cover Manager: Paul Gourhan
Manufacturing Buyer: Alan Fischer
Assistant Editor: Audra Walsh

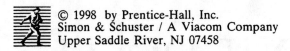 © 1998 by Prentice-Hall, Inc.
Simon & Schuster / A Viacom Company
Upper Saddle River, NJ 07458

Printed in the United States of America

10 9 8 7 6 5 4 3 2

ISBN 0-13-872755-4

Prentice-Hall International (UK) Limited, *London*
Prentice-Hall of Australia Pty. Limited, *Sydney*
Prentice-Hall Canada, Inc., *London*
Prentice-Hall Hispanoamericana, S.A., *Mexico*
Prentice-Hall of India Private Limited, *New Delhi*
Prentice-Hall of Japan, Inc., *Tokyo*
Simon & Schuster Asia Pte. Ltd., *Singapore*
Editora Prentice-Hall do Brazil, Ltda., *Rio de Janeiro*

Contents

Chapter 1

2. $\sqrt{9} = 3, 3, \dfrac{6}{2} = 3, 0$

4. $30 \div (-6) + 3 - 2(-5)$
$= -5 + 3 + 10$
$= 8$

6. $3^3 - \sqrt{4(-5) + 29}$
$= 27 - \sqrt{-20 + 29}$
$= 27 - \sqrt{9}$
$= 27 - 3$
$= 24$

8. $(-7a^2 b)(-2a^0 b^3 c^2)(-a^{-3})$
$= (-7)(-2)(-1)a^{2+0-3}b^{1+3}c^2$
$= -14a^{-1}b^4 c^2$
$= -\dfrac{14b^4 c^2}{a}$

10. $\dfrac{4x^3 y^2}{-16x^2 y^{-3}}$
$= -\dfrac{1}{4}x^{3-2}y^{2-(-3)}$
$= -\dfrac{xy^5}{4}$

12. $(-2x^3 y^{-2})^{-2}$
$= (-2)^{-2}(x^3)^{-2}(y^{-2})^{-2}$
$= \dfrac{1}{(-2)^2}x^{-6}y^4$
$= \dfrac{y^4}{4x^6}$

14. $8.95 \times 10^7 = 89,500,000$

16. $3ab^2(-2a^2 + 3ab^2 - 1)$
$= (3ab^2)(-2a^2) + (3ab^2)(3ab^2) - (3ab^2)(1)$
$= -6a^3 b^2 + 9a^2 b^4 - 3ab^2$

18. $5a^2 - 3ab + 2b$
$= 5(-3)^2 - 3(-3)(-2) + 2(-2)$
$= 45 - 18 - 4$
$= 23$

20. $T = 2\pi\sqrt{\dfrac{L}{g}}$
$= 2(3.14)\sqrt{\dfrac{512}{32}}$
$= 6.28\sqrt{16}$
$= 6.28(4)$
$= 25.12$
$= 25.12 \text{ sec}$

1.1 Exercises

2. A rational number can be written as $\dfrac{x}{y}$, where x and y are integers. Rational numbers can be thought of as fractional parts of integers.

4. A repeating decimal contains digits that repeat without end.

6. Whole, Integer, Rational, Real

8. Natural, Whole, Integer, Rational, Real

10. Rational, Real

12. Rational, Real

14. Irrational, Real

16. Irrational, Real

18. Rational, Real

20. $-25, -\dfrac{28}{7} = -4$

22. $0, 9$

24. $-\pi, \dfrac{\pi}{4}, \sqrt{3}$

26. $-25, -\dfrac{28}{7}, -\dfrac{18}{5}, -0.763, -0.333\ldots$

28. $1, 2, 3, 4, 5, 6, 7$

30. $-4, -3, -2$

32. True

34. False

36. Associative Property of Addition

38. Inverse Property of Multiplication

40. Identity Property of Addition

42. Commutative Property of Multiplication

44. Distributive Property of Multiplication over Addition

46. Commutative Property of Addition

48. Inverse Property of Multiplication

50. Associative Property of Multiplication

52. Associative Property of Addition

54. Commutative Property of Addition

56. Distributive Property of Multiplication over Addition

58. Inverse Property of Addition

60. a. $\dfrac{3}{8} = 0.375$

   37.5%

   b. $\dfrac{5}{8} = 0.625$

   62.5%

1.2 Exercises

2. $|12| = 12$

4. $|-23| = 23$

6. $\left|3\dfrac{1}{2}\right| = 3\dfrac{1}{2}$

8. $|9 - 14| = |-5| = 5$

10. $|-b| = b$

12. $-6 + (-12) = -18$

14. $-6 - (+4) = -6 + (-4) = -10$

16. $3 - 7 - 6 + 1$
$= 3 + (-7) + (-6) + 1$
$= 4 + (-13)$
$= -9$

18. $(-24) \div (4) = -6$

20. $(-16)(-2) = 32$

22. $-12.6 + 8.3 = -4.3$

24. $1.4 - (-3.6)$
$= 1.4 + 3.6$
$= 5$

26. $-\dfrac{1}{3} + \dfrac{3}{4} = -\dfrac{4}{12} + \dfrac{9}{12} = \dfrac{5}{12}$

28. $-\dfrac{5}{6} + \dfrac{1}{8} = -\dfrac{20}{24} + \dfrac{3}{24} = -\dfrac{17}{24}$

30. $-\dfrac{2}{5} - \dfrac{3}{7}$
$= -\dfrac{2}{5} + \left(-\dfrac{3}{7}\right)$
$= -\dfrac{14}{35} + \left(-\dfrac{15}{35}\right)$
$= -\dfrac{29}{35}$

32. $(18)\left(-\dfrac{1}{2}\right)(3)(-1) = 27$

34. $-12 - (-3)(2)$
$= -12 - (-6)$
$= -12 + 6$
$= -6$

36. $\dfrac{\frac{2}{7}}{-\frac{3}{5}} = \dfrac{2}{7} \cdot \left(-\dfrac{5}{3}\right) = -\dfrac{10}{21}$

38. $-\dfrac{\frac{3}{4}}{-24} = -\dfrac{3}{4} \cdot \left(\dfrac{1}{-24}\right) = \dfrac{1}{32}$

40. $8(0.5) - 9 \div (-0.3)$
$= 4 + 30$
$= 34$

42. $-6.2 + 6.2 = 0$

44. Not possible

46. $\dfrac{0}{4} = 0$

48. $\dfrac{-5+5}{6} = \dfrac{0}{6} = 0$

50. $\dfrac{-6+(-6)}{-18} = \dfrac{-12}{-18} = \dfrac{2}{3}$

52. $12 - 3 - (-4) + 6 - 5 - 8$
$= 12 + (-3) + 4 + 6 + (-5) + (-8)$
$= 22 + (-16)$
$= 6$

54. $\dfrac{8(-2)+6}{1-6}$
$= \dfrac{-16+6}{-5}$
$= \dfrac{-10}{-5}$
$= 2$

56. $-8(-4) + 3(-2) + 5 - 7$
$= 32 - 6 + 5 - 7$
$= 37 - 13$
$= 24$

58. $100 \div 2 \div 5 + 3(-2) - (-6)$
$= 50 \div 5 - 6 + 6$
$= 10 - 6 + 6$
$= 10$

60. $\dfrac{72 \div (-4) + 3(-4)}{5 - (-5)}$
$= \dfrac{-18 - 12}{10}$
$= \dfrac{-30}{10}$
$= -3$

62. $(-2.5)(4) - (3.2)(2)$
$= -10 - 6.4$
$= -16.4$

64. $(1.783)(2.5725) - (1.0526)(-5.9812)$
$= 4.5867675 + 6.29581112$
$= 10.88257862$

66. Either two quantities are negative or all are positive.

Cumulative Review Problems

68. Associative Property of Multiplication

70. $\left\{-16, 0, \dfrac{19}{2}, 9.36, 10.\overline{5}\right\}$

72. $12\dfrac{1}{2} + 2 \times 6 + 5 \times 18\dfrac{3}{4} + 7 \times 10 + 3 \times 25$
$= 12\dfrac{1}{2} + 12 + 93\dfrac{3}{4} + 70 + 75$
$= 263\dfrac{1}{4}$

Two dollars and $63\dfrac{1}{4}$ cents

1.3 Exercises

2. Negative

4. No, $-a^n$ means the opposite of a^n. If a^n is negative then $-a^n$ will be positive.

6. The principal square root is the non-negative square root.

8. $5 \cdot 5 \cdot 5 \cdot 5 \cdot 5 \cdot 5 \cdot 5 \cdot 5 \cdot 5 = 5^9$

10. $y \cdot y \cdot y \cdot y \cdot y \cdot y \cdot y = y^7$

12. $(-8)(-8)(-8) = (-8)^3$

14. $2^5 = 2 \cdot 2 \cdot 2 \cdot 2 \cdot 2 = 32$

16. $(-5)^2 = (-5)(-5) = 25$

18. $-2^4 = -1 \cdot 2 \cdot 2 \cdot 2 \cdot 2 = -16$

20. $(-3)^2 = (-3)(-3) = 9$

22. $-3^2 = -9$

24. $\left(\dfrac{3}{4}\right)^2 = \left(\dfrac{3}{4}\right)\left(\dfrac{3}{4}\right) = \dfrac{9}{16}$

26. $\left(-\dfrac{1}{6}\right)^3 = \left(-\dfrac{1}{6}\right)\left(-\dfrac{1}{6}\right)\left(-\dfrac{1}{6}\right) = -\dfrac{1}{216}$

28. $(0.7)^2 = (0.7)(0.7) = 0.49$

30. $(0.05)^3 = (0.05)(0.05)(0.05) = 0.000125$

32. $(-1.2)^4 = (-1.2)(-1.2)(-1.2)(-1.2) = 2.0736$

34. $\sqrt{36} = \sqrt{6^2} = 6$

36. $\sqrt{49} = \sqrt{7^2} = 7$

38. $-\sqrt{64} = -\sqrt{8^2} = -8$

40. $\sqrt{\dfrac{1}{100}} = \sqrt{\left(\dfrac{1}{10}\right)^2} = \dfrac{1}{10}$

42. $\sqrt{0.25} = \sqrt{(0.5)^2} = 0.5$

44. $\sqrt{0.0016} = \sqrt{(0.04)^2} = 0.04$

46. $\sqrt{8101-1}$
$= \sqrt{8100}$
$= \sqrt{90^2}$
$= 90$

48. $\sqrt{5+4} = \sqrt{9} = 3$

50. $\sqrt{\dfrac{1}{9} + \dfrac{3}{9}} = \sqrt{\dfrac{4}{9}} = \dfrac{2}{3}$

52. Does not exist

54. $6(2-4)+5$
$= 6(-2)+5$
$= -12+5$
$= -7$

56. $27 \div 3 \cdot 2 - (-1)$
$= 9 \cdot 2 + 1$
$= 18 + 1$
$= 19$

58. $\sqrt{(-3)^2 + (2)^2 + 3}$
$= \sqrt{9+4+3}$
$= \sqrt{16}$
$= 4$

60. $(8-6-7)^2 \div 5 - 6$
$= (-5)^2 \div 5 - 6$
$= 25 \div 5 - 6$
$= 5 - 6$
$= -1$

62. $2\sqrt{16} + (-4)^2 - 3$
$= 2(4) + 16 - 3$
$= 8 + 16 - 3$
$= 21$

64. $3\sqrt{25} + 2(0) - 8$
$= 3(5) + 2(0) - 8$
$= 15 + 0 - 8$
$= 7$

66. $8 + 5[6 - (3+4)]$
$= 8 + 5(6-7)$
$= 8 + 5(-1)$
$= 8 - 5$
$= 3$

68. $9[(7-2)+6]$
$= 9(5+6)$
$= 9(11)$
$= 99$

70. $\dfrac{2^3 + 3^2 - 5}{4}$
$= \dfrac{8+9-5}{4}$
$= \dfrac{12}{4}$
$= 3$

72. $\dfrac{4 + 2(3^2 - 12)}{-2}$
$= \dfrac{4 + 2(9-12)}{-2}$
$= \dfrac{4 + 2(-3)}{-2}$
$= \dfrac{4-6}{-2}$
$= \dfrac{-2}{-2}$
$= 1$

74. $\dfrac{\sqrt{(-5)^2 - 3 + 14}}{|19 - 6 + 3 - 25|}$

$= \dfrac{\sqrt{25 - 3 + 14}}{|-9|}$

$= \dfrac{\sqrt{36}}{9}$

$= \dfrac{6}{9} = \dfrac{2}{3}$

76. $\dfrac{\left|6 - 2^5\right| - 4}{19 + 3}$

$= \dfrac{|6 - 32| - 4}{22}$

$= \dfrac{|-26| - 4}{22}$

$= \dfrac{26 - 4}{22}$

$= \dfrac{22}{22}$

$= 1$

78. $(0.325)^4 = 0.0111566406$

80. $\sqrt{13,593,969} = 3687$

Cumulative Review Problems

82. Distributive Property

84. $\dfrac{81,000}{27,000} = 3$

3 times greater

1.4 Exercises

2. $4^{-3} = \dfrac{1}{4^3} = \dfrac{1}{64}$

4. $y^{-4} = \dfrac{1}{y^4}$

6. $\left(\dfrac{4}{5}\right)^{-2} = \dfrac{1}{\left(\frac{4}{5}\right)^2} = \dfrac{1}{\frac{16}{25}} = \dfrac{25}{16}$

8. $\left(-\dfrac{1}{5}\right)^{-3} = \dfrac{1}{\left(-\frac{1}{5}\right)^3} = \dfrac{1}{-\frac{1}{125}} = -125$

10. $\left(\dfrac{1}{y}\right)^{-5} = \dfrac{1}{\left(\frac{1}{y}\right)^5} = \dfrac{1}{\frac{1}{y^5}} = y^5$

12. $y^{10} \cdot y = y^{10+1} = y^{11}$

14. $y^5 \cdot y \cdot y^0 \cdot y^3 = y^{5+1+0+3} = y^9$

16. $2^{18} \cdot 2^{10} = 2^{18+10} = 2^{28}$

18. $(5y^2)(3y) = (5)(3)y^{2+1} = 15y^3$

20. $(-20a^3b^2)(5ab)$

$= (-20)(5)a^{3+1}b^{2+1}$

$= -100a^4b^3$

22. $(4^0 x^2 y^3)(-3x^0 y^6)$

$= (1)(-3)x^{2+0}y^{3+6}$

$= -3x^2 y^9$

24. $(-4a^4b^{-3})(a^{-4}b)$

$= (-4)(1)a^{4-4}b^{-3+1}$

$= -4b^{-2}$

$= -\dfrac{4}{b^2}$

26. $(-5x^{-8}y^{-2})(3x^{-5}y^2)$

$= (-5)(3)x^{-8+(-5)}y^{-2+2}$

$= -15x^{-13}y^0$

$= -\dfrac{15}{x^{13}}$

28. $\dfrac{y^{18}}{y^{20}} = y^{18-20} = y^{-2} = \dfrac{1}{y^2}$

30. $\dfrac{x^4}{x^7} = x^{4-7} = x^{-3} = \dfrac{1}{x^3}$

32. $\dfrac{3^{16}}{3^{18}} = 3^{16-18} = 3^{-2} = \dfrac{1}{3^2} = \dfrac{1}{9}$

34. $\dfrac{4y^3}{8y} = \dfrac{1}{2}y^{3-1} = \dfrac{1}{2}y^2$ or $\dfrac{y^2}{2}$

36. $\dfrac{-64x^2y}{4x^2}$

$= -16x^{2-2}y$

$= -16y$

38. $\dfrac{-15x^8yz^{-4}}{-35x^0y^5z^{-2}}$

$= \dfrac{3}{7}x^{8-0}y^{1-5}z^{-4-(-2)}$

$= \dfrac{3}{7}x^8y^{-4}z^{-2}$

$= \dfrac{3x^8}{7y^4z^2}$

40. $\dfrac{21x^{-12}y^{-3}}{-14x^{-16}y^{-8}}$

$= -\dfrac{3}{2}x^{-12-(-16)}y^{-3-(-8)}$

$= -\dfrac{3}{2}x^4y^5$

42. $(a^5)^7 = a^{5\cdot7} = a^{35}$

44. $(2xy^6)^5 = 2^5x^5(y^6)^5 = 32x^5y^{30}$

46. $\left(\dfrac{x^3}{y^5z^8}\right)^4$

$= \dfrac{(x^3)^4}{(y^5)^4(z^8)^4}$

$= \dfrac{x^{12}}{y^{20}z^{32}}$

48. $\left(\dfrac{-5x^4yz^3}{z^2}\right)^2$

$= \dfrac{25x^8y^2z^6}{z^4}$

$= 25x^8y^2z^2$

50. $\left(\dfrac{5a^3bc^0}{-3a^{-2}b^5}\right)^3$

$= \dfrac{125a^9b^3c^0}{-27a^{-6}b^{15}}$

$= -\dfrac{125a^{15}}{27b^{12}}$

52. $\left(\dfrac{3x^{-4}y}{x^{-3}y^2}\right)^{-2}$

$= \dfrac{3^{-2}x^8y^{-2}}{x^6y^{-4}}$

$= \dfrac{x^8y^4}{3^2x^6y^2}$

$= \dfrac{x^2y^2}{9}$

54. $(x^3y^{-2})^{-2}(5x^{-5}y)^2$

$= (x^{-6}y^4)(5^2x^{-10}y^2)$

$= 25x^{-6-10}y^{4+2}$

$= \dfrac{25y^6}{x^{16}}$

56. $\dfrac{(-5ab^3)^{-2}}{(-2a^8b^{-3})^3}$

$= \dfrac{(-5)^{-2}a^{-2}b^{-6}}{(-2)^3a^{24}b^{-9}}$

$= \dfrac{b^9}{(-5)^2(-2)^3a^2a^{24}b^6}$

$= \dfrac{b^9}{(25)(-8)a^{26}b^6}$

$= -\dfrac{b^3}{200a^{26}}$

58. $\dfrac{3^4a^{-3}b^2c^{-4}}{3^3a^4b^{-2}c^0}$

$= 3^{4-3}a^{-3-4}b^{2-(-2)}c^{-4-0}$

$= 3a^{-7}b^4c^{-4}$

$= \dfrac{3b^4}{a^7c^4}$

60. $(2x^{-3}y^2)^{-3}$

$= 2^{-3}x^9y^{-6}$

$= \dfrac{x^9}{2^3y^6}$

$= \dfrac{x^9}{8y^6}$

62. $\left(\dfrac{2^{-1}y^{-5}}{x^{-6}}\right)^{-2}$

$= \dfrac{2^2 y^{10}}{x^{12}}$

$= \dfrac{4y^{10}}{x^{12}}$

64. $\dfrac{b^{-2}c^4 d^0}{b^{-3}c^4 d^{-3}}$

$= b^{-2+3}c^{4-4}d^{0+3}$

$= b^1 c^0 d^3$

$= bd^3$

66. $\left(\dfrac{25x^{-1}y^{-6}}{5x^{-4}y^{-6}}\right)^{-2}$

$= (5x^3 y^0)^{-2}$

$= 5^{-2}x^{-6}y^0$

$= \dfrac{1}{5^2 x^6}$

$= \dfrac{1}{25x^6}$

68. $\dfrac{9^{-2}\cdot 8^{-10}\cdot 4^0}{9^{-1}\cdot 8^{-9}}$

$= 9^{-2-(-1)}\cdot 8^{-10-(-9)}$

$= 9^{-1}\cdot 8^{-1}$

$= \dfrac{1}{9\cdot 8} = \dfrac{1}{72}$

70. $(-4x^3 y^{-5})(2x^{-8}y^{-5})$

$= -8x^{-5}y^{-10}$

$= -\dfrac{8}{x^5 y^{10}}$

72. $\dfrac{(4a^2 b^3)^2}{(2ab)^{-2}}$

$= \dfrac{16a^4 b^6}{2^{-2}a^{-2}b^{-2}}$

$= (16a^4 b^6)(4a^2 b^2)$

$= 64a^6 b^8$

74. $\dfrac{1.98364\times 10^{-14}}{4.32571\times 10^{-16}}$

$= 0.458569807\times 10^2$

$= 4.58569807\times 10^1$

76. $\dfrac{300,000}{200} = 1500$

Moths and butterflies are 1500 times more sensitive.

78. $1230 = 1.23\times 10^3$

80. $5,318,000,000 = 5.318\times 10^9$

82. $0.093 = 9.3\times 10^{-2}$

84. $0.000007116 = 7.116\times 10^{-6}$

86. $2.75\times 10^6 = 2,750,000$

88. $7.07\times 10^{-3} = 0.00707$

90. $6.668\times 10^{-9} = 0.000000006668$

92. $(3.1\times 10^{-5})(2.0\times 10^8)$

$= (3.1)(2.0)\times 10^{-5+8}$

$= 6.2\times 10^3$

94. $\dfrac{4.6\times 10^{-12}}{2.3\times 10^5}$

$= \left(\dfrac{4.6}{2.3}\right)\times 10^{-12-5}$

$= 2\times 10^{-17}$

96. $(5.87\times 10^{12})(5\times 10^3)$

$(5.87)(5)\times 10^{12+3}$

$= 29.35\times 10^{15}$

$= 2.935\times 10^{16}$

2.935×10^{16} miles

98. $\dfrac{4.90\times 10^{11}}{2\times 10^4}$

$= \left(\dfrac{4.90}{2}\right)\times 10^{11-4}$

$= 2.45\times 10^7$

2.45×10^7 sec

Cumulative Review Problems

100. $5 + 2(-3) + 12 \div (-6)$
$= 5 - 6 - 2$
$= -3$

102. $\dfrac{5 + 3 - 4}{32 \div (-8)}$
$= \dfrac{4}{-4} = -1$

1.5 Exercises

2. $3y^3 z$

4. $5x^3; 3x^2; -2y; -8$

6. $1; 2; 8$

8. $6; -1; -6$

10. $-\dfrac{1}{2}; -\dfrac{10}{3}; -\dfrac{4}{5}$

12. $7ab - 5ab$
$= (7 - 5)ab$
$= 2ab$

14. $2a - 8a + 3b + 5a$
$= (2 - 8 + 5)a + 3b$
$= -a + 3b$

16. $y^2 + 5y - 4y - 5y^2$
$= (1 - 5)y^2 + (5 - 4)y$
$= -4y^2 + y$

18. $2a - ab - 2a - ab$
$= (2 - 2)a + (-1 - 1)ab$
$= -2ab$

20. $5x^2 - 8x - 10x^2 + 8$
$= (5 - 10)x^2 - 8x + 8$
$= -5x^2 - 8x + 8$

22. $0.7x^2 - 6x + 0.4x^2$
$= (0.7 + 0.4)x^2 - 6x$
$= 1.1x^2 - 6x$

24. $\dfrac{1}{4}x + \dfrac{1}{3}y - \dfrac{1}{12}x + \dfrac{1}{6}y$
$= \left(\dfrac{1}{4} - \dfrac{1}{12}\right)x + \left(\dfrac{1}{3} + \dfrac{1}{6}\right)y$
$= \dfrac{x}{6} + \dfrac{y}{2}$

26. $\dfrac{1}{2}x^2 + 6y - \dfrac{1}{7}x^2 - 8y$
$= \left(\dfrac{1}{2} - \dfrac{1}{7}\right)x^2 + (6 - 8)y$
$= \dfrac{5}{14}x^2 - 2y$

28. $4y^2 - 2.1y - 8.6y - 2.2y^2$
$= (4 - 2.2)y^2 + (-2.1 - 8.6)y$
$= 1.8y^2 - 10.7y$

30. $12mn + 8m^2 n - 6mn^2 + mn - 16m^2 n - 4mn^2$
$= (12 + 1)mn + (8 - 16)m^2 n + (-6 - 4)mn^2$
$= 13mn - 8m^2 n - 10mn^2$

32. $5y(3x - 2)$
$= (5y)(3x) - (5y)(2)$
$= 15xy - 10y$

34. $-2y(y^2 - 3y + 1)$
$= -2y(y^2) - 2y(-3y) - 2y(1)$
$= -2y^3 + 6y^2 - 2y$

36. $-6(4a + 2ab - 7b^2)$
$= -6(4a) - 6(2ab) - 6(-7b^2)$
$= -24a - 12ab + 42b^2$

38. $4ab(a^2 - 6ab - 2b^2)$
$= 4ab(a^2) - 4ab(6ab) - 4ab(2b^2)$
$= 4a^3 b - 24a^2 b^2 - 8ab^3$

40. $\dfrac{1}{4}(7x^2 - 4x + 8)$
$= \dfrac{1}{4}(7x^2) - \dfrac{1}{4}(4x) + \dfrac{1}{4}(8)$
$= \dfrac{7}{4}x^2 - x + 2$

42. $\dfrac{x}{2}(7x^2 - 4x + 1)$

$= \dfrac{x}{2}(7x^2) - \dfrac{x}{2}(4x) + \dfrac{x}{2}(1)$

$= \dfrac{7}{2}x^3 - 2x^2 + \dfrac{x}{2}$

44. $5xy^2(y^3 - y^2 + 3x + 1)$

$= 5xy^2(y^3) - 5xy^2(y^2) + 5xy^2(3x) + 5xy^2(1)$

$= 5xy^5 - 5xy^4 + 15x^2y^2 + 5xy^2$

46. $8(x + 5y) - 2y(x + 1)$

$= 8x + 40y - 2xy - 2y$

$= 8x + 38y - 2xy$

48. $5x + 2(-x - 6)$

$= 5x - 2x - 12$

$= 3x - 12$

50. $5(x - 2) + (3x - 8) - (x - 2)$

$= 5x - 10 + 3x - 8 - x + 2$

$= 7x - 16$

52. $3[2x + (y - 2x)] - 2[x - (3y - x)]$

$= 3(y) - 2(x - 3y + x)$

$= 3y - 2(2x - 3y)$

$= 3y - 4x + 6y$

$= 9y - 4x$

54. $-3\{3y + 2[y + 2(y - 4)]\}$

$= -3[3y + 2(y + 2y - 8)]$

$= -3[3y + 2(3y - 8)]$

$= -3(3y + 6y - 16)$

$= -3(9y - 16)$

$= -27y + 48$

56. $-5(b + a^2) - 6[a + a(-3 - a)]$

$= -5b - 5a^2 - 6(a - 3a - a^2)$

$= -5b - 5a^2 - 6a + 18a + 6a^2$

$= a^2 + 12a - 5b$

Cumulative Review Problems

58. $4(2 - 3 + 6) + \sqrt{36}$

$= 4(5) + 6$

$= 20 + 6$

$= 26$

60. $(-3)^5 + 2(-3)$

$= -243 - 6$

$= -249$

62. $\dfrac{2\%}{1000\ \text{feet}} \times \dfrac{1\ \text{foot}}{0.305\ \text{meter}} \times 4167\ \text{meters}$

$= 27.3\%$

1.6 Exercises

2. $2x - 6$

$= 2(4) - 6$

$= 8 - 6$

$= 2$

4. $8x + 5$

$= 8(-6) + 5$

$= -48 + 5$

$= -43$

6. $x^2 + 7x + 12$

$= (-2)^2 + 7(-2) + 12$

$= 4 - 14 + 12$

$= 2$

8. $-3x^2 + 5x + 2$

$= -3(-1)^2 + 5(-1) + 2$

$= -3(1) - 5 + 2$

$= -3 - 5 + 2$

$= -6$

10. $6x^2 - 3x + 5$

$= 6(5)^2 - 3(5) + 5$

$= 6(25) - 15 + 5$

$= 140$

12. $3ay - 2by + x$

$= 3(4)(-1) - 2(-6)(-1) + 1$

$= -12 - 12 + 1$

$= -23$

14. $x^3 + ax^2 + aby$

$= (-2)^3 + (1)(-2)^2 + (1)(-3)(5)$

$= -8 + 4 - 15$

$= -19$

16. $\sqrt{b^2 - 4ac}$

$= \sqrt{(-5)^2 - 4(2)(-3)}$

$= \sqrt{25 + 24}$

$= \sqrt{49}$

$= 7$

18. $3x^2 - 7x - 2$

$= 3(-0.56736)^2 - 7(-0.56736) - 2$

$= 2.93721$

20. $F = \dfrac{9}{5}C + 32$

$= \dfrac{9}{5}(85) + 32$

$= 153 + 32$

$= 185$

185°F

22. $C = \dfrac{5F - 160}{9}$

$= \dfrac{5(-40) - 160}{9}$

$= \dfrac{-200 - 160}{9}$

$= \dfrac{-360}{9}$

$= -40$

-40°C

24. $T = 2\pi\sqrt{\dfrac{L}{g}}$

$= 2(3.14)\sqrt{\dfrac{512}{32}}$

$= 6.28\sqrt{16}$

$= 6.28(4)$

$= 25.12$

25.12 sec

26. $A = p(1 + rt)$

$= 3200[1 + (0.07)(2)]$

$= 3200(1 + 0.14)$

$= 3200(1.14)$

$= 3648$

$3648

28. $A = p(1 + rt)$

$= 1900[1 + (0.06)(3)]$

$= 1900(1 + 0.18)$

$= 1900(1.18)$

$= 2242$

$2242

30. $S = \dfrac{1}{2}gt^2$

$= \dfrac{1}{2}(32)(3)^2$

$= (16)(9)$

$= 144$

144 ft

32. $S = \dfrac{1}{2}gt^2$

$= \dfrac{1}{2}(32)(7)^2$

$= (16)(49)$

$= 784$

784 ft

34. $z = \dfrac{Rr}{R + r}$

$= \dfrac{(35)(15)}{35 + 15}$

$= \dfrac{525}{50} = \dfrac{21}{2}$

36. $S = \dfrac{n}{2}[2a + (n - 1)d]$

$= \dfrac{16}{2}[2(4) + (16 - 1)(-3)]$

$= 8[8 + (15)(-3)]$

$= 8(8 - 45)$

$= 8(-37)$

$= -296$

38. $C = \pi d$

$= (3.14)0.2)$

$= 0.628$

0.628 meters

40. $A = \dfrac{1}{2}ab = \dfrac{1}{2}(16)(7) = 56$

56 sq. cm

42. $A = ab$
$= (5)(16)$
$= 80$
80 sq. cm

44. $S = 2lw + 2lh + 2wh$
$= 2(12.4)(6.7) + 2(12.4)(1.2) + 2(6.7)(1.2)$
$= 166.16 + 29.76 + 16.08$
$= 212$
212 sq. cm

46. $P = b + c + d + e$
$= 5.2 + 6.1 + 3.5 + 2.2$
$= 17$
17 m

48. **(a)** $V = \dfrac{4}{3}\pi r^3$
$= \dfrac{4}{3}(3.14)(6)^3$
$= 904.32$
904.32 cu. m

(b) $S = 4\pi r^2$
$= 4(3.14)(6)^2$
$= 452.16$
452.16 sq. m

50. $A = \pi r^2$
$= \pi(9.05263)^2$
$= 257.45386$
257.45386 sq. cm

52. $A = \pi r^2$
$= 3.14(8)^2$
$= 200.96$
200.96 sq. cm
$C = 2\pi r$
$= 2(3.14)(8)$
$= 50.24$
50.24 cm

54. $-126.9 + 47.4 = -79.5$
$-79.5°F$ or $-61.9°C$

Cumulative Review Problems

56. $3x(x - y) + x(y - 2x)$
$= 3x^2 - 3xy + xy - 2x^2$
$= x^2 - 2xy$

58. $2\{5 - 2[x - 3(2x + 1)]\}$
$= 2[5 - 2(x - 6x - 3)]$
$= 2[5 - 2(-5x - 3)]$
$= 2(5 + 10x + 6)$
$= 2(10x + 11)$
$= 20x + 22$

Putting Your Skills To Work

2. $V = \dfrac{4}{3}(3.1416)(2,439,000 \text{ m})^3$
$= 6.0775 \times 10^{19} \text{ m}^3$
Mass $= 6.0775 \times 10^{19} \text{ m}^3 \times 5430 \text{ kg/m}^3$
$= 3.300 \times 10^{23}$ kg
$\dfrac{3.3 \times 10^{23}}{5.999 \times 10^{24}}$
$= 0.055$
The mass of Mercury is approximately 5.5% of the mass of Earth.

4. None of the factors by itself. The escape velocity is closest.

Chapter 1 Review Problems

2. Rational, Real

4. Rational, Real

6. Commutative Property of Addition

8. Yes

10. $-1.6 + (-5.2) = -6.8$

12. $-12 \div (+3) = -4$

14. $\left(-\dfrac{5}{7}\right) \div \left(\dfrac{5}{-13}\right)$
$= -\dfrac{5}{7} \cdot \dfrac{-13}{5}$
$= \dfrac{13}{7}$ or $1\dfrac{6}{7}$

16. $5 + 6 - 2 - 5$

$= 11 - 2 - 5$

$= 9 - 5$

$= 4$

18. $0 \div (-6) = 0$

20. $-12 + (+12) = 0$

22. $\dfrac{5-8}{2-7-(-2)}$

$= \dfrac{-3}{-5+2}$

$= \dfrac{-3}{-3}$

$= 1$

24. $4 - 2 + 6\left(-\dfrac{1}{3}\right)$

$= 4 - 2 - 2$

$= 2 - 2$

$= 0$

26. $\sqrt{(-3)^2} + (-2)^3$

$= \sqrt{9} - 8$

$= 3 - 8$

$= -5$

28. $2\sqrt{16} + 3(-4)(0)(2) - 2^2$

$= 2(4) + 0 - 4$

$= 8 - 4$

$= 4$

30. $(3xy^2)(-2x^0 y)(4x^3 y^3)$

$= (3)(-2)(4)x^{1+0+3} y^{2+1+3}$

$= -24x^4 y^6$

32. $\dfrac{5^{-3} x^{-3} y^6}{5^{-5} x^{-5} y^8}$

$= 5^{-3-(-5)} x^{-3-(-5)} y^{6-8}$

$= 5^2 x^2 y^{-2}$

$= \dfrac{25x^2}{y^2}$

34. $\left(\dfrac{-3x^3 y}{2x^4 z^2}\right)^4$

$= \dfrac{(-3)^4 x^{12} y^4}{2^4 x^{16} z^8}$

$= \dfrac{81y^4}{16x^4 z^8}$

36. $(2^{-1} a^2 b^{-4})^3$

$= 2^{-3} a^6 b^{-12}$

$= \dfrac{a^6}{2^3 b^{12}}$

$= \dfrac{a^6}{8b^{12}}$

38. $\dfrac{(3^{-1} x^{-2} y)^{-2}}{(4^{-1} xy^{-2})^{-1}}$

$= \dfrac{3^2 x^4 y^{-2}}{4x^{-1} y^2}$

$= \dfrac{9x^4 x^1}{4y^2 y^2}$

$= \dfrac{9x^5}{4y^4}$

40. $\left(\dfrac{a^5 b^2}{3^{-1} a^{-5} b^{-4}}\right)^3$

$= \dfrac{a^{15} b^6}{3^{-3} a^{-15} b^{-12}}$

$= 3^3 a^{15} a^{15} b^6 b^{12}$

$= 27a^{30} b^{18}$

42. $0.00721 = 7.21 \times 10^{-3}$

44. $2ab - 4a^2 b - 6b^2 - 3ab + 2a^2 b + 5b^3$

$= (2-3)ab + (-4+2)a^2 b - 6b^2 + 5b^3$

$-ab - 2a^2 b - 6b^2 + 5b^3$

46. $3a[2a - 3(a+4)]$

$= 3a(2a - 3a - 12)$

$= 3a(-a - 12)$

$= -3a^2 - 36a$

48. $5x^2 - 3xy - 2y^3$

$= 5(2)^2 - 3(2)(-1) - 2(-1)^3$

$= 20 + 6 + 2$

$= 28$

Chapter 1 Test

2. $-2, 12, \dfrac{9}{3}, \dfrac{25}{25}, 0, \sqrt{4}$

4. $(7-5)^3 - 18 \div (-3) + 3\sqrt{10+6}$
$= (2)^3 - 18 \div -3 + 3\sqrt{16}$
$= 8 - 18 \div -3 + 3(4)$
$= 8 + 6 + 12$
$= 26$

6. $(5x^{-3}y^{-5})(-3xy)(-2x^3y^0)$
$= (5)(-3)(-2)x^{-3+1+3}y^{-5+1+0}$
$= 30xy^{-4}$
$= \dfrac{30x}{y^4}$

8. $\left(\dfrac{2x^{-3}y^{-1}}{-8x^2y^{-4}}\right)^{-2}$

$= \dfrac{2^{-2}x^6y^2}{(-8)^{-2}x^{-4}y^8}$

$= \dfrac{(-8)^2 x^6 x^4 y^2}{2^2 y^8}$

$= \dfrac{64x^{10}y^2}{4y^8}$

$= \dfrac{16x^{10}}{y^6}$

10. $2a + 3b - 6a^2 + b - 8a - 3a^2$
$= (2-8)a + (3+1)b + (-6-3)a^2$
$= -6a + 4b - 9a^2$

12. $0.000002186 = 2.186 \times 10^{-6}$

14. $(3.8 \times 10^{-5})(4 \times 10^{-2})$
$= (3.8)(4) \times 10^{-5+(-2)}$
$= 15.2 \times 10^{-7}$
$= 1.52 \times 10^{-6}$

16. $2\{3x - 2[x - 3(x+5)]\}$
$= 2[3x - 2(x - 3x - 15)]$
$= 2[3x - 2(-2x - 15)]$
$= 2(3x + 4x + 30)$
$= 2(7x + 30)$
$= 14x + 60$

18. $5x^2 + 3xy - y^2$
$5(3)^2 + 3(3)(-3) - (-3)^2$
$= 45 - 27 - 9$
$= 9$

20. $A = \pi r^2$
$= 3.14\left(\dfrac{12}{2}\right)^2$
$= 3.14(6)^2$
$= 113.04$
113.04 sq. m

Chapter 2

Pretest Chapter 2

2.
$$\frac{x-2}{4}=\frac{1}{2}x+4$$
$$4\left(\frac{x-2}{4}\right)=4\left(\frac{1}{2}x\right)+4(4)$$
$$x-2=2x+16$$
$$-2=x+16$$
$$-18=x$$

4.
$$0.7x-1=0.4$$
$$10(0.7x)-10(1)=10(0.4)$$
$$7x-10=4$$
$$7x=14$$
$$x=2$$

6.
$$5ab-2b=16ab-3(8+b)$$
$$5ab-2b=16ab-24-3b$$
$$-11ab=-24-b$$
$$a=\frac{-24-b}{-11b}$$
$$a=\frac{24+b}{11b}$$

8.
$$|3x-2|=7$$
$$3x-2=7 \text{ or } 3x-2=-7$$
$$3x=9 \text{ or } \quad 3x=-5$$
$$x=3 \text{ or } \quad x=-\frac{5}{3}$$

10.
$$\left|\frac{2x+3}{4}\right|=2$$
$$\frac{2x+3}{4}=2 \text{ or } \frac{2x+3}{4}=-2$$
$$2x+3=8 \text{ or } 2x+3=-8$$
$$2x=5 \quad \text{or} \quad 2x=-11$$
$$x=2.5 \quad \text{or} \quad x=-5.5$$

12. width: x
length: $3x-4$
$$P=2w+2l$$
$$64=2x+2(3x-4)$$
$$64=2x+6x-8$$
$$64=8x-8$$
$$72=8x$$
$$9=x$$
$$3x-4=3(9)-4=23$$
9 cm $\times$ 23 cm

14. amount at 77%: x
amount at 92%: $100-x$
$$0.77x+0.92(100-x)=0.80(100)$$
$$77x+92(100-x)=80(100)$$
$$77x+9200-92x=8000$$
$$9200-15x=8000$$
$$-15x=-1200$$
$$x=80$$
$$100-x=100-80=20$$
80 g at 77%; 20 g at 92%

16.
$$7x+12<9x$$
$$12<2x$$
$$6<x$$

18.
$$\frac{2}{3}x-\frac{5}{6}x-3\le\frac{1}{2}x-5$$
$$6\left(\frac{2}{3}x\right)-6\left(\frac{5}{6}x\right)-6(3)\le6\left(\frac{1}{2}x\right)-6(5)$$
$$4x-5x-18\le3x-30$$
$$-x-18\le3x-30$$
$$-18\le4x-30$$
$$12\le4x$$
$$3\le x$$

20. $x<-3$ or $x>0$

22.
$$2x+3<-5 \text{ or } x-2>1$$
$$2x<-8 \quad \text{or} \quad x>3$$
$$x<-4 \quad \text{or} \quad x>3$$

24.
$$\left|\frac{2}{3}x-\frac{1}{2}\right|\le3$$
$$-3\le\frac{2}{3}x-\frac{1}{2}\le3$$
$$-18\le4x-3\le18$$
$$-15\le4x\le21$$
$$-\frac{15}{4}\le x\le\frac{21}{4}$$

2.1 Exercises

2.
$$5y + 9 = 12$$
$$5\left(\frac{3}{5}\right) + 9 = 12$$
$$3 + 9 = 12$$
$$12 = 12$$
$$\text{True}$$

$y = \dfrac{3}{5}$ is a solution

4. Multiply both sides of the equation by 100 to clear the decimals.

6. No, it would be easier to add $\dfrac{1}{4}$ to both sides of the equation.

8.
$$17 + x = -24$$
$$x = -41$$

10.
$$-12x = -48$$
$$x = 4$$

12.
$$5x + 3 = 43$$
$$5x = 40$$
$$x = 8$$

14.
$$8y - 3 = 2y + 3$$
$$6y - 3 = 3$$
$$6y = 6$$
$$y = 1$$

16.
$$-10 + 3x = 2 - 3x$$
$$6x = 12$$
$$x = 2$$

18.
$$-3x + 6 - 8x = -5$$
$$-11x + 6 = -5$$
$$-11x = -11$$
$$x = 1$$

20.
$$5a - 2 + 4a = 2a + 12$$
$$9a - 2 = 2a + 12$$
$$7a - 2 = 12$$
$$7a = 14$$
$$a = 2$$

22.
$$5(2 - y) = 3(y - 2)$$
$$10 - 5y = 3y - 6$$
$$16 = 8y$$
$$2 = y$$

24.
$$8 - (4x - 5) = x - 7$$
$$8 - 4x + 5 = x - 7$$
$$13 - 4x = x - 7$$
$$13 = 5x - 7$$
$$20 = 5x$$
$$4 = x$$

26.
$$5 - 2(3 - y) = 2(2y + 5) + 1$$
$$5 - 6 + 2y = 4y + 10 + 1$$
$$-1 + 2y = 4y + 11$$
$$-1 = 2y + 11$$
$$-12 = 2y$$
$$-6 = y$$

28.
$$\frac{y}{5} + \frac{1}{3} = \frac{7}{15}$$
$$15\left(\frac{y}{5} + \frac{1}{3}\right) = 15\left(\frac{7}{15}\right)$$
$$3y + 5 = 7$$
$$3y = 2$$
$$y = \frac{2}{3}$$

30.
$$\frac{y}{2} + 4 = \frac{1}{6}$$
$$6\left(\frac{y}{2} + 4\right) = 6\left(\frac{1}{6}\right)$$
$$3y + 24 = 1$$
$$3y = -23$$
$$y = -\frac{23}{3}$$

32.
$$\frac{1}{2} + \frac{3x}{7} = \frac{x}{4}$$
$$28\left(\frac{1}{2} + \frac{3x}{7}\right) = 28\left(\frac{x}{4}\right)$$
$$14 + 12x = 7x$$
$$14 = -5x$$
$$-\frac{14}{5} = x$$

34.
$$\frac{x}{5} - \frac{4}{6} = \frac{x}{6} - \frac{2}{3}$$
$$30\left(\frac{x}{5} - \frac{4}{6}\right) = 30\left(\frac{x}{6} - \frac{2}{3}\right)$$
$$6x - 20 = 5x - 20$$
$$x - 20 = -20$$
$$x = 0$$

36. $5 - \dfrac{2}{3}(x+2) = 3$

$$5 - \dfrac{2}{3}x - \dfrac{4}{3} = 3$$
$$15 - 2x - 4 = 9$$
$$2 = 2x$$
$$1 = x$$

38. $\dfrac{5x}{6} - 8 = 2x - 8$

$$6\left(\dfrac{5x}{6} - 8\right) = 6(2x - 8)$$
$$5x - 48 = 12x - 48$$
$$5x = 12x$$
$$-7x = 0$$
$$x = 0$$

40. $0.7x - 0.2 = 0.5x + 0.8$

$$10(0.7x - 0.2) = 10(0.5x + 0.8)$$
$$7x - 2 = 5x + 8$$
$$2x - 2 = 8$$
$$2x = 10$$
$$x = 5$$

42. $0.6(2x+1) = 1$

$$1.2x + 0.6 = 1$$
$$12x + 6 = 10$$
$$12x = 4$$
$$x = \dfrac{1}{3}$$

44. $0.8x + 3 = 0.6x + 2$

$$10(0.8x + 3) = 10(0.6x + 2)$$
$$8x + 30 = 6x + 20$$
$$2x + 30 = 20$$
$$2x = -10$$
$$x = -5$$

46. $0.04x - 0.03 = 0.05 + 0.12x$

$$100(0.04x - 0.03) = 100(0.05 + 0.12x)$$
$$4x - 3 = 5 + 12x$$
$$-3 = 5 + 8x$$
$$-8 = 8x$$
$$-1 = x$$

48. $0.17 = 0.5x + 3$

$$100(0.17) = 100(0.5x + 3)$$
$$17 = 50x + 300$$
$$-283 = 50x$$
$$-5.66 = x$$

50. $2y - 5 - \dfrac{4}{3}(2y+6) = -\dfrac{5}{3}$

$$3\left[2y - 5 - \dfrac{4}{3}(2y+6)\right] = 3\left(-\dfrac{5}{3}\right)$$
$$6y - 15 - 4(2y+6) = -5$$
$$6y - 15 - 8y - 24 = -5$$
$$-2y - 39 = -5$$
$$-2y = 34$$
$$y = -17$$

52. $\dfrac{1}{6} - \dfrac{x}{2} = \dfrac{x-5}{3}$

$$6\left(\dfrac{1}{6} - \dfrac{x}{2}\right) = 6\left(\dfrac{x-5}{3}\right)$$
$$1 - 3x = 2(x-5)$$
$$1 - 3x = 2x - 10$$
$$1 = 5x - 10$$
$$11 = 5x$$
$$\dfrac{11}{5} = x$$

54. $\dfrac{y+5}{7} = \dfrac{5}{14} - \dfrac{y-3}{4}$

$$28\left(\dfrac{y+5}{7}\right) = 28\left(\dfrac{5}{14} - \dfrac{y-3}{4}\right)$$
$$4(y+5) = 10 - 7(y-3)$$
$$4y + 20 = 10 - 7y + 21$$
$$4y + 20 = -7y + 31$$
$$11y + 20 = 31$$
$$11y = 11$$
$$y = 1$$

56. $3(4x+5) - x(2x+1) + 2x(x-3) = 0$

$$12x + 15 - 2x^2 - x + 2x^2 - 6x = 0$$
$$5x + 15 = 0$$
$$x = -3$$

58. $3(0.3 + 0.1x) + 0.1 = 0.5(x+2)$

$$10[3(0.3 + 0.1x) + 0.1] = 10[0.5(x+2)]$$
$$3(3 + x) + 1 = 5(x+2)$$
$$9 + 3x + 1 = 5x + 10$$
$$3x + 10 = 5x + 10$$
$$3x = 5x$$
$$0 = 2x$$
$$0 = x$$

60. $x - \dfrac{5}{3}(x-2) = \dfrac{1}{9}(x+2)$

$$9\left[x - \dfrac{5}{3}(x-2)\right] = 9\left[\dfrac{1}{9}(x+2)\right]$$

$$9x - 15(x - 2) = x + 2$$
$$9x - 15x + 30 = x + 2$$
$$-6x + 30 = x + 2$$
$$30 = 7x + 2$$
$$28 = 7x$$
$$4 = x$$

62. $2x + \dfrac{36,942}{79,603} = 5x - \dfrac{88,032}{91,264}$

$$2x + 0.4641 = 5x - 0.9646$$
$$0.4641 = 3x - 0.9646$$
$$1.4287 = 3x$$
$$0.4762 = x$$

64. (a) $\dfrac{3966 - 1460}{10,545} = 0.238$

Approximately 23.8% wore skirts or dresses

(b) 5491 to (6579 − 5491) or 323 to 64

Cumulative Review Problems

66. $\left(\dfrac{3xy^2}{2x^2y}\right)^3 = \dfrac{3^3 x^3 y^6}{2^3 x^6 y^3} = \dfrac{27y^3}{8x^3}$

68. $(2x^{-2}y^{-3})^2(4xy^{-2})^{-2}$

$$= (4x^{-4}y^{-6})(4^{-2}x^{-2}y^4)$$

$$= \dfrac{4y^4}{4^2 x^4 y^6 x^2}$$

$$= \dfrac{1}{4x^6 y^2}$$

2.2 Exercises

2. $-7y + 8x = -13$
$$8x = 7y - 13$$
$$x = \dfrac{7y - 13}{8}$$

4. $2a - 3(x + a) = 2x$
$$2a - 3x - 3a = 2x$$
$$-3x - a = 2x$$
$$-a = 5x$$
$$-\dfrac{a}{5} = x$$

6. $8d + 8cdx - 3d = 5cdx$
$$5d + 8cdx = 5cdx$$
$$5d = -3cdx$$
$$-\dfrac{5}{3c} = x$$

8. $7x - 2y + 4 = 8$
$$7x - 2y = 4$$
$$7x = 2y + 4$$
$$x = \dfrac{2y + 4}{7}$$

10. $y = -\dfrac{1}{3}x + 2$
$$3y = 3\left(-\dfrac{1}{3}x + 2\right)$$
$$3y = -x + 6$$
$$3y - 6 = -x$$
$$-3y + 6 = x$$

12. $3x - 4(x - 2b) = x + 4a$
$$3x - 4x + 8b = x + 4a$$
$$-x + 8b = x + 4a$$
$$8b = 2x + 4a$$
$$8b - 4a = 2x$$
$$4b - 2a = x$$

14. $I = prt$
$$\dfrac{I}{rt} = p$$

16. $C = \dfrac{5}{9}(F - 32)$
$$9C = 5(F - 32)$$
$$9C = 5F - 160$$
$$9C + 160 = 5F$$
$$\dfrac{9C + 160}{5} = F$$

18. $\dfrac{1}{5}(a + 2b) = 3(a + 2b)$
$$5\left[\dfrac{1}{5}(a + 2b)\right] = 5[3(a + 2b)]$$
$$a + 2b = 15(a + 2b)$$
$$a + 2b = 15a + 30b$$
$$a = 15a + 28b$$
$$-14a = 28b$$
$$-\dfrac{a}{2} = b$$

20. $-6dex + 3y = 5(dex - 3y)$
$$-6dex + 3y = 5dex - 15y$$
$$3y = 11dex - 15y$$
$$18y = 11dex$$
$$\dfrac{18y}{11ex} = d$$

22.
$$\frac{1}{2}A + 3B = \frac{1}{3}B + 6$$
$$6\left(\frac{1}{2}A + 3B\right) = 6\left(\frac{1}{3}B + 6\right)$$
$$3A + 18B = 2B + 36$$
$$3A + 16B = 36$$
$$16B = 36 - 3A$$
$$B = \frac{36 - 3A}{16}$$

24. $16.932x - 19.832 = 15.428 + 19.3(56x - 12)$
$16.932x - 19.832 = 15.428 + 1080.8x - 231.6$
$16.932x - 19.832 = 1080.8x - 216.172$
$-19.832 = 1063.868x - 216.172$
$196.34 = 1063.868x$
$0.1846 = x$

26. (a)
$$F = \frac{9}{5}C + 32$$
$$5F = 5\left(\frac{9}{5}C + 32\right)$$
$$5F = 9C + 160$$
$$5F - 160 = 9C$$
$$\frac{5F - 160}{9} = C$$

(b) $C = \dfrac{5(23) - 160}{9} = -5°$

28. (a)
$$A = p + prt$$
$$A - p = prt$$
$$\frac{A - p}{pr} = t$$

(b) $t = \dfrac{3400 - 1700}{(1700)(0.06)} = 16.\overline{6}$

30. (a)
$$A = \frac{\pi r^2 S}{360}$$
$$360A = \pi r^2 S$$
$$\frac{360A}{\pi r^2} = S$$

(b) $S = \dfrac{360(0.314)}{(3.14)(2)^2} = 9$

32. (a) $NI = 1.08T$
$$N = \frac{1.08T}{I}$$

(b) $N = \dfrac{(1.08)(360)}{15} = 25.92$
26 patients

34. (a) $C = 0.7649D + 6.1275$
$C - 6.1275 = 0.7649D$
$$\frac{C - 6.1275}{0.7649} = D$$

(b) $D = \dfrac{12.48 - 6.1275}{0.7649} = 8.3$
\$8.3 billion

Cumulative Review Problems

36. $\left(\dfrac{5x^2 y^{-3}}{x^{-4}y^2}\right)^{-3}$
$$= \frac{5^{-3}x^{-6}y^9}{x^{12}y^{-6}}$$
$$= \frac{y^6 y^9}{5^3 x^{12} x^6}$$
$$= \frac{y^{15}}{125x^{18}}$$

38. Miles $= 46{,}622.1 - 45{,}711.3$
$= 910.8$
Gallons $= 9.9 + 11.7 + 10.6 + 5.8 + 8$
$= 46$
$910.8 \div 46 = 19.8$
19.8 miles per gallon

2.3 Exercises

2. $|x| = 19$
$x = 19$ or $x = -19$

4. $|x - 3| = 6$
$x - 3 = 6$ or $x - 3 = -6$
$x = 9 \qquad\qquad x = -3$

6. $|2x + 1| = 15$
$2x + 1 = 15$ or $2x + 1 = -15$
$2x = 14 \qquad\qquad 2x = -16$
$x = 7 \qquad\qquad\quad x = -8$

8. $|2 - 3x| = 13$
$2 - 3x = 13$ or $2 - 3x = -13$
$-3x = 11 \qquad\qquad -3x = -15$
$x = -\dfrac{11}{3} \qquad\qquad x = 5$

10. $\left|\dfrac{1}{4}x+5\right|=3$

$\dfrac{1}{4}x+5=3$ or $\dfrac{1}{4}x+5=-3$

$\dfrac{1}{4}x=-2$ $\dfrac{1}{4}x=-8$

$x=-8$ $x=-32$

12. $\left|0.7-0.3x\right|=2$

$0.7-0.3x=2$ or $0.7-0.3x=-2$

$7-3x=20$ $7-3x=-20$

$x=-\dfrac{13}{3}$ $x=9$

14. $\left|x+3\right|-4=8$

$\left|x+3\right|=12$

$x+3=12$ or $x+3=-12$

$x=9$ $x=-15$

16. $\left|3x+5\right|+3=14$

$\left|3x+5\right|=11$

$3x+5=11$ or $3x+5=-11$

$3x=6$ $3x=-16$

$x=2$ $x=-\dfrac{16}{3}$

18. $\left|2x-9\right|-1=15$

$\left|2x-9\right|=16$

$2x-9=16$ or $2x-9=-16$

$2x=25$ $2x=-7$

$x=\dfrac{25}{2}$ $x=-\dfrac{7}{2}$

20. $\left|4-\dfrac{5}{2}x\right|+3=15$

$\left|4-\dfrac{5}{2}x\right|=12$

$4-\dfrac{5}{2}x=12$ or $4-\dfrac{5}{2}x=-12$

$-\dfrac{5}{2}x=8$ $-\dfrac{5}{2}x=-16$

$x=-\dfrac{16}{5}$ $x=\dfrac{32}{5}$

22. $\left|x-4\right|=\left|2x+5\right|$

$x-4=2x+5$ or $x-4=-(2x+5)$

$-4=x+5$ $x-4=-2x-5$

$-9=x$ $3x-4=-5$

                 $3x=-1$

                 $x=-\dfrac{1}{3}$

24. $\left|6x-2\right|=\left|3x+1\right|$

$6x-2=3x+1$ or $6x-2=-(3x+1)$

$3x-2=1$ $6x-2=-3x-1$

$3x=3$ $9x-2=-1$

$x=1$ $9x=1$

               $x=\dfrac{1}{9}$

26. $\left|5+x\right|=\left|3-4x\right|$

$5+x=3-4x$ or $5+x=-(3-4x)$

$5+5x=3$ $5+x=-3+4x$

$5x=-2$ $5=-3+3x$

$x=-\dfrac{2}{5}$ $8=3x$

               $\dfrac{8}{3}=x$

28. $\left|2.2x+2\right|=\left|1-2.8x\right|$

$2.2x+2=1-2.8x$ or $2.2x+2=-1+2.8x$

$22x+20=10-28x$ $22x+20=-10+28x$

$50x=-10$ $-6x=-30$

$x=-\dfrac{1}{5}$ $x=5$

30. $\left|1.62x+3.14\right|=2.19$

$1.62x+3.14=2.19$ or $1.62x+3.14=-2.19$

$1.62x=-0.95$ $1.62x=-5.33$

$x=-0.59$ $x=-3.29$

32. $\left|9.63x+1.52\right|=\left|-8.61x+3.76\right|$

$9.63x+1.52=-8.61x+3.76$ or $9.63x+1.52=-(-8.61x+3.76)$

$18.24x+1.52=3.76$ $9.63x+1.52=8.61x-3.76$

$18.24x=2.24$ $1.02x=-5.28$

$x=0.12$ $x=-5.18$

34. $|3(x+4)|+2=14$

$|3x+12|=12$

$3x+12=12$ or $3x+12=-12$

$\quad 3x=0 \qquad\qquad 3x=-24$

$\quad\quad x=0 \qquad\qquad\ \ x=-8$

36. $|4x-20|=0$

$4x-20=0$

$\quad 4x=20$

$\quad\ \ x=5$

38. $\left|\dfrac{2}{3}x+\dfrac{1}{7}\right|=-4$

No solution

(Absolute value will never be negative)

40. $\left|\dfrac{2x-1}{3}\right|=\dfrac{5}{6}$

$\dfrac{2x-1}{3}=\dfrac{5}{6}$ or $\dfrac{2x-1}{3}=-\dfrac{5}{6}$

$6\left(\dfrac{2x-1}{3}\right)=6\left(\dfrac{5}{6}\right) \qquad 6\left(\dfrac{2x-1}{3}\right)=6\left(-\dfrac{5}{6}\right)$

$4x-2=5 \qquad\qquad 4x-2=-5$

$\quad 4x=7 \qquad\qquad\quad 4x=-3$

$\quad\ \ x=\dfrac{7}{4} \qquad\qquad\quad\ x=-\dfrac{3}{4}$

42. $\left|\dfrac{1}{2}x+3\right|=\left|\dfrac{1}{4}x-6\right|$

$\dfrac{1}{2}x+3=\dfrac{1}{4}x-6$ or $\dfrac{1}{2}x+3=-\left(\dfrac{1}{4}x-6\right)$

$4\left(\dfrac{1}{2}x+3\right)=4\left(\dfrac{1}{4}x-6\right) \quad \dfrac{1}{2}x+3=-\dfrac{1}{4}x+6$

$2x+12=x-24 \quad 4\left(\dfrac{1}{2}x+3\right)=4\left(-\dfrac{1}{4}x+6\right)$

$x+12=-24 \qquad 2x+12=-x+24$

$\quad\ \ x=-36 \qquad\quad 3x+12=24$

$\qquad\qquad\qquad\qquad\ 3x=12$

$\qquad\qquad\qquad\qquad\ \ x=4$

44. $\dfrac{|x+2|}{-3}=-5$

$|x+2|=15$

$x+2=15$ or $x+2=-15$

$\quad x=13 \qquad\quad x=-17$

Cumulative Review Problems

46. $2(3x+1)-3(x-2)=2x+5$

$6x+2-3x+6=2x+5$

$\quad 3x+8=2x+5$

$\quad\ \ x+8=5$

$\qquad\ x=-3$

48. $\left(\dfrac{2x^{-2}y}{z^{-1}}\right)^3=\dfrac{8x^{-6}y^3}{z^{-3}}=\dfrac{8y^3z^3}{x^6}$

Putting Your Skills to Work

2. $21.9-21.0=0.9$

$\dfrac{0.9}{21.0}\approx 0.04286$

The rate of increase from 1990 to 1995 was approximately 4.286%.

2000: $21.9+21.9(0.04286)\approx 22.84$

2005: $22.84+22.84(0.04286)\approx 23.82$

In 2005, gas mileage will be approximately 23.8 miles per gallon.

4. From problem 2, the mileage in 2000 will be 22.84 miles per gallon.

2005: $22.84+22.84(0.02143)\approx 23.33$

2010: $23.33+23.33(0.010715)\approx 23.58$

2015: $23.58+23.58(0.0053575)\approx 23.71$

The gas mileage in 2015 will be approximately 23.7 miles per gallon.

2.4 Exercises

2. number: x

$\dfrac{7}{8}x=-63$

$\quad x=-72$

The number is –72.

4. Original budget in millions: x

$3x+2.7=14.4$

$\quad 3x=11.7$

$\quad\ \ x=3.9$

$3.9 million

6. number of hours parked at $3.50 per hour: x

$5+3.5x=82$

$\quad 3.5x=77$

$\quad\ \ x=22$

Including the first hour, the car has been parked 23 hours.

8. number of checks: x

$$8(4) + 0.10x = 39.70$$
$$32 + 0.10x = 39.70$$
$$0.10x = 7.70$$
$$x = 77$$

77 checks

10. 1st odd integer: x

2nd odd integer: $x + 2$

3rd odd integer: $x + 4$

$$x + x + 2 + x + 4 = 237$$
$$3x + 6 = 237$$
$$3x = 231$$
$$x = 77$$
$$x + 2 = 79$$
$$x + 4 = 81$$

The integers are 77, 79, 81.

12. 1st number: $\dfrac{1}{3}x$

2nd number: x

3rd number: $2x$

$$\frac{1}{3}x + x + 2x = 70$$
$$\frac{10}{3}x = 70$$
$$x = 21$$
$$\frac{1}{3}x = 7$$
$$2x = 42$$

1st number: 7; 2nd number: 21;

3rd number: 42

14. width: x

length: $3x - 6$

$$2(x) + 2(3x - 6) = 340$$
$$2x + 6x - 12 = 340$$
$$8x - 12 = 340$$
$$8x = 352$$
$$x = 44$$
$$3x - 6 = 126$$

44 yd by 126 yd

16. 1st side: x

2nd side: $\dfrac{2}{3}x$

3rd side: $x - 10$

$$x + \frac{2}{3}x + x - 10 = 62$$
$$\frac{8}{3}x - 10 = 62$$
$$\frac{8}{3}x = 72$$
$$x = 27$$
$$\frac{2}{3}x = 18$$
$$x - 10 = 17$$

1st side: 27 mm; 2nd side: 18 mm;

3rd side: 17 mm

18. number of Digital Center employees: x

number of Computer Village employees: $3x - 50$

$$x + 3x - 50 = 470$$
$$4x - 50 = 470$$
$$4x = 520$$
$$x = 130$$
$$3x - 50 = 340$$

Digital Center: 130 people

Computer Village: 340 people

20. time spent climbing, in minutes: x

time spent at level altitude: $3x$

time spent descending: $x - 4$

(a) $$x + 3x + x - 4 = 2(60) + 6$$
$$5x - 4 = 126$$
$$5x = 130$$
$$x = 26$$
$$x - 4 = 22$$

Climbed for 26 minutes, descended for 22 minutes.

(b) $\dfrac{33,000 \text{ ft}}{26 \text{ min}} \approx 1270 \text{ ft / min}$

22. width: x

length: $2x$

$$2(x) + 2(2x) = 0.05052$$
$$2x + 4x = 0.05052$$
$$6x = 0.05052$$
$$x = 0.00842$$
$$2x = 0.01684$$

0.00842 cm by 0.01684 cm

Cumulative Review Problems

24. Associative Property of Multiplication

2.5 Exercises

2. $x = 1990$ debt in trillions
$$x + 0.62x = 5.207$$
$$1.62x = 5.207$$
$$x = 3.214$$
$3.214 trillion

4. original price: x
$$0.80x = 340$$
$$x = 425$$
$425

6. number of trees: x
$$0.65x = 95$$
$$x \approx 146$$
146 trees

8. 1st number: x
2nd number: $128 - x$
$$3x + 2(128 - x) = 311$$
$$3x + 256 - 2x = 311$$
$$x = 55$$
$$128 - 55 = 73$$
The numbers are 55 and 73.

10. mg in packet A: x
mg in packet B: $8 - x$
$$17x + 14(8 - x) = 127$$
$$17x + 112 - 14x = 127$$
$$3x + 112 = 127$$
$$3x = 15$$
$$x = 5$$
$$8 - x = 3$$
packet A: 5 mg; packet B: 3 mg

12. $I = prt$
$$= (900)(0.14)(2)$$
$$= 252$$
$252

14. $I = prt$
$$= (3000)(0.08)\left(\frac{1}{4}\right)$$
$$= 60$$
$60

16. amount at 13%: x
amount at 16%: $45,000 - x$
$$0.13x + 0.16(45,000 - x) = 6570$$
$$13x + 720,000 - 16x = 657,000$$
$$-3x = -63,000$$
$$x = 21,000$$
$$45,000 - 21,000 = 24,000$$
amount at 13%: \$21,000;
amount at 16%: \$24,000

18. amount at 14%: x
amount at 11%: $7000 - x$
$$0.14x + 0.11(7000 - x) = 902$$
$$14x + 11(7000 - x) = 90200$$
$$14x + 77000 - 11x = 90200$$
$$3x + 77000 = 90200$$
$$3x = 13200$$
$$x = 4400$$
$$7000 - x = 2600$$
amount at 14%: \$4400;
amount at 11%: \$2600

20. amount at 16%: x
amount at 9%: $350 - x$
$$0.16x + 0.09(350 - x) = 0.12(350)$$
$$16x + 3150 - 9x = 4200$$
$$7x = 1050$$
$$x = 150$$
150 ml at 16% strength;
200 ml at 9% strength

22. amount at 30%: x
amount at 10%: $100 - x$
$$0.30x + 0.10(100 - x) = 0.25(100)$$
$$30x + 10(100 - x) = 25(100)$$
$$30x + 1000 - 10x = 2500$$
$$20x = 1500$$
$$x = 75$$
$$100 - x = 25$$
amount at 30%: 75 lb;
amount at 10%: 25 lb

24. amount at 15%: x
$$0.30(40) + 0.15x = 0.27(40 + x)$$
$$30(40) + 15x = 27(40 + x)$$
$$1200 + 15x = 1080 + 27x$$
$$1200 = 1080 + 12x$$
$$120 = 12x$$
$$10 = x$$
10 liters of 15% solution

26. maximum speed: x

cruising speed: $x - 60$

$$3x + 2(x - 60) = 930$$
$$3x + 2x - 120 = 930$$
$$5x - 120 = 930$$
$$5x = 1050$$
$$x = 210$$

210 mph

28. amount of time: x

$$14x = 6x + 20$$
$$8x = 20$$
$$x = 2.5$$

2.5 hr

30. amount at 5.9%: x

amount at 7.8%: $18,375 - x$

$$0.059x + 0.078(18,375 - x) = 1243.25$$
$$0.059x + 1433.25 - 0.078x = 1243.25$$
$$-0.019x + 1433.25 = 1243.25$$
$$-0.019x = -190$$
$$x = 10,000$$
$$18,375 - x = 8375$$

amount at 5.9%: $10,000;

amount at 7.8%: $8375

32. number of passengers: x

$$0.72x + 0.23x + 36 = x$$
$$36 = 0.05x$$
$$720 = x$$

720 passengers

34. $V_{\text{sphere}} = \dfrac{4}{3}\pi r^3$

$$38,808 = \frac{4}{3}\left(\frac{22}{7}\right)r^3$$

$$9261 = r^3$$
$$21 = r$$

$V_{\text{cyl}} = \pi r^2 h$

$$= \left(\frac{22}{7}\right)(21)^2(42)$$
$$= 58,212$$

58,212 cm^3

Cumulative Review Problems

36. $5a - 2b + c$

$$= 5(1) - 2(-3) + (-4)$$
$$= 5 + 6 - 4$$
$$= 7$$

38. $\dfrac{9}{5}C + 32$

$$\frac{9}{5}(-25) + 32$$
$$= -45 + 32$$
$$= -13$$

2.6 Exercises

2. False

4. True

6. False

8. $<$

10. $>$

12. $\dfrac{5}{6} = \dfrac{35}{42}; \dfrac{5}{7} = \dfrac{30}{42}$

$$\frac{5}{6} > \frac{5}{7}$$

14. $>$

16. $-12 + 6 = -6; 18 - 3 = 15$

$$(-12 + 6) < (18 - 3)$$

18. $-3 > -\dfrac{15}{4}$

20. $x \geq 4$

22. $x < 9$

24. $x < \dfrac{2}{3}$

26. $x \geq -7.5$

28. $2x - 8 \leq 10$

$$2x \leq 18$$
$$x \leq 9$$

30. $2x + 5 > 4x - 5$
$-2x + 5 > -5$
$-2x > -10$
$x < 5$

32. $15 - 3x < -x - 5$
$15 - 2x < -5$
$-2x < -20$
$x > 10$

34. $7 - 9x - 12 \geq 3x + 5 - 8x$
$-9x - 5 \geq -5x + 5$
$-4x - 5 \geq 5$
$-4x \geq 10$
$x \leq -\dfrac{5}{2}$

36. $2x - 11 + 3(x + 2) < 0$
$2x - 11 + 3x + 6 < 0$
$5x - 5 < 0$
$5x < 5$
$x < 1$

38. $1 - (x + 3) + 2x > 4$
$1 - x - 3 + 2x > 4$
$x - 2 > 4$
$x > 6$

40. $-0.3x + 0.4 \leq 2.2$
$10(-0.3x + 0.4) \leq 10(2.2)$
$-3x + 4 \leq 22$
$-3x \leq 18$
$x \geq -6$

42. $0.5x - 0.2 > 2.8$
$10(0.5x - 0.2) > 10(2.8)$
$5x - 2 > 28$
$5x > 30$
$x > 6$

44. $-4.5 + 0.4x \geq 0.5(x + 0.8)$
$-4.5 + 0.4x \geq 0.5x + 0.4$
$-45 + 4x \geq 5x + 4$
$-x \geq 49$
$x \leq -49$

46. $\dfrac{7}{6} - \dfrac{1}{3}x + \dfrac{5}{6}x \leq 1x - \dfrac{4}{3}$
$6\left(\dfrac{7}{6} - \dfrac{1}{3}x + \dfrac{5}{6}x\right) \leq 6\left(x - \dfrac{4}{3}\right)$
$7 - 2x + 5x \leq 6x - 8$
$7 + 3x \leq 6x - 8$

$7 - 3x \leq -8$
$-3x \leq -15$
$x \geq 5$

48. $\dfrac{1}{4}(x + 3) \geq 4x - 2(x - 3)$

$4\left[\dfrac{1}{4}(x + 3)\right] \geq 4[4x - 2(x - 3)]$
$x + 3 \geq 4(4x - 2x + 6)$
$x + 3 \geq 4(2x + 6)$
$x + 3 \geq 8x + 24$
$-7x + 3 \geq 24$
$-7x \geq 21$
$x \leq -3$

50. $\dfrac{2}{3}x - x + \dfrac{3}{2} < \dfrac{1}{3}(x + 3) + \dfrac{1}{2}$

$6\left(\dfrac{2}{3}x - x + \dfrac{3}{2}\right) < 6 \cdot \dfrac{1}{3}(x + 3) + 6 \cdot \dfrac{1}{2}$
$4x - 6x + 9 < 2x + 6 + 3$
$-2x + 9 < 2x + 9$
$-2x < 2x$
True for all $x > 0$

52. $1.92(6.3x + 4.9) \geq 7.06x - 4.371$
$12.096x + 9.408 \geq 7.06x - 4.371$
$5.036x + 9.408 \geq -4.371$
$5.036x \geq -13.779$
$x \geq -2.74$

54. number of tables: x
$3(4) + 4x > 52$
$12 + 4x > 52$
$4x > 40$
$x > 10$
She would have to serve more than 10 tables.

56. $I = prt$
$192 > 3200(r)(1)$
$192 > 3200r$
$0.06 > r$
More than 6%

58. number of hours: x
$250 + 6x > 8x$
$250 > 2x$
$125 > x$
It is a better decision to pay \$8 per hour if less than 125 hours is spent digging up the old gardens.

Cumulative Review Problems

60. $(2x^2y^{-3})^2 = 2^2x^4y^{-6} = \dfrac{4x^4}{y^6}$

62. $(-4x^{-2}y^4z^{-6})^{-2}$
$= (-4)^{-2}x^4y^{-8}z^{12}$
$= \dfrac{x^4z^{12}}{(-4)^2y^8}$
$= \dfrac{x^4z^{12}}{16y^8}$

2.7 Exercises

2. $5 < x$ and $x < 10$

4. $-7 < x$ and $x < 1$

6. $3 < x < 5$

8. $-1 \le x \le 6$

10. $x > 7$ or $x < 2$

12. $x < -2$ or $x > 4$

14. $x \le -6$ or $x \ge 2$

16. $4x - 1 < 7$ and $x \ge -1$
$4x < 8$ and $x \ge -1$
$x < 2$ and $x \ge -1$
$-1 \le x < 2$

18. $x + 1 \ge 5$ or $x + 5 < 2.5$
$x \ge 4$ or $x < -2.5$

20. $x < 6$ and $x > 9$
$\varnothing$, no solution

22. $t < 10.9$ or $t > 11.2$

24. $5000 \le c \le 12{,}000$

26. $-20 \le C \le 11$
$-20 \le \dfrac{5}{9}(F - 32) \le 11$
$-180 \le 5F - 160 \le 99$
$-20 \le 5F \le 259$
$-4 \le F \le 51.8$
$-4° \le F \le 51.8°$

28. $17{,}000 \le Y \le 29{,}000$
$131.78 \le d - 4 \le 224.81$
$135.78 \le d \le 228.81$
$\$135.78 \le d \le \$228.81$

30. $x + 3 < 7$ and $x - 2 < -3$
$x < 4$ and $x < -1$
$x < -1$

32. $2x - 5 \ge 1$ and $3x - 3 \le 6$
$2x \ge 6$ and $3x \le 9$
$x \ge 3$ and $x \le 3$
$x = 3$

34. $3x + 2 < 5$ or $5x - 7 > 8$
$3x < 3$ or $5x > 15$
$x < 1$ or $x > 3$

36. $-6x - 8 > 2x$ or $-4x + 6 < 8x$
$-8x > 8$ or $-12x < -6$
$x < -1$ or $x > \dfrac{1}{2}$

38. $4x + 3 < -1$ or $2x - 3 > -11$
$4x < -4$ or $2x > -8$
$x < -1$ or $x > -4$
All real numbers

40. $5x - 6 < 14$ and $6x + 5 < -1$
$5x < 20$ and $6x < -6$
$x < 4$ and $x < -1$
$x < -1$

42. $6x - 10 < 8$ and $2x + 1 > 9$
$6x < 18$ and $2x > 8$
$x < 3$ and $x > 4$
$\varnothing$, no solution

44. $-7x + 3 \ge -11$ and $1 - x < 4.2$
$-7x \ge -14$ and $-x < 3.2$
$x \le 2$ and $x > -3.2$
$-3.2 < x \le 2$

46. $-3x - 7 < 2$ and $x + 1 > 4x + 7$
$\quad\quad -3x < 9$ and $-3x > 6$
$\quad\quad\;\; x > -3$ and $\quad x < -2$
$\quad\quad\quad\quad -3 < x < -2$

48. $x - 4 \geq 1$ or $-3x + 1 \geq -5 - x$
$\quad\quad x \geq 5$ or $\quad\quad -2x \geq -6$
$\quad\quad x \geq 5$ or $\quad\quad\quad x \leq 3$

50. $2.35x + 6.62 \geq 5.04x - 1.23$ or $9.28x \geq 52.71$
$\quad\quad\quad 6.62 \geq 2.69x - 1.23$ or $\;\; x \geq 5.68$
$\quad\quad\quad 7.85 \geq 2.69x$
$\quad\quad\quad\quad x \leq 2.92$

52. $x > -2.5$ and $x > 6$ and $x < 3.5$ and $x \leq 14$
$\quad\quad\quad\quad x > 6$ and $x < 3.5$
$\quad\quad\quad\quad \varnothing$, no solution

54. $\dfrac{x-4}{6} - \dfrac{x-2}{9} \leq \dfrac{5}{18}$ or $-\dfrac{2}{5}(x+3) \leq -\dfrac{6}{5}$
$\quad 3(x-4) - 2(x-2) \leq 5$ or $\;\; -2(x+3) \leq -6$
$\quad 3x - 12 - 2x + 4 \leq 5$ or $\quad -2x - 6 \leq -6$
$\quad\quad\quad x - 8 \leq 5$ or $\quad\quad -2x \leq 0$
$\quad\quad\quad\quad x \leq 13$ or $\quad\quad\quad x \geq 0$
$\quad\quad\quad\quad$ All real numbers

Cumulative Review Problems

56. $7x + 6y = -12$
$\quad\quad 6y = -7x - 12$
$\quad\quad y = \dfrac{-7x - 12}{6}$

58. $I = prt$
$\quad\quad \dfrac{I}{rt} = p$

2.8 Exercises

2. $|x| < 6$
$\quad -6 < x < 6$

4. $|x| \geq 7$
$\quad x \geq 7$ or $x \leq -7$

6. $|x + 6| < 3.5$
$\quad -3.5 < x + 6 < 3.5$
$\quad -9.5 < x < -2.5$

8. $|x - 7| \leq 10$
$\quad -10 \leq x - 7 \leq 10$
$\quad -3 \leq x \leq 17$

10. $|3x + 2| \leq 12$
$\quad -12 \leq 3x + 2 \leq 12$
$\quad -14 \leq 3x \leq 10$
$\quad -\dfrac{14}{3} \leq x \leq \dfrac{10}{3}$

12. $|0.2x - 0.7| \leq 0.3$
$\quad -0.3 \leq 0.2x - 0.7 \leq 0.3$
$\quad -3 \leq 2x - 7 \leq 3$
$\quad 4 \leq 2x \leq 10$
$\quad 2 \leq x \leq 5$

14. $\left|x - \dfrac{3}{2}\right| < \dfrac{1}{2}$
$\quad -\dfrac{1}{2} < x - \dfrac{3}{2} < \dfrac{1}{2}$
$\quad 1 < x < 2$

16. $\left|\dfrac{1}{5}x + 1\right| < 5$
$\quad -5 < \dfrac{1}{5}x + 1 < 5$
$\quad -6 < \dfrac{1}{5}x < 4$
$\quad -30 < x < 20$

18. $|-3 + 4(x + 1)| \leq 3$
$\quad |-3 + 4x + 4| \leq 3$
$\quad |4x + 1| \leq 3$
$\quad -3 \leq 4x + 1 \leq 3$
$\quad -4 \leq 4x \leq 2$
$\quad -1 \leq x \leq \dfrac{1}{2}$

20. $\left|\dfrac{3}{4}(x - 1)\right| < 6$
$\quad -6 < \dfrac{3}{4}(x - 1) < 6$
$\quad -24 < 3(x - 1) < 24$
$\quad -8 < x - 1 < 8$
$\quad -7 < x < 9$

22. $\left|\dfrac{5x - 3}{2}\right| < 4$
$\quad -4 < \dfrac{5x - 3}{2} < 4$
$\quad -8 < 5x - 3 < 8$

$$-5 < 5x < 11$$
$$-1 < x < \frac{11}{5}$$

24. $|x+4| > 7$
$x + 4 > 7$ or $x + 4 < -7$
$\quad x > 3 \quad$ or $\quad x < -11$

26. $|x-1| \geq 2$
$x - 1 \geq 2$ or $x - 1 \leq -2$
$\quad x \geq 3 \quad$ or $\quad x \leq -1$

28. $|5x-2| \geq 13$
$5x - 2 \geq 13$ or $5x - 2 \leq -13$
$\quad 5x \geq 15 \quad$ or $\quad 5x \leq -11$
$\quad x \geq 3 \quad$ or $\quad x \leq -\frac{11}{5}$

30. $\left|3 - \frac{2}{3}x\right| > 5$

$3 - \frac{2}{3}x > 5$ or $3 - \frac{2}{3}x < -5$

$-\frac{2}{3}x > 2 \quad$ or $\quad -\frac{2}{3}x < -8$

$\quad x < -3 \quad$ or $\quad x > 12$

32. $\left|\frac{1}{4}x - \frac{3}{8}\right| > 1$

$\frac{1}{4}x - \frac{3}{8} > 1$ or $\frac{1}{4}x - \frac{3}{8} < -1$

$\quad \frac{1}{4}x > \frac{11}{8} \quad$ or $\quad \frac{1}{4}x < -\frac{5}{8}$

$\quad x > \frac{11}{2} \quad$ or $\quad x < -\frac{5}{2}$

34. $|11-6x| \geq 7$
$11 - 6x \geq 7$ or $11 - 6x \leq -7$
$\quad -6x \geq -4 \quad$ or $\quad -6x \leq -18$
$\quad x \leq \frac{2}{3} \quad$ or $\quad x \geq 3$

36. $\left|\frac{2}{5}(x-2)\right| \leq 4$

$-4 \leq \frac{2}{5}(x-2) \leq 4$
$-10 \leq x - 2 \leq 10$
$-8 \leq x \leq 12$

38. $|m - 17.48| \leq 0.12$
$-0.12 \leq m - 17.48 \leq 0.12$
$17.36 \leq m \leq 17.60$

40. $|n - 7.84| \leq 0.05$
$-0.05 \leq n - 7.84 \leq 0.05$
$7.79 \leq n \leq 7.89$

42. In Step 3 division by a negative number was carried out, but he failed to reverse the inequality symbols.

Cumulative Review Problems

44. $(6-4)^3 \div (-4) + 2^2$
$= 2^3 \div (-4) + 4$
$= 8 \div (-4) + 4$
$= -2 + 4$
$= 2$

46. $C = 2\pi r = 2(3.14)(30) = 188.14$

$d = 2\left(\frac{1}{6}C\right) = \frac{188.14}{3} = 62.8$

$t = \frac{d}{r} = \frac{62.8}{8} = 7.85$ seconds

Chapter 2 Review Problems

2. $6 - (3x + 5) = 15 - (x - 6)$
$6 - 3x - 5 = 15 - x + 6$
$-3x + 1 = -x + 21$
$-2x + 1 = 21$
$-2x = 20$
$x = -10$

4. $\quad x - \frac{7}{5} = \frac{1}{3}x + \frac{7}{15}$

$15\left(x - \frac{7}{5}\right) = 15\left(\frac{1}{3}x + \frac{7}{15}\right)$

$15x - 21 = 5x + 7$
$10x - 21 = 7$
$10x = 28$
$x = \frac{14}{5}$

6. $\quad \frac{1}{9}x - 1 = \frac{1}{2}\left(x + \frac{1}{3}\right)$

$18\left(\frac{1}{9}x - 1\right) = 18\left[\frac{1}{2}\left(x + \frac{1}{3}\right)\right]$

$2x - 18 = 9\left(x + \frac{1}{3}\right)$

$2x - 18 = 9x + 3$
$-18 = 7x + 3$
$-21 = 7x$
$-3 = x$

8.
$$0.6 - 0.2(x-3) + 0.5 = 1.5$$
$$10[0.6 - 0.2(x-3) + 0.5] = 10(1.5)$$
$$6 - 2(x-3) + 5 = 15$$
$$6 - 2x + 6 + 5 = 15$$
$$-2x + 17 = 15$$
$$-2x = -2$$
$$x = 1$$

10.
$$2(3ax - 2y) - 6ax = -3(ax + 2y)$$
$$6ax - 4y - 6ax = -3ax - 6y$$
$$-4y = -3ax - 6y$$
$$2y = -3ax$$
$$-\frac{2y}{3x} = a$$

12. (a)
$$C = \frac{5F - 160}{9}$$
$$9C = 5F - 160$$
$$9C + 160 = 5F$$
$$\frac{9C + 160}{5} = F$$

(b) $F = \dfrac{9(10) + 160}{5} = 50°$

14. $|x - 3| = 12$
$$x - 3 = 12 \text{ or } x - 3 = -12$$
$$x = 15 \qquad x = -9$$

16. $|3x + 2| = 20$
$$3x + 2 = 20 \text{ or } 3x + 2 = -20$$
$$3x = 18 \qquad 3x = -22$$
$$x = 6 \qquad x = -\frac{22}{3}$$

18. $|3 - x| = |5 - 2x|$
$$3 - x = 5 - 2x \text{ or } 3 - x = -(5x - 2x)$$
$$3 + x = 5 \qquad 3 - x = -5 + 2x$$
$$x = 2 \qquad 3 = -5 + 3x$$
$$8 = 3x$$
$$\frac{8}{3} = x$$

20. $|4 - 7x| = 25$
$$4 - 7x = 25 \text{ or } 4 - 7x = -25$$
$$-7x = 21 \qquad -7x = -29$$
$$x = -3 \qquad x = \frac{29}{7}$$

22. number: x
$$\frac{5}{8}x = 290$$
$$x = 464$$
The number is 464.

24. number of miles: x
$$30(2) + 0.12x = 102$$
$$60 + 0.12x = 102$$
$$0.12x = 42$$
$$x = 350$$
350 miles

26. width: x
length: $3x + 8$
$$2(x) + 2(3x + 8) = 88$$
$$2x + 6x + 16 = 88$$
$$8x + 16 = 88$$
$$8x = 72$$
$$x = 9$$
$$3x + 8 = 35$$
9 mm by 35 mm

28. number of students last year: x
$$0.88x = 2332$$
$$x = 2650$$
2650 students

30. amount at 12%: x
amount at 8%: $7000 - x$
$$0.12x + 0.08(7000 - x) = 740$$
$$100[0.12x + 0.08(7000 - x)] = 100(740)$$
$$12x + 8(7000 - x) = 74,000$$
$$12x + 56,000 - 8x = 74,000$$
$$4x + 56,000 = 74,000$$
$$4x = 18,000$$
$$x = 4500$$
$$7000 - x = 2500$$
amount at 12%: $4500
amount at 8%: $2500

32. amount at $4.25/lb: x
amount at $4.50/lb: $30 - x$
$$4.25x + 4.50(30 - x) = 4.40(30)$$
$$100[4.25x + 4.50(30 - x)] = 100[4.40(30)]$$
$$425x + 450(30 - x) = 440(30)$$
$$425x + 13,500 - 450x = 13,200$$
$$-25x + 13,500 = 13,200$$
$$-25x = -300$$
$$x = 12$$
$$30 - x = 18$$
12 lb at $4.25; 18 lb at $4.50

34. $8x + 3 < 5x$
$$3 < -3x$$
$$-1 > x$$

36. $2 - x \geq 3x + 10$
$$2 \geq 4x + 10$$
$$-8 \geq 4x$$
$$-2 \geq x$$

38. $4x - 1 < 3(x + 2)$
$$4x - 1 < 3x + 6$$
$$x - 1 < 6$$
$$x < 7$$

40. $(x + 6) - (2x + 7) \leq 3x - 9$
$$x + 6 - 2x - 7 \leq 3x - 9$$
$$-x - 1 \leq 3x - 9$$
$$-1 \leq 4x - 9$$
$$8 \leq 4x$$
$$2 \leq x$$

42.
$$\frac{1}{9}x + \frac{2}{9} > \frac{1}{3}$$
$$9\left(\frac{1}{9}x + \frac{2}{9}\right) > 9\left(\frac{1}{3}\right)$$
$$x + 2 > 3$$
$$x > 1$$

44.
$$\frac{6}{5} - x \geq \frac{3}{5}x + \frac{14}{5}$$
$$5\left(\frac{6}{5} - x\right) \geq 5\left(\frac{3}{5}x + \frac{14}{5}\right)$$
$$6 - 5x \geq 3x + 14$$
$$6 \geq 8x + 14$$
$$-8 \geq 8x$$
$$-1 \geq x$$

46. $\frac{1}{3}(x - 2) < \frac{1}{4}(x + 5) - \frac{5}{3}$
$$12\left[\frac{1}{3}(x - 2)\right] < 12\left[\frac{1}{4}(x + 5) - \frac{5}{3}\right]$$
$$4(x - 2) < 3(x + 5) - 20$$
$$4x - 8 < 3x + 15 - 20$$
$$4x - 8 < 3x - 5$$
$$x - 8 < -5$$
$$x < 3$$

48.
$$7x - 6 \leq \frac{1}{3}(-2x + 5)$$
$$3(7x - 6) \leq 3\left[\frac{1}{3}(-2x + 5)\right]$$
$$21x - 18 \leq -2x + 5$$
$$23x - 18 \leq 5$$
$$23x \leq 23$$
$$x \leq 1$$

50. $-4 < x \leq 5$

52. $-9 \leq x \leq -6$

54. $x < -3$ or $x \geq 6$

56. $x > -8$ and $x < -3$

58. $x - 2 > 7$ or $x + 3 < 2$
$$x > 9 \quad \text{or} \quad x < -1$$

60. $-1 < x + 5 < 8$
$$-6 < x < 3$$

62. $2x - 7 < 3$ and $5x - 1 \geq 8$
$$2x < 10 \text{ and } 5x \geq 9$$
$$x < 5 \text{ and } x \geq \frac{9}{5}$$
$$\frac{9}{5} \leq x < 5$$

64. $|x + 3| < 10$
$$-10 < x + 3 < 10$$
$$-13 < x < 7$$

66. $|2x - 1| \leq 15$
$$-15 \leq 2x - 1 \leq 15$$
$$-14 \leq 2x \leq 16$$
$$-7 \leq x \leq 8$$

68. $\left|\frac{1}{2}x + 2\right| < \frac{7}{4}$
$$-\frac{7}{4} < \frac{1}{2}x + 2 < \frac{7}{4}$$
$$-7 < 2x + 8 < 7$$
$$-15 < 2x < -1$$
$$-\frac{15}{2} < x < -\frac{1}{2}$$

70. $|2x - 1| \geq 9$
$$2x - 1 \geq 9 \text{ or } 2x - 1 \leq -9$$
$$2x \geq 10 \text{ or } 2x \leq -8$$
$$x \geq 5 \text{ or } x \leq -4$$

72. $|3(x-1)| \geq 5$

$|3x-3| \geq 5$

$3x-3 \geq 5$ or $3x-3 \leq -5$

$3x \geq 8$ or $3x \leq -2$

$x \geq \dfrac{8}{3}$ or $x \leq -\dfrac{2}{3}$

74. $|7+x-3| > 10$

$|x+4| > 10$

$x+4 > 10$ or $x+4 < -10$

$x > 6$ or $x < -14$

Chapter 2 Test

2. $3(7-2x) = 14 - 8(x-1)$

$21 - 6x = 14 - 8x + 8$

$21 - 6x = -8x + 22$

$21 + 2x = 22$

$2x = 1$

$x = \dfrac{1}{2}$

4. $0.5x + 1.2 = 4x - 3.05$

$100(0.5x + 1.2) = 100(4x - 3.05)$

$50x + 120 = 400x - 305$

$120 = 350x - 305$

$425 = 350x$

$\dfrac{17}{14} = x$

6. $F = \dfrac{9}{5}C + 32$

$5F = 5\left(\dfrac{9}{5}C + 32\right)$

$5F = 9C + 160$

$5F - 160 = 9C$

$\dfrac{5F - 160}{9} = C$

8. $H = \dfrac{1}{2}r + 3b - \dfrac{1}{4}$

$4H = 4\left(\dfrac{1}{2}r + 3b - \dfrac{1}{4}\right)$

$4H = 2r + 12b - 1$

$4H - 12b + 1 = 2r$

$\dfrac{4H - 12b + 1}{2} = r$

10. $\left|\dfrac{1}{2}x + 3\right| - 2 = 4$

$\left|\dfrac{1}{2}x + 3\right| = 6$

$\dfrac{1}{2}x + 3 = 6$ or $\dfrac{1}{2}x + 3 = -6$

$\dfrac{1}{2}x = 3$ $\qquad$ $\dfrac{1}{2}x = -9$

$x = 6$ $\qquad$ $x = -18$

12. number of hours: x

$200 + 12(280) + 10x = 12{,}560$

$200 + 3360 + 10x = 12{,}560$

$3560 + 10x = 12{,}560$

$10x = 9000$

$x = 900$

900 hr

14. amount at 6%: x

amount at 10%: $5000 - x$

$0.06x + 0.10(5000 - x) = 428$

$100[0.06x + 0.10(5000 - x)] = 100(428)$

$6x + 10(5000 - x) = 42{,}800$

$6x + 50{,}000 - 10x = 42{,}800$

$50{,}000 - 4x = 42{,}800$

$-4x = -7200$

$x = 1800$

$5000 - x = 3200$

$1800 at 6%; $3200 at 10%

16. $-\dfrac{1}{2} + \dfrac{1}{3}(2 - 3x) \geq \dfrac{1}{2}x + \dfrac{5}{3}$

$6\left[-\dfrac{1}{2} + \dfrac{1}{3}(2 - 3x)\right] \geq 6\left(\dfrac{1}{2}x + \dfrac{5}{3}\right)$

$-3 + 2(2 - 3x) \geq 3x + 10$

$-3 + 4 - 6x \geq 3x + 10$

$1 - 6x \geq 3x + 10$

$1 - 9x \geq 10$

$-9x \geq 9$

$x \leq -1$

18. $x - 4 \leq -6$ or $2x + 1 \geq 3$

$x \leq -2$ or $2x \geq 2$

$x \geq 1$

20. $|3x+1| > 7$

$3x+1 > 7$ or $3x+1 < -7$

$3x > 6$ or $3x < -8$

$x > 2$ or $x < -\dfrac{8}{3}$

Cumulative Test For Chapters 1–2

2. Associative property for addition

4. $(-2x^{-3}y^4)^{-2}$
$= (-2)^{-2}x^6y^{-8}$
$= \dfrac{x^6}{(-2)^2 y^8}$
$= \dfrac{x^6}{4y^8}$

6. $P = 2w + 2l$
$= 2(9) + 2(18)$
$= 18 + 36$
$= 54$
54 cm

8. $2x(3x - 4) - 5x^2(2 - 6x)$
$= 6x^2 - 8x - 10x^2 + 30x^3$
$= 30x^3 - 4x^2 - 8x$

10. $\quad h = \dfrac{2}{3}(b + d)$
$3h = 2(b + d)$
$3h = 2b + 2d$
$3h - 2d = 2b$
$\dfrac{3h - 2d}{2} = b$

12. number of miles: x
$19(4) + 0.23x = 154.20$
$76 + 0.23x = 154.20$
$0.23x = 78.20$
$x = 340$
340 miles

14. amount at 80%: x
amount at 50%: $9 - x$
$0.80x + 0.50(9 - x) = 0.70(9)$
$10[0.80x + 0.50(9 - x)] = 10(0.70)(9)$
$8x + 5(9 - x) = 63$
$8x + 45 - 5x = 63$
$3x + 45 = 63$
$3x = 18$
$x = 6$
$9 - x = 3$
6 gal at 80%; 3 gal at 50%

16. $\quad \dfrac{1}{3}(x + 2) \le \dfrac{1}{5}(x + 6)$
$15\left[\dfrac{1}{3}(x + 2)\right] \le 15\left[\dfrac{1}{5}(x + 6)\right]$
$5(x + 2) \le 3(x + 6)$
$5x + 10 \le 3x + 18$
$2x + 10 \le 18$
$2x \le 8$
$x \le 4$

18. $x + 5 \le -4$ or $2 - 7x \le 16$
$x \le -9 \quad$ or $\quad -7x \le 14$
$x \ge -2$

20. $|3x - 4| > 11$
$3x - 4 > 11$ or $3x - 4 < -11$
$3x > 15 \qquad 3x < -7$
$x > 5 \qquad x < -\dfrac{7}{3}$

Chapter 3

2. $y = -\dfrac{1}{2}x + 5$

x	y
0	5
2	4
4	3

4. $m = \dfrac{y_2 - y_1}{x_2 - x_1}$

$= \dfrac{8 - (-6)}{2 - (-1)}$

$= \dfrac{14}{3}$

6. $y - y_1 = m(x - x_1)$

$y - (-3) = -2(x - 7)$

$y + 3 = -2x + 14$

$y = -2x + 11$

8. $y > -\dfrac{1}{2}x + 3$

Test point: $(0, 0)$

$0 > -\dfrac{1}{2}(0) + 3$

$0 > 3$

False; shade the half-plane not containing $(0, 0)$.

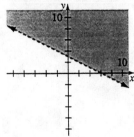

10. Domain: $\{0, 3, 4, 5\}$

Range: $\{1, 2, 4, 6, 7\}$

It is not a function since there are two different ordered pairs having 3 as the first coordinate.

12. Not a function; there are many different ordered pairs with the same first coordinate

14. $g(-1) = |2(-1) - 3|$

$= |-2 - 3|$

$= |-5|$

$= 5$

16. $h(x) = |x - 2|$

x	$h(x)$
−1	3
0	2
1	1
2	0
3	1
4	2

3.1 Exercises

2. origin

4. If you substitute 5 for x and 1 for y in the equation you will get a true statement.

6. $y = 4 - 3x$

$= 4 - 3(-3)$

$= 13$

8. $6x - 24y = 12$
  $6x - 24(2) = 12$
  $6x - 48 = 12$
  $6x = 60$
  $x = 10$

10. $-6x + 3y = 15$
  $-6(0) + 3y = 15$
  $3y = 15$
  $y = 5$

12. $y = -2x + 1$

x	y
0	1
1	-1
2	-3

14. $y = -5x - 2$

x	y
-1	3
0	-2
1	-7
2	-12

16. $y = \dfrac{3}{5}x + 2$

x	y
0	2
5	5
10	8

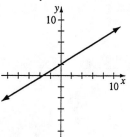

18. $2x + 5y = 10$
  x-intercept: $2x + 5(0) = 10$
  $2x = 10$
  $x = 5$
  $(5, 0)$
  y-intercept: $2(0) + 5y = 10$
  $5y = 10$
  $y = 2$
  $(0, 2)$
  Additional point: Let $y = 4$:
  $2x + 5(4) = 10$
  $2x + 20 = 10$
  $2x = -10$
  $x = -5$
  $(-5, 4)$

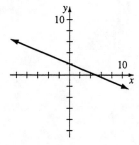

20. $-3x - 4y = 8$
  x-intercept: $-3x - 4(0) = 8$
  $-3x + 0 = 8$
  $-3x = 8$
  $x = -\dfrac{8}{3}$
  $\left(-\dfrac{8}{3},\ 0\right)$

y-intercept: $-3(0) - 4y = 8$
$-4y = 8$
$y = -2$
$(0, -2)$
Additional point: Let $x = 4$:
$-3(4) - 4y = 8$
$-12 - 4y = 8$
$-4y = 20$
$y = -5$
$(4, -5)$

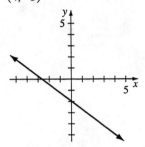

22. $y = -3x$
x-intercept: $0 = -3x$
$0 = x$
$(0, 0)$
This is also the y-intercept.

x	y
-1	3
1	-3

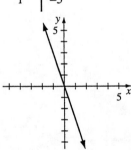

24. $-2x + 5y - 6 = -6$
$-2x + 5y = 0$
x-intercept: $-2x + 5(0) = 0$
$-2x = 0$
$x = 0$
$(0, 0)$
This is also the y-intercept.

x	y
-5	-2
5	2

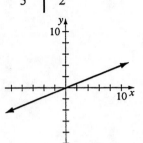

26. $x = 6$
Vertical line

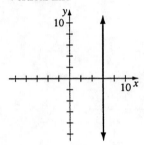

28. $5y + 6 = 2y$
$6 = -3y$
$-2 = y$
Horizontal line

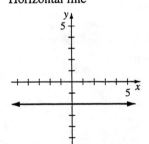

30. $x = 0$
Vertical line, the y-axis

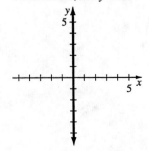

32. $y = -1.5x + 2$

x	y
0	2
2	-1
4	-4

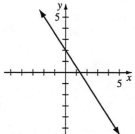

34. $5x + y + 4 = 8x$
$y = 3x - 4$

x	y
0	-4
1	-1
2	2

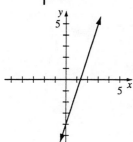

36. $7x + 8y = 2 + 7y + 7x$
$8y = 2 + 7y$
$y = 2$
Horizontal line

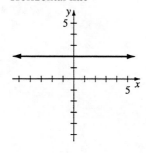

38. $y = 82x + 150$

x	y
-1	68
0	150
1	232

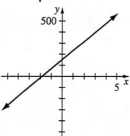

40. $V = 120 - 32T$

(a)

T	V
0	$120 - 32(0) = 120$
1	$120 - 32(1) = 88$
2	$120 - 32(2) = 56$
3	$120 - 32(3) = 24$
4	$120 - 32(4) = -8$

(b)

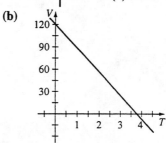

(c) The baseball is moving downward instead of upward at $T = 4$ seconds.

42. $P = 14.7 - 0.0005d$

d	P
0	$14.7 - 0.0005(0) = 14.7$
1000	$14.7 - 0.0005(1000) = 14.2$
2000	$14.7 - 0.0005(2000) = 13.7$
3000	$14.7 - 0.0005(3000) = 13.2$
9000	$14.7 - 0.0005(9000) = 10.2$
15000	$14.7 - 0.0005(15000) = 7.2$

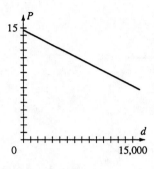

44. $y = -2.15x + 2.73$

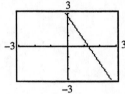

46. $y = 0.713x + 25.82$

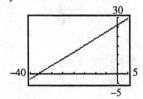

3.2 Exercises

2. upward

4. equal

6. $\dfrac{y_2 - y_1}{x_2 - x_1} = \dfrac{5 - (-3)}{-4 - (-6)}$

$= \dfrac{8}{2}$

$= 4$

$\dfrac{y_1 - y_2}{x_1 - x_2} = \dfrac{-3 - 5}{-6 - (-4)}$

$= \dfrac{-8}{-2}$

$= 4$

The results are the same. The slope of a line is constant and it doesn't matter what order you use to compute the slope.

8. $m = \dfrac{6 - 5}{-3 - 2}$

$= -\dfrac{1}{5}$

10. $m = \dfrac{-1 - 3}{2 - (-6)}$

$= \dfrac{-4}{8}$

$= -\dfrac{1}{2}$

12. $m = \dfrac{1 - \frac{1}{3}}{6 - 0}$

$= \dfrac{\frac{2}{3}}{6}$

$= \dfrac{1}{9}$

14. $m = \dfrac{-8 - (-8)}{-2 - 5}$

$= \dfrac{0}{-7}$

$= 0$

16. $m = \dfrac{5.2 - (-1.6)}{-2 - 4.8}$

$= \dfrac{6.8}{-6.8}$

$= -1$

18. $m = \dfrac{-6 - \frac{1}{6}}{\frac{7}{3} - \frac{7}{3}}$

$= \dfrac{-\frac{37}{6}}{0}$

undefined; no slope

20. $\text{grade} = \dfrac{\text{rise}}{\text{run}}$

$= \dfrac{6.3}{126}$

$= 0.05$

22. $m = \dfrac{\text{rise}}{\text{run}}$

$= \dfrac{3.15}{10.50}$

$= 0.3$

24. $m = \dfrac{\text{rise}}{\text{run}}$

$0.18 = \dfrac{\text{rise}}{700}$

$126 = \text{rise}$

126 ft

26. $m = \dfrac{6-5}{2.8-3}$

$= \dfrac{1}{-0.2}$

$= -5$

A parallel line has slope -5.

28. $m = \dfrac{-6-(-8)}{2-(-5)}$

$= \dfrac{2}{7}$

A parallel line has slope $\dfrac{2}{7}$.

30. $m = \dfrac{16-(-5)}{2-2}$

$= \dfrac{21}{0}$

A parallel line has no slope. (Division by zero is undefined.)

32. $m = \dfrac{5-3}{-2-1}$

$= -\dfrac{2}{3}$

A perpendicular line has slope $-\dfrac{1}{m} = \dfrac{3}{2}$.

34. $m = \dfrac{\frac{1}{3}-(-2)}{-3-\left(-\frac{2}{3}\right)}$

$\dfrac{\frac{7}{3}}{-\frac{7}{3}}$

$= -1$

A perpendicular line has slope $-\dfrac{1}{m} = 1$.

36. $m = \dfrac{-5-0}{0-(-2)}$

$= -\dfrac{5}{2}$

A perpendicular line has slope $-\dfrac{1}{m} = \dfrac{2}{5}$.

38. $m_{AB} = \dfrac{-2-(-1)}{-1-2} = \dfrac{1}{3}$

$m_{BC} = \dfrac{1-(-1)}{8-2} = \dfrac{2}{6} = \dfrac{1}{3}$

Since $m_{AB} = m_{BC}$ and B is a common point, all the points lie on one straight line.

40. **(a)** $m = \dfrac{\text{rise}}{\text{run}} = \dfrac{4300-3000}{2-1} = 1300$ ft/mi

$4.8 - 2 = 2.8$

$m = \dfrac{\text{rise}}{2.8} = 1300$

rise $= 2.8(1300) = 3640$ feet, so the plane rises 3640 feet while it goes from 2 to 4.8 miles from the airport. Thus, the plane's altitude is $4300 + 3640 = 7940$ feet.

(b) $6000 - 3000 = 3000$

$m = \dfrac{3000}{\text{run}} = 1300$

run $= \dfrac{3000}{1300} \approx 2.3$ miles, so the plane covers a horizontal distance of about 2.3 miles while it goes from 3000 to 6000 feet in altitude. The total distance from the airport is approximately $1 + 2.3 = 3.3$ miles.

(c) $m = \dfrac{\text{rise}}{\text{run}} = \dfrac{4040-3000}{1.8-1} = 1300$ ft/min

Yes, the Lear jet is being flown at the same rate of climb as the Cessna.

Cumulative Review Problems

42. $\dfrac{5+3\sqrt{9}}{|2-9|}$

$= \dfrac{5+3(3)}{|-7|}$

$= \dfrac{14}{7}$

$= 2$

44. $\dfrac{-15x^6y^3}{-3x^{-4}y^6}$

$= 5x^{6-(-4)}y^{3-6}$

$= 5x^{10}y^{-3}$

$= \dfrac{5x^{10}}{y^3}$

3.3 Exercises

2. The y-intercept is 5 and the slope is $-\dfrac{2}{7}$.

4. $y = mx + b$

$y = 10x - 2$

6. $y = mx + b$

$$y = -\frac{2}{3}x + 5$$

8. $y = mx + b$

$y = -6x - 9$

$6x + y = -9$

10. $y = mx + b$

$$y = \frac{5}{6}x + \frac{1}{3}$$

$6y = 5x + 2$

$5x - 6y = -2$

12. y-intercept $(0, -2)$, $m = -1$

$y = mx + b$

$y = -x - 2$

14. y-intercept $(0, -2)$, $m = \frac{1}{3}$

$y = mx + b$

$$y = \frac{1}{3}x - 2$$

16. y-intercept $(0, -8)$, $m = 1$

$y = mx + b$

$y = x - 8$

18. $y - 8x = 12$

$y = 8x + 12$

$m = 8,\ b = 12$

20. $5x - 4y = -20$

$-4y = -5x - 20$

$$y = \frac{5}{4}x + 5$$

$$m = \frac{5}{4},\ b = 5$$

22. $3x + \dfrac{2}{3}y = -2$

$$\frac{2}{3}y = -3x - 2$$

$$y = -\frac{9}{2}x - 3$$

$$m = -\frac{9}{2},\ b = -3$$

24. $3x - y = 10$

$-y = -3x + 10$

$y = 3x - 10$

$m = 3,\ b = -10$

26. $y = \dfrac{1}{2}x - 3$

$$m = \frac{1}{2},\ b = -3$$

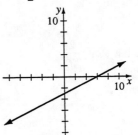

28. $5x - 4y = -20$

$-4y = -5x - 20$

$$y = \frac{5}{4}x + 5$$

$$m = \frac{5}{4},\ b = 5$$

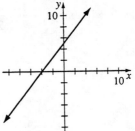

30. $5x + 3y = 18$

$3y = -5x + 18$

$$y = -\frac{5}{3}x + 6$$

$$m = -\frac{5}{3},\ b = 6$$

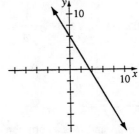

32. $y - y_1 = m(x - x_1)$

$y - 5 = 7[x - (-4)]$

$y - 5 = 7(x + 4)$

$y - 5 = 7x + 28$

$y = 7x + 33$

34. $y - y_1 = m(x - x_1)$

$y - 0 = -3(x - 8)$

$y = -3x + 24$

36. $y - y_1 = m(x - x_1)$

$y - 1 = -\dfrac{1}{4}[x - (-3)]$

$y - 1 = -\dfrac{1}{4}(x + 3)$

$y - 1 = -\dfrac{1}{4}x - \dfrac{3}{4}$

$y = -\dfrac{1}{4}x + \dfrac{1}{4}$

38. $m = \dfrac{-1 - 2}{6 - 3} = -1$

$y - y_1 = m(x - x_1)$

$y - 2 = -1(x - 3)$

$y - 2 = -x + 3$

$x + y = 5$

40. $m = \dfrac{4 - (-1)}{3 - (-4)} = \dfrac{5}{7}$

$y - y_1 = m(x - x_1)$

$y - 4 = \dfrac{5}{7}(x - 3)$

$7y - 28 = 5(x - 3)$

$7y - 28 = 5x - 15$

$5x - 7y = -13$

42. $m = \dfrac{-8 - 0}{3 - (-5)} = -1$

$y - y_1 = m(x - x_1)$

$y - 0 = -1[x - (-5)]$

$y = -1(x + 5)$

$y = -x - 5$

$x + y = -5$

44. $y = 5x - 4$

$m = 5$

$y - y_1 = m(x - x_1)$

$y - 0 = 5(x + 2)$

$y = 5x + 10$

$5x - y = -10$

46. $x = 3y - 8$

$3y = x + 8$

$y = \dfrac{1}{3}x + \dfrac{8}{3}$

$m = \dfrac{1}{3}$

$y - y_1 = m(x - x_1)$

$y - (-1) = \dfrac{1}{3}(x - 5)$

$y + 1 = \dfrac{1}{3}(x - 5)$

$3y + 3 = x - 5$

$x - 3y = 8$

48. $y = -\dfrac{2}{3}x$

$m = -\dfrac{2}{3}$

A perpendicular line has slope $m = \dfrac{3}{2}$.

$y - y_1 = m(x - x_1)$

$y - 1 = \dfrac{3}{2}[x - (-3)]$

$2y - 2 = 3(x + 3)$

$2y - 2 = 3x + 9$

$3x - 2y = -11$

50. $x + 7y = -12$

$7y = -x - 12$

$y = -\dfrac{1}{7}x - \dfrac{12}{7}$

$m = -\dfrac{1}{7}$

A perpendicular line has slope $m = 7$.

$y - y_1 = m(x - x_1)$

$y - (-1) = 7[x - (-4)]$

$y + 1 = 7(x + 4)$

$y + 1 = 7x + 28$

$7x - y = -27$

52. $x = 4$ (Vertical line)

54. $-3x + 5y = 40$

$5y + 3x = 17$

$y = \dfrac{3}{5}x + 8$

$m_1 = \dfrac{3}{5}$

$5y + 3x = 17$

$5y = -3x + 17$

$y = -\dfrac{3}{5}x + \dfrac{17}{5}$

$m_2 = -\dfrac{3}{5}$

Neither since $m_1 \neq m_2$ and $m_1 m_2 \neq -1$.

56. $y = -\dfrac{3}{4}x - 2$

$m_1 = -\dfrac{3}{4}$

$6x + 8y = -5$

$8y = -6x - 5$

$y = -\dfrac{3}{4}x - \dfrac{5}{8}$

$m_2 = -\dfrac{3}{4}$

Parallel since $m_1 = m_2$.

58. $y = \dfrac{5}{6}x - \dfrac{1}{3}$

$m_1 = \dfrac{5}{6}$

$6x + 5y = -12$

$5y = -6x - 12$

$y = -\dfrac{6}{5}x - \dfrac{12}{5}$

$m_2 = -\dfrac{6}{5}$

Perpendicular since $m_1 m_2 = -1$.

60. $y = 1.43x - 2.17$

$y = 1.43x + 0.39$

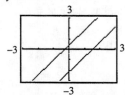

Yes, they are parallel.

Putting Your Skills to Work

2. $m = -0.8$

The negative slope indicates a decrease in demand for each increase in price.

The y-intercept is 160. This is the number of calculators in thousands that would be sold for a price of \$0. (This is not realistic.)

4. $y = -0.8x + 160$

$y = -0.8(110) + 160$

$y = 72$

72,000 calculators

6. $R = 90n$

$R = 90(72,000)$

$R = 6,480,000$

Profit $= 6,480,000 - 5,250,000$

Profit $= 1,230,000$

\$1,230,000

3.4 Exercises

2. $y > -3x + 2$ (dashed line)

Test point: $(0, 0)$

$0 > -3(0) + 2$

$0 > 2$

False; shade the half-plane not containing $(0, 0)$.

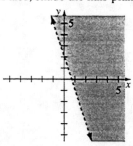

4. $y < \dfrac{3}{4}x - 3$ (dashed line)

Test point: $(0, 0)$

$0 < \dfrac{3}{4}(0) - 3$

$0 < -3$

False; shade the half-plane not containing (0, 0).

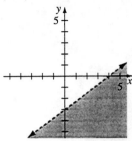

6. $y \le -\dfrac{2}{3}x + 4$ (solid line)

Test point: (0, 0)

$0 \le -\dfrac{2}{3}(0) + 4$

$0 \le 4$

True; shade the half-plane containing (0, 0).

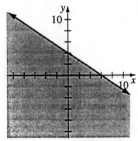

8. $-x + 3y \le 12$ (solid line)

Test point: (0, 0)

$0 + 3(0) \le 12$

$0 \le 12$

True; shade the half-plane containing (0, 0).

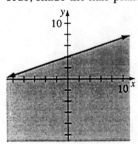

10. $-2x - y > 1$ (dashed line)

Test point: (0, 0)

$-2(0) - 0 > 1$

$0 > 1$

False; shade the half-plane not containing (0, 0).

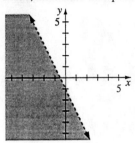

12. $-4x + 2y > -10$ (dashed line)

Test point: (0, 0)

$-4(0) + 2(0) > -10$

$0 > -10$

True; shade the half-plane containing (0, 0).

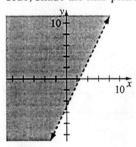

14. $y > -3x$ (dashed line)

Test point: (1, 1)

$1 > -3(1)$

$1 > -3$

True; shade the half-plane containing (1, 1).

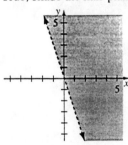

16. $4x - 3y \ge 0$ (solid line)

Test point: (1, 1)

$4(1) - 3(1) \ge 0$

$4 - 3 \ge 0$

$1 \ge 0$

True; shade the half-plane containing (1, 1).

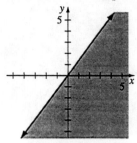

18. The point $(0, 0)$ is on the line.
$4(6) - 3(-5) \geq 0$
$24 + 15 \geq 0$
$39 \geq 0$
True.

20. $x < 3$

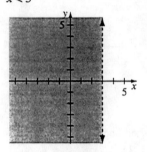

22. $y \geq -1$

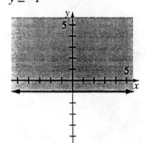

24. $-5x \leq -10$
$x \geq 2$

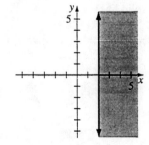

26. $-8y \geq 24$
$y \leq -3$

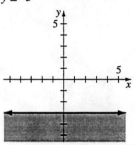

28. $x + y \leq 3, x \geq 0, y \geq 0$
Test point $(1, 1)$
$1 + 1 \leq 3$
$2 \leq 3$ True

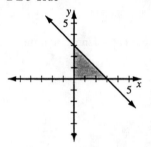

30. $75x + 175y < 2100$
Test point: $(0, 0)$
$75(0) + 175(0) < 2100$
$0 < 2100$
True

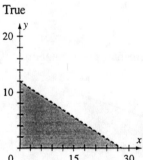

Cumulative Review Problems

32. $A = \dfrac{1}{2}a(b + c)$

$= \dfrac{1}{2}(6.0)(2.5 + 5.5)$

$= 3(8)$

$= 24$

3.5 Exercises

2. The domain consists of all the first items of each ordered pair in a relation. The range consists of all the second items of each ordered pair in a relation.

4. $(-5, 8)$; $x = -5$, $y = 8$

6. Domain = $\{1, 2, 3, 4\}$
Range = $\{4, 9, 16, 25\}$
The relation is function.

8. Domain = $\{0, 5, 7\}$
Range = $\{0, 11, 13\}$
The relation is not a function since 5 is used as a first coordinate in two different ordered pairs.

10. Domain = $\{-7, -6, -3\}$
Range = $\{-6, -1, 2, 4\}$
The relation is not a function since -7 is used as a first coordinate in two different ordered pairs.

12. Domain = $\{0, 1.3, 4\}$
Range = $\{0, -2, 8.6\}$
The relation is not a function since 1.3 is used as a first coordinate in two different ordered pairs.

14. Domain = $\{40, 42, 44, 46, 48\}$
Range = $\{14, 15, 16, 17, 18\}$
The relation is a function.

16. Domain = {Jan., Feb., Mar., Apr., May, June, July, Aug., Sept., Oct., Nov., Dec.}
Range = $\{79, 80, 81\}$
The relation is a function.

18. Domain = $\{32, 41, 50, 59, 68, 95\}$
Range = $\{0, 5, 10, 15, 20, 35\}$
The relation is a function.

20. Function; no different ordered pairs have the same first coordinate

22. Not a function; many different ordered pairs have the same first coordinate

24. Function; no different ordered pairs have the same first coordinate

26. Not a function; many different ordered pairs have the same first coordinate

28. Function; no different ordered pairs have the same first coordinate

30. $f(x) = 3x + 4$
$f(6) = 3(6) + 4 = 18 + 4 = 22$

32. $f(x) = 3x + 4$
$f(-2) = 3(-2) + 4 = -6 + 4 = -2$

34. $g(x) = 2x - 5$
$g(-2.4) = 2(-2.4) - 5 = -4.8 - 5 = -9.8$

36. $g(x) = 2x - 5$
$g\left(\dfrac{1}{2}\right) = 2\left(\dfrac{1}{2}\right) - 5 = 1 - 5 = -4$

38. $h(x) = \dfrac{2}{3}x + 2$
$h(-6) = \dfrac{2}{3}(-6) + 2 = -4 + 2 = -2$

40. $h(x) = \dfrac{2}{3}x + 2$
$h(2) = \dfrac{2}{3}(2) + 2 = \dfrac{4}{3} + 2 = \dfrac{10}{3} = 3\dfrac{1}{3}$

42. $r(x) = 2x^2 - 4x + 1$
$r\left(\dfrac{1}{3}\right) = 2\left(\dfrac{1}{3}\right)^2 - 4\left(\dfrac{1}{3}\right) + 1$
$= \dfrac{2}{9} - \dfrac{4}{3} + 1$
$= -\dfrac{1}{9}$

44. $r(x) = 2x^2 - 4x + 1$
$r(-3) = 2(-3)^2 - 4(-3) + 1$
$= 18 + 12 + 1$
$= 31$

46. $t(x) = x^3 - 3x^2 + 2x - 3$
$t(-3) = (-3)^3 - 3(-3)^2 + 2(-3) - 3$
$= -27 - 27 - 6 - 3 = -63$

48. $t(x) = x^3 - 3x^2 + 2x - 3$
$t(-2) = (-2)^3 - 3(-2)^2 + 2(-2) - 3$
$= -8 - 12 - 4 - 3 = -27$

50. $g(x) = x^2 + 3$

$g(-2) = (-2)^2 + 3 = 7$

$g(-1) = (-1)^2 + 3 = 4$

$g(0) = 0^2 + 3 = 3$

$g(1) = 1^2 + 3 = 4$

$g(2) = 2^2 + 3 = 7$

Range: $\{3, 4, 7\}$

52. $d(x) = 3 - \dfrac{1}{4}x$

$0 = 3 - \dfrac{1}{4}x$

$\dfrac{1}{4}x = 3$

$x = 12$

$\dfrac{1}{4} = 3 - \dfrac{1}{4}x$

$-\dfrac{11}{4} = -\dfrac{1}{4}x$

$11 = x$

$\dfrac{3}{4} = 3 - \dfrac{1}{4}x$

$-\dfrac{9}{4} = -\dfrac{1}{4}x$

$9 = x$

$4 = 3 - \dfrac{1}{4}x$

$1 = -\dfrac{1}{4}x$

$-4 = x$

Domain: $\{-4, 9, 11, 12\}$

Cumulative Review Problems

54. $-3\{x + 2[x - 3(2 + x)]\}$

$= -3[x + 2(x - 6 - 3x)]$

$= -3[x + 2(-2x - 6)]$

$= -3(x - 4x - 12)$

$= -3(-3x - 12)$

$= 9x + 36$

56. $20(81 + 76)$

$= 20(157)$

$= 3140$

3140 tons of raw material

3.6 Exercises

2. $f(x) = 2x - 1$

x	$f(x)$
0	-1
1	1
2	3

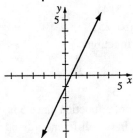

4. $f(x) = \dfrac{3}{4}x + 2$

x	$f(x)$
-4	-1
0	2
4	5

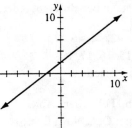

6. $f(x) = -\dfrac{1}{2}x - 1$

x	$f(x)$
-4	1
0	-1
2	-2

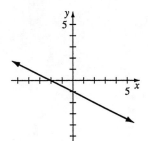

8. $f(x) = -\dfrac{2}{3}x - \dfrac{1}{2}$

x	$f(x)$
0	$-\dfrac{1}{2}$
-3	$\dfrac{3}{2}$
3	$-\dfrac{5}{2}$

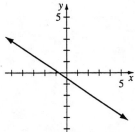

10. $c(x) = 0.10x + 35$

x	$c(x)$
0	35
100	45
200	55
250	60

12. $p(x) = -1500x + 45,000$

x	$p(x)$
0	45,000
10	30,000
30	0

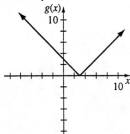

When $x = 30$, $p(x) = 0$ and the river will not support any fish.

14. $g(x) = |x - 3|$

x	$g(x)$
0	3
2	1
3	0
4	1
6	3

16. $g(x) = |x| - 5$

x	$g(x)$
-2	-3
-1	-4
0	-5
1	-4
2	-3

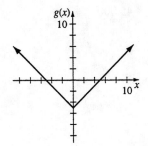

18. $g(x) = x^2 - 4$

x	$g(x)$
−2	0
−1	−3
0	−4
1	−3
2	0

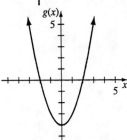

20. $g(x) = (x+1)^2$

x	$g(x)$
−3	4
−2	1
−1	0
0	1
1	4

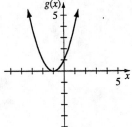

22. $g(x) = x^3 - 3$

x	$g(x)$
−2	−11
−1	−4
0	−3
1	−2
2	5

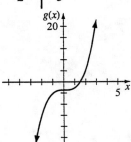

24. $s(x) = (x-3)^3$

x	$s(x)$
0	−27
2	−1
3	0
4	1
6	27

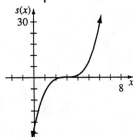

26. $g(x) = -\dfrac{3}{x}$

x	$g(x)$
-2	$\dfrac{3}{2}$
-1	3
$-\dfrac{1}{2}$	6
$\dfrac{1}{2}$	-6
1	-3
2	$-\dfrac{3}{2}$

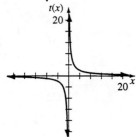

28. $t(x) = \dfrac{8}{x}$

x	$t(x)$
-4	-2
-2	-4
$-\dfrac{1}{2}$	-16
$\dfrac{1}{2}$	16
2	4
4	2

30.

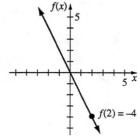

$f(2) = -4$

32.

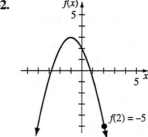

$f(2) = -5$

34.

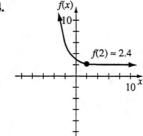

$f(2) \approx 2.4$

36. (a)

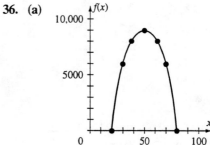

(b) 50

(c) Between 40 and 60

(d) They will operate at a loss

(e) $8700

38. (a)

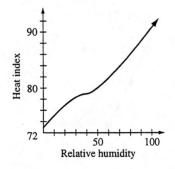

No. Because there is not a constant rate of change.

(b) 80

(c) Between 80% and 100%

(d) Between 45% and 50%

(e) At 20% humidity, 80° feels relatively cool.

Cumulative Review Problems

40. $\frac{1}{2}(3x + 5y) = 2(x - 3y)$
$3x + 5y = 4(x - 3y)$
$3x + 5y = 4x - 12y$
$17y = x$

42. $0.12(x - 4) = 1.16x - 8.02$
$12(x - 4) = 116x - 802$
$12x - 48 = 116x - 802$
$-48 = 104x - 802$
$754 = 104x$
$7.25 = x$

44. $10(24)(31 + 31 + 29) = 240(91) = 21{,}840$
It will breathe 21,840 times.

Chapter 3 Review Problems

2. $-5x = 3(y + 4)$
$-5(3) = 3(b + 4)$
$-15 = 3b + 12$
$-27 = 3b$
$-9 = b$

4. $y = -\frac{1}{4}x - 1$
$m = -\frac{1}{4},\ b = -1$

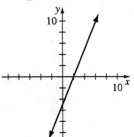

6. $5(x - y) = 10 - 3y$
$5x - 5y = 10 - 3y$
$5x - 10 = 2y$
$\frac{5}{2}x - 5 = y$
$m = \frac{5}{2},\ b = -5$

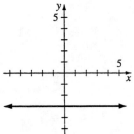

8. $-3y + 2 = -8y - 13$
$5y + 2 = -13$
$5y = -15$
$y = -3$

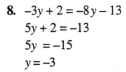

10. $m = \dfrac{-4 - (-3)}{-8 - 2}$
$= \dfrac{1}{10}$

12. No slope (vertical line)

14. $A(3, -5)$; $B(2, 1)$; $C(-2, 10)$

$m_{AB} = \dfrac{-5-1}{3-2} = -6$

$m_{BC} = \dfrac{10-1}{-2-2} = -\dfrac{9}{4}$

They do not lie on the same line since $m_{AB} \neq m_{BC}$.

16. $y = mx + b$

$y = \dfrac{2}{3}x - 4$

$3y = 2x - 12$

$2x - 3y = 12$

18. Slope 0 indicates a horizontal line.

$y = 1$

20. No slope indicates a vertical line.

$x = -6$

22. $7x + 8y - 12 = 0$

$8y = -7x + 12$

$y = -\dfrac{7}{8}x + \dfrac{3}{2}$

$m = -\dfrac{7}{8}$

A perpendicular line has slope $m = \dfrac{8}{7}$.

$y - y_1 = m(x - x_1)$

$y - 5 = \dfrac{8}{7}[x - (-2)]$

$7y - 35 = 8(x + 2)$

$7y - 35 = 8x + 16$

$8x - 7y = -51$

24. $y < 2x + 4$ (dashed line)

Test point: $(0, 0)$

$0 < 2(0) + 4$

$0 < 4$

True; shade the half-plane containing $(0, 0)$.

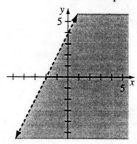

26. $y > -\dfrac{2}{3}x + 1$ (dashed line)

Test point: $(0, 0)$

$0 > -\dfrac{2}{3}(0) + 1$

$0 > 1$

False; shade the half-plane not containing $(0, 0)$.

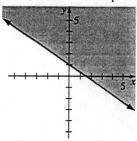

28. $5x + 3y \leq -15$ (solid line)

Test point: $(0, 0)$

$5(0) + 3(0) \leq -15$

$0 \leq -15$

False; shade the half-plane not containing $(0, 0)$.

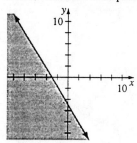

30. $3x - 5 < 7$

$3x < 12$

$x < 4$ (dashed line)

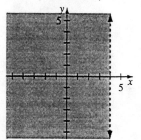

32. Domain = $\{0, 1, 2, 3\}$

Range = $\{0, 1, 4, 9, 16\}$

The relation is not a function since 1 is the first coordinate in two different ordered pairs.

34. Function; no different ordered pairs have the same first coordinate

36. Not a function; many different ordered pairs have the same first coordinate

38. $g(x) = 2x^2 - 3x - 5$

$g(-3) = 2(-3)^2 - 3(-3) - 5$

$= 18 + 9 - 5$

$= 22$

40. $p(x) = |-6x - 3|$

$p(3) = |-6(3) - 3|$

$= |-21|$

$= 21$

42. $g(x) = x^2 - 3$

x	$g(x)$
-2	1
-1	-2
0	-3
1	-2
2	1

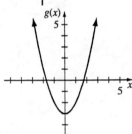

44.

$f(-2) = 0$

46. $f(x) = -\dfrac{4}{5}x + 3$

x	$f(x)$
-5	7
0	3
10	-5

48. $f(x) = 3x^3 - 4$

x	$f(x)$
-1	-7
0	-4
2	20

Chapter 3 Test

2. $m = \dfrac{-3 - (-6)}{2 - \frac{1}{2}}$

$= \dfrac{3}{\frac{3}{2}}$

$= 2$

4. $m = \dfrac{-2 - (-1)}{5 - (-3)}$

$= -\dfrac{1}{8}$

$y - y_1 = m(x - x_1)$

$y - (-2) = -\dfrac{1}{8}(x - 5)$

$y + 2 = -\dfrac{1}{8}(x - 5)$

$8y + 16 = -x + 5$

$x + 8y = -11$

6. $y = 2$

8. $4x - 2y < -6$

$2x - y < -3$ (dashed line)

Test point: (0, 0)

$2(0) - 0 < -3$

$0 < -3$

False; shade the half-plane not containing (0, 0).

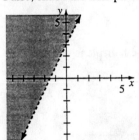

10. $f(x) = 2x - 3$

$f\left(\dfrac{3}{4}\right) = 2\left(\dfrac{3}{4}\right) - 3 = \dfrac{3}{2} - \dfrac{6}{2} = -\dfrac{3}{2} = -1\dfrac{1}{2}$

12. $h(x) = \left| -\dfrac{2}{3}x + 4 \right|$

$h(-9) = \left| -\dfrac{2}{3}(-9) + 4 \right|$

$= |6 + 4|$

$= |10|$

$= 10$

14. $g(x) = 5 - x^2$

x	$g(x)$
-2	1
-1	4
0	5
1	4
2	1

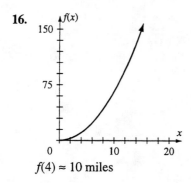

16.

$f(4) \approx 10$ miles

Cumulative Test For Chapters 1–3

2. $3(4-6)^2 + \sqrt{16} + 12 \div (-3)$

$= 3(-2)^2 + 4 + 12 \div (-3)$

$= 3(4) + 4 + 12 \div (-3)$

$= 12 + 4 - 4$

$= 12$

4. $5x(2x - 3y) - 3(x^2 + 4)$

$= 10x^2 - 15xy - 3x^2 - 12$

$= 7x^2 - 15xy - 12$

6. $3(x-2) > 6$ or $5 - 3(x+1) > 8$

$3x - 6 > 6$ or $5 - 3x - 3 > 8$

$3x > 12$ or $2 - 3x > 8$

$x > 4$ or $-3x > 6$

$x > 4$ or $x < -2$

8. width: x

length: $2x + 1$

$2(x) + 2(2x + 1) = 92$

$2x + 4x + 2 = 92$

$6x + 2 = 92$

$6x = 90$

$x = 15$

$2x + 1 = 30 + 1 = 31$

width $= 15$ cm; length $= 31$ cm

10. $A = \dfrac{1}{2}\pi r^2$

$= \dfrac{1}{2}(3.14)(3)^2$

$= 14.13$

14.13 sq in.

12. $m = \dfrac{5-1}{6-(-2)} = \dfrac{4}{8}$

$= \dfrac{1}{2}$

14. $y = \dfrac{2}{3}x - 4$

$m = \dfrac{2}{3}$

A perpendicular line has slope $m = -\dfrac{3}{2}$.

$y - y_1 = m(x - x_1)$

$y - (-3) = -\dfrac{3}{2}[x - (-2)]$

$y + 3 = -\dfrac{3}{2}(x + 2)$

$2y + 6 = -3x - 6$

$3x + 2y = -12$

16. $f(x) = -2x^2 - 4x + 1$

$f(-3) = -2(-3)^2 - 4(-3) + 1$

$= -18 + 12 + 1$

$= -5$

18. $h(x) = |x - 2|$

x	$h(x)$
−1	3
0	2
1	1
2	0
3	1
4	2

20. $f(x) = x^2 - 3$

x	$f(x)$
−2	1
−1	−2
0	−3
1	−2
2	1

22. $f(x) = -2x^3 + 4$

x	$f(x)$
−2	20
0	4
3	−50

Chapter 4

Pretest Chapter 4

2. $7x + 3y = 15$

$\dfrac{1}{3}x - \dfrac{1}{2}y = 2$

$7x + 3y = 15$
$\underline{2x - 3y = 12}$
$9x = 27$
$x = 3$

$7(3) + 3y = 15$
$21 + 3y = 15$
$3y = -6$
$y = -2$
$x = 3,\ y = -2$

4. $5x - 2y + z = -1$
$3x + y - 2z = 6$
$-2x + 3y - 5z = 7$

$10x - 4y + 2z = -2$ $25x - 10y + 5z = -5$
$\underline{3x + y - 2z = 6}$ $\underline{-2x + 3y - 5z = 7}$
$13x - 3y = 4$ $23x - 7y = 2$

$91x - 21y = 28$
$\underline{-69x + 21y = -6}$
$22x = 22$
$x = 1$

$13(1) - 3y = 4$
$13 - 3y = 4$
$-3y = -9$
$y = 3$

$5(1) - 2(3) + z = -1$
$5 - 6 + z = -1$
$-1 + z = -1$
$z = 0$
$x = 1,\ y = 3,\ z = 0$

6. cost of shirt: x
cost of pants: y
$2x + 3y = 75$
$3x + 5y = 121$

$-6x - 9y = -225$
$\underline{6x + 10y = 242}$
$y = 17$

$2x + 3(17) = 75$
$2x + 51 = 75$
$2x = 24$
$x = 12$
shirt: \$12; pants: \$17

8. $\begin{vmatrix} 2 & -4 \\ 3 & -5 \end{vmatrix} = 2(-5) - (3)(-4)$
$= -10 + 12$
$= 2$

10. $\begin{vmatrix} 3 & 0 \\ 4 & 0 \end{vmatrix} = 3(0) - 4(0) = 0$

12. $D = \begin{vmatrix} 2 & 7 \\ 5 & 6 \end{vmatrix} = (2)(6) - (5)(7) = -23$

$D_x = \begin{vmatrix} -10 & 7 \\ -2 & 6 \end{vmatrix} = (-10)(6) - (-2)(7) = -46$

$D_y = \begin{vmatrix} 2 & -10 \\ 5 & -2 \end{vmatrix} = (2)(-2) - (5)(-10) = 46$

$x = \dfrac{D_x}{D} = \dfrac{-46}{-23} = 2$

$y = \dfrac{D_y}{D} = \dfrac{46}{-23} = -2$

14. $2x + 2y \geq -4$
$-3x + y \leq 2$

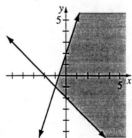

4.1 Exercises

2. $3x - 5y = 15$
$3(-5) - 5(-6) \overset{?}{=} 15$
$-15 + 30 \overset{?}{=} 15$
$15 = 15$ ✔

$-2x + y = 4$

$-2(-5) - 6 \overset{?}{=} 4$

$10 - 6 \overset{?}{=} 4$

$4 = 4$ ✔

$(-5, -6)$ is a solution to the system.

4. $3x = 2y + 12$

$3(8) \overset{?}{=} 2(6) + 12$

$24 \overset{?}{=} 12 + 12$

$24 = 24$ ✔

$8y = -3x + 62$

$8(6) \overset{?}{=} -3(8) + 62$

$48 \overset{?}{=} -24 + 62$

$48 \neq 38$

$(8, 6)$ is not a solution to the system.

6. $4x + 3y = -4$

$4(-2) + 3\left(\dfrac{4}{3}\right) \overset{?}{=} -4$

$-8 + 4 \overset{?}{=} -4$

$-4 = -4$ ✔

$x - 6y = -10$

$-2 - 6\left(\dfrac{4}{3}\right) \overset{?}{=} -10$

$-2 - 8 \overset{?}{=} -10$

$-10 = -10$ ✔

$\left(-2, \dfrac{4}{3}\right)$ is a solution to the system.

8. $3x + y = 2$

$2x - y = 3$

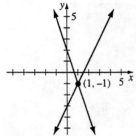

$(1, -1)$ is a solution to the system.

10. $2x + 3y = 6$

$2x + y = -2$

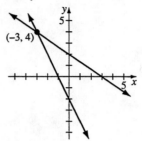

$(-3, 4)$ is a solution to the system.

12. $y = \dfrac{1}{3}x - 2$

$-x + 3y = 9$

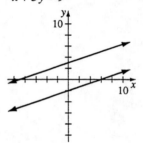

No solution

14. $2x + 3y = 9$

$x = 2 + y$

$2(2 + y) + 3y = 9$

$4 + 2y + 3y = 9$

$4 + 5y = 9$

$5y = 5$

$y = 1$

$x = 2 + 1 = 3$

$x = 3, \ y = 1$

Check

$2(3) + 3(1) \overset{?}{=} 9$ $3 \overset{?}{=} 2 + 1$

$6 + 3 \overset{?}{=} 9$ $3 = 3$ ✔

$9 = 9$ ✔

16. $5x - 2y = 8$

$3x - y = 7$

$y = 3x - 7$

$5x - 2(3x - 7) = 8$

$5x - 6x + 14 = 8$

$-x = -6$

$x = 6$

$y = 3(6) - 7 = 11$
$x = 6,\ y = 11$
Check
$5(6) - 2(11) \overset{?}{=} 8$ $11 \overset{?}{=} 3(6) - 7$
$30 - 22 \overset{?}{=} 8$ $11 \overset{?}{=} 18 - 7$
$8 = 8$ ✔ $11 = 11$ ✔

18. $5x - 2y = 8$
     $3x + y = 7$

     $y = 7 - 3x$
     $5x - 2(7 - 3x) = 8$
     $5x - 14 + 6x = 8$
     $11x - 14 = 8$
     $11x = 22$
     $x = 2$

     $y = 7 - 3(2) = 1$
     $x = 2,\ y = 1$

20. $-3a + 4b = -18$
     $2a + b = 1$

     $b = 1 - 2a$
     $-3a + 4(1 - 2a) = -18$
     $-3a + 4 - 8a = -18$
     $-11a + 4 = -18$
     $-11a = -22$
     $a = 2$

     $b = 1 - 2(2) = -3$
     $a = 2,\ b = -3$

22. $\dfrac{1}{5}x - \dfrac{1}{2}y = -1$
     $\dfrac{3}{5} - 3y = -9$

     $x - \dfrac{5}{2}y = -5$
     $3x - 15y = -45$
     $x = \dfrac{5}{2}y - 5$

     $3\left(\dfrac{5}{2}y - 5\right) - 15y = -45$
     $\dfrac{15}{2}y - 15 - 15y = -45$
     $15y - 30 - 30y = -90$

$-15y - 30 = -90$
$-15y = -60$
$y = 4$
$x = \dfrac{5}{2}(4) - 5 = 5$
$x = 5,\ y = 4$

24. $2(x - 2) + 3(y + 1) = -2$
     $x + 2(y - 1) = -4$

     $x = -2(y - 1) - 4$
     $= -2y + 2 - 4$
     $= -2y - 2$

     $2(-2y - 2 - 2) + 3(y + 1) = -2$
     $2(-2y - 4) + 3(y + 1) = -2$
     $-4y - 8 + 3y + 3 = -2$
     $-y - 5 = -2$
     $-y = 3$
     $y = -3$
     $x = -2(-3) - 2 = 4$
     $x = 4,\ y = -3$

26. $x + 3y = 2$
     $4x + 5y = 1$

     $-4x - 12y = -8$
     $\underline{4x + 5y = 1}$
     $-7y = -7$
     $y = 1$

     $x + 3(1) = 2$
     $x + 3 = 2$
     $x = -1$
     $x = -1,\ y = 1$

28. $2a + b = 3$
     $a - 2b = -1$

     $4a + 2b = 6$
     $\underline{a - 2b = -1}$
     $5a = 5$
     $a = 1$

     $2(1) + b = 3$
     $2 + b = 3$
     $b = 1$
     $a = 1,\ b = 1$

30. $2s + 3t = 5$
$3s - 6t = 18$

$4s + 6t = 10$
$\underline{3s - 6t = 18}$
$7s = 28$
$s = 4$

$2(4) + 3t = 5$
$8 + 3t = 5$
$3t = -3$
$t = -1$
$s = 4,\ t = -1$

32. $\dfrac{4}{3}x - y = 4$

$\dfrac{3}{4}x - y = \dfrac{1}{2}$

$4x - 3y = 12$
$3x - 4y = 2$

$12x - 9y = 36$
$\underline{-12x + 16y = -8}$
$7y = 28$
$y = 4$

$4x - 3(4) = 12$
$4x - 12 = 12$
$4x = 24$
$x = 6$
$x = 6,\ y = 4$

34. $0.9x + 0.4y = 0$
$0.5x - 0.8y = 2.3$

$9x + 4y = 0$
$5x - 8y = 23$

$18x + 8y = 0$
$\underline{5x - 8y = 23}$
$23x = 23$
$x = 1$

$9(1) + 4y = 0$
$9 + 4y = 0$
$4y = -9$
$y = -\dfrac{9}{4}$

$x = 1,\ y = -\dfrac{9}{4}$

36. $3(x + 1) + y = -7$
$2(x + 4) + 3(y + 1) = -5$

$3x + 3 + y = -7$
$3x + y = -10$

$2x + 8 + 3y + 3 = -5$
$2x + 3y = -16$

$3x + y = -10$
$2x + 3y = -16$

$-9x - 3y = 30$
$\underline{2x + 3y = -16}$
$-7x = 14$
$x = -2$

$3(-2) + y = -10$
$-6 + y = -10$
$y = -4$
$x = -2,\ y = -4$

38. $2x + 3y = 16$
$5x - \dfrac{3}{4}y = 7$

$2x + 3y = 16$
$\underline{20x - 3y = 28}$
$22x = 44$
$x = 2$

$2(2) + 3y = 16$
$4 + 3y = 16$
$3y = 12$
$y = 4$
$x = 2,\ y = 4$

40. $0.1x - 0.6 = 0.3y$
$0.3x + 0.1y + 2.2 = 0$

$x - 6 = 3y$
$3x + y + 22 = 0$

$x = 3y + 6$
$3(3y + 6) + y + 22 = 0$
$9y + 18 + y + 22 = 0$
$10y + 40 = 0$
$10y = -40$
$y = -4$

$x = 3(-4) + 6 = -6$
$x = -6, \ y = -4$

42. $3x - 11y = 9$
$-9x + 33y = 18$

$9x - 33y = 27$
$\underline{-9x + 33y = 18}$
$0 = 45$
No solution; inconsistent system of equations.

44. $-9x + 6y - 10 = 0$
$6x = 4y - 8$
$x = \dfrac{2}{3}y - \dfrac{4}{3}$
$-9\left(\dfrac{2}{3}y - \dfrac{4}{3}\right) + 6y - 10 = 0$
$-6y + 12 + 6y - 10 = 0$
$2 = 0$
No solution; inconsistent system of equations.

46. $3a - 2b = \dfrac{3}{2}$
$\dfrac{3a}{2} = \dfrac{3}{4} + b$

$6a - 4b = 3$
$6a = 3 + 4b$

$3 + 4b - 4b = 3$
$3 = 3$
Infinite number of solutions; dependent equations.

48. $\dfrac{2}{5}x + \dfrac{3}{5}y = 1$
$x - \dfrac{2}{3}y = \dfrac{1}{3}$

$2x + 3y = 5$
$3x - 2y = 1$

$4x + 6y = 10$
$\underline{9x - 6y = 3}$
$13x = 13$
$x = 1$

$2(1) + 3y = 5$
$2 + 3y = 5$
$3y = 3$
$y = 1$
$x = 1, \ y = 1$

50. $0.0052x - 0.0093y = 0.1256$
$-0.0104x + 0.0521y = 0.9315$

Multiply 1st equation by 2:
$0.0104x - 0.0186y = 0.2512$
$\underline{-0.0104x + 0.0521y = 0.9315}$
$0.0335y = 1.1827$
$y = 35.3045$

$0.0052x - 0.0093(35.3045) = 0.1256$
$x = 87.2946$
$x = 87.2946, \ y = 35.3045$

52. $y_1 = -0.81x + 2.3$
$y_2 = 1.6x + 0.8$

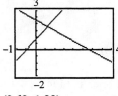

$(0.62, 1.80)$

54. $5.86x + 6.22y = -8.89$

$-2.33x + 4.72y = -10.61$

$y_1 = \dfrac{-8.89 - 5.86x}{6.22}$

$y_2 = \dfrac{-10.61 + 2.33x}{4.72}$

$(0.57, -1.97)$

Cumulative Review Problems

56. $\dfrac{5}{4} \times 273{,}511 = 341{,}888.75$

341,889 cars

Putting Your Skills to Work

2. $\dfrac{A - 0.10A}{32} \times \dfrac{144 \text{ in}^2}{1 \text{ ft}^2} = 4.5(A - 0.10A)$

$N = 4.5(A - 0.10A)$

$N = 4.5A - 0.45A$

$N = 4.05A$

$N = 4.05(9 \times 9) = 328.05$

A minimum of 329 bricks will be needed.

4. $23(11) + 17z = d$

$45(11) + 36z = d + 508$

$17z - d = -253$

$\underline{-36z + d = -13}$

$-19z = -266$

$z = 14$

$17(14) - d = -253$

$d = 491$

The length of the brick is 14 inches. The original distance is 491 inches.

4.2 Exercises

2. $3x + 4y + 2z = -1$

$3(5) + 4(-3) + 2(-2) \overset{?}{=} -1$

$15 - 12 - 4 \overset{?}{=} -1$?

$-1 = -1$

$-x - 2y + 3z = -5$

$-5 - 2(-3) + 3(-2) \overset{?}{=} -5$

$-5 + 6 - 6 \overset{?}{=} -5$?

$-5 = -5$

$x + y + z = 0$

$5 - 3 - 2 \overset{?}{=} 0$

$0 = 0$

$(5, -3, -2)$ is a solution to the system.

4. $2x + y + 3z = 2$

$x - y + 2z = -4$

$x + 3y - z = 1$

$\begin{array}{ll} 2x + y + 3z = 2 \\ \underline{x - y + 2z = -4} \\ 3x + 5z = -2 \end{array}$
$\qquad$
$\begin{array}{ll} 3x - 3y + 6z = -12 \\ \underline{x + 3y - z = 1} \\ 4x + 5z = -11 \end{array}$

$-12x - 20z = 8$

$\underline{12x + 15z = -33}$

$-5z = -25$

$z = 5$

$3x + 5(5) = -2$

$3x = -27$

$x = -9$

$2(-9) + y + 3(5) = 2$

$-18 + y + 15 = 2$

$y = 5$

$x = -9, \ y = 5, \ z = 5$

6. $-5x + 3y + 2z = 1$

$x + y + z = 7$

$2x - y + z = 7$

$\begin{array}{ll} x + y + z = 7 \\ \underline{2x - y + z = 7} \\ 3x + 2z = 14 \end{array}$
$\qquad$
$\begin{array}{ll} -5x + 3y + 2z = 1 \\ \underline{6x - 3y + 3z = 21} \\ x + 5z = 22 \end{array}$

$3x + 2z = 14$
$\underline{-3x - 15z = -66}$
$-13z = -52$
$z = 4$

$x + 5(4) = 22$
$x = 2$

$2 + y + 4 = 7$
$y = 1$
$x = 2, y = 1, z = 4$

8. $3x - y + 4z = 4$
$x - 2y + 2z = 4$
$2x + y - 3z = 5$

$3x - y + 4z = 4$ $x - 2y + 2z = 4$
$\underline{2x + y - 3z = 5}$ $\underline{4x + 2y - 6z = 10}$
$5x + z = 9$ $5x - 4z = 14$

$20x + 4z = 36$
$\underline{5x - 4z = 14}$
$25x = 50$
$x = 2$

$5(2) + z = 9$
$z = -1$

$2(2) + y - 3(-1) = 5$
$4 + y + 3 = 5$
$y = -2$
$x = 2, y = -2, z = -1$

10. Multiply the second equation by 2 to clear fractions.
$x - 4y + 4z = -1$
$-2x + y - 5z = -6$
$-x + 3y - z = 5$

$x - 4y + 4z = -1$ $2x - 8y + 8z = -2$
$\underline{-x + 3y - z = 5}$ $\underline{-2x + y - 5z = -6}$
$-y + 3z = 4$ $-7y + 3z = -8$

$y - 3z = -4$
$\underline{-7y + 3z = -8}$
$-6y = -12$
$y = 2$

$-2 + 3z = 4$
$3z = 6$
$z = 2$

$x - 4(2) + 4(2) = -1$
$x = -1$
$x = -1, y = 2, z = 2$

12. $-2x + y - 2z = 0$
$4x + 2y + 2z = -6$
$3x - 2y + 2z = -3$

$-2x + y - 2z = 0$ $-2x + y - 2z = 0$
$\underline{4x + 2y + 2z = -6}$ $\underline{3x - 2y + 2z = -3}$
$2x + 3y = -6$ $x - y = -3$

$2x + 3y = -6$
$\underline{3x - 3y = -9}$
$5x = -15$
$x = -3$

$-3 - y = -3$
$-y = 0$
$y = 0$
$-2(-3) + 0 - 2z = 0$
$-2z = -6$
$z = 3$
$x = -3, y = 0, z = 3$

14. $a = c - b$
$3a - 2b + 6c = 1$
$c = 4 - 3b - 7a$

$3(c - b) - 2b + 6c = 1$ $c = 4 - 3b - 7(c - b)$
$3c - 3b - 2b + 6c = 1$ $c = 4 - 3b - 7c + 7b$
$-5b + 9c = 1$ $-4b + 8c = 4$

$-20b + 36c = 4$
$\underline{20b - 40c = -20}$
$-4c = -16$
$c = 4$

$-4b + 8(4) = 4$
$-4b = -28$
$b = 7$

$a = 4 - 7 = -3$
$a = -3, b = 7, c = 4$

16. $4a + 2b + 3c = 9$
$3a + 5b + 4c = 19$
$9a + 3b + 2c = 3$

$\begin{array}{l}-16a - 8b - 12c = -36 \\ \underline{9a + 15b + 12c = 57} \\ -7a + 7b = 21\end{array}$　　$\begin{array}{l}3a + 5b + 4c = 19 \\ \underline{-18a - 6b - 4c = -6} \\ -15a - b = 13\end{array}$

$\begin{array}{l}-7a + 7b = 21 \\ \underline{-105a - 7b = 91} \\ -112a = 112 \\ a = -1\end{array}$

$-15(-1) - b = 13$
$-b = -2$
$b = 2$

$9(-1) + 3(2) + 2c = 3$
$-9 + 6 + 2c = 3$
$2c = 6$
$c = 3$
$a = -1, b = 2, c = 3$

18. $-3x - 2y + 3z = 2$
$2x - 5y + 2z + 2 = 0$
$4x - 3y + 4z = 10$

$-3x - 2y + 3z = 2$
$2x - 5y + 2z = -2$
$4x - 3y + 4z = 10$

$\begin{array}{l}-6x - 4y + 6z = 4 \\ \underline{6x - 15y + 6z = -6} \\ -19y + 12z = -2\end{array}$　　$\begin{array}{l}-4x + 10y - 4z = 4 \\ \underline{4x - 3y + 4z = 10} \\ 7y = 14\end{array}$

$y = 2$

$-19(2) + 12z = -2$
$12z = 36$
$z = 3$

$2x - 5(2) + 2(3) = -2$
$2x - 10 + 6 = -2$
$2x = 2$
$x = 1$
$x = 1, y = 2, z = 3$

20. $4x + 2y + 3z = 9$
$9x + 3y + 2z = 3$
$2.987x + 5.027y + 3.867z = 18.642$

$\begin{array}{l}-8x - 4y - 6z = -18 \\ \underline{27x + 9y + 6z = 9} \\ 19x + 5y = -9\end{array}$

$\begin{array}{l}-5.156x - 2.578y - 3.867z = -11.601 \\ \underline{2.987x + 5.027y + 3.867z = 18.642} \\ -2.169x + 2.449y = 7.041\end{array}$

$\begin{array}{l}-9.3062x - 2.449y = 4.4082 \\ \underline{-2.169x + 2.449y = 7.041} \\ -11.4752x = 11.4492 \\ x = -0.99773\end{array}$

$19(-0.99773) + 5y = -9$
$5y = 9.95687$
$y = 1.99137$

$4(-0.99773) + 2(1.99137) + 3z = 9$
$-3.99092 + 3.98274 + 3z = 9$
$3z = 9.00818$
$z = 3.00273$
$x = -0.99773, y = 1.99137, z = 3.00273$

22. $y - 2z = 5$
$2x + z = -1$
$3x + y - z = 4$

$\begin{array}{l}-6x - 3z = 3 \\ \underline{6x + 2y - 2z = 8} \\ 2y - 5z = 11\end{array}$

$\begin{array}{l}-2y + 4z = -10 \\ \underline{2y - 5z = 11} \\ -z = 1 \\ z = -1\end{array}$

$y - 2(-1) = 5$
$y = 3$

$2x - 1 = -1$

$2x = 0$

$x = 0$

$x = 0, y = 3, z = -1$

24. $-2x + y - 3z = 0$

$-2y - z = -1$

$x + 2y - z = 5$

$-2x + y - 3z = 0$

$\underline{2x + 4y - 2z = 10}$

$5y - 5z = 10$

$-y + z = -2$

$-y + z = -2$

$\underline{-2y - z = -1}$

$-3y = -3$

$y = 1$

$-2(1) - z = -1$

$-z = 1$

$z = -1$

$x + 2(1) - (-1) = 5$

$x + 2 + 1 = 5$

$x = 2$

$x = 2, y = 1, z = -1$

26. $x + 2z = 0$

$3x + 3y + z = 6$

$6y + 5z = -3$

$-6x - 6y - 2z = -12$

$\underline{6y + 5z = -3}$

$-6x + 3z = -15$

$6x + 12z = 0$

$\underline{-6x + 3z = -15}$

$15z = -15$

$z = -1$

$x + 2(-1) = 0$

$x = 2$

$6y + 5(-1) = -3$

$6y = 2$

$y = \dfrac{1}{3}$

$x = 2, \; y = \dfrac{1}{3}, \; z = -1$

28. $a + 2b + c = 5$

$4a + 2c = 10$

$-b - 5c = -6$

$a + 2b + c = 5$

$\underline{-2b - 10c = -12}$

$a - 9c = -7$

$-4a + 36c = 28$

$\underline{4a + 2c = 10}$

$38c = 38$

$c = 1$

$4a + 2(1) = 10$

$4a = 8$

$a = 2$

$-b - 5(1) = -6$

$-b = -1$

$b = 1$

$a = 2, \; b = 1, \; c = 1$

30. $-3x - 4y = -15$

$2x - 5z = -3$

$-4y + 3z = -9$

$3x + 4y = 15$

$\underline{-4y + 3z = -9}$

$3x + 3z = 6$

$x + z = 2$

$-2x - 2z = -4$

$\underline{2x - 5z = -3}$

$-7z = -7$

$z = 1$

$-4y + 3(1) = -9$

$-4y = -12$

$y = 3$

$-3x - 4(3) = -15$
$-3x = -3$
$x = 1$
$x = 1, y = 3, z = 1$

32. $3x = 11 + 2y - 4z$
$6x = 1 - 6y$
$z = 1 - 2y$

$3x - 2y + 4z = 11$
$6x + 6y = 1$
$2y + z = 1$

$3x - 2y + 4z = 11$
$\underline{-8y - 4z = -4}$
$3x - 10y = 7$

$-6x + 20y = -14$
$\underline{6x + 6y = 1}$
$26y = -13$
$y = -\dfrac{1}{2}$

$2y + z = 1$
$2\left(-\dfrac{1}{2}\right) + z = 1$
$z = 2$

$6x + 6y = 1$
$6x + 6\left(-\dfrac{1}{2}\right) = 1$
$6x = 4$
$x = \dfrac{2}{3}$

$x = \dfrac{2}{3}, \; y = -\dfrac{1}{2}, \; z = 2$

34. $6x - 2y + 2z = 2$
$4x + 8y - 2z = 5$
$-2x - 4y + z = -2$

$4x + 8y - 2z = 5$
$\underline{-4x - 8y + 2z = -4}$
$0 = 1$
No solution; inconsistent system of equations.

36. $-3x + 4y - z = -4$
$x + 2y + z = 4$
$-12x + 16y - 4z = -16$

$12x - 16y + 4z = 16$
$\underline{-12x + 16y - 4z = -16}$
$0 = 0$
Infinite number of solutions; dependent equation.

Cumulative Review Problems

38. $y = -\dfrac{2}{3}x + 4$
$m = -\dfrac{2}{3}$
$m_\perp = \dfrac{3}{2}$
$y - y_1 = m(x - x_1)$
$y - 2 = \dfrac{3}{2}[x - (-4)]$
$2y - 4 = 3(x + 4)$
$2y - 4 = 3x + 12$
$3x - 2y = -16$

40. Let $x =$ speed of boat
$48 = 3(x + 3.5)$
$48 = 3x + 10.5$
$37.5 = 3x$
$12.5 = x$
12.5 miles per hour

4.3 Exercises

2. $x =$ number of mezzanine tickets sold
$y =$ number of orchestra tickets sold
$x + y = 530$ (1)
$9x + 14y = 5870$ (2)
Add -9 times (1) to (2)
$-9x - 9y = -4770$
$\underline{9x + 14y = 5870}$
$5y = 1100$
$y = 220$
Substitute 220 for y in (1)
$x + 220 = 530$
$x = 310$
The number of mezzanine tickets = 310.
The number of orchestra tickets = 220.

4. x = number of acres of corn
y = number of acres of wheat
$x + y = 450$
$42x + 35y = 16{,}520$

$-42x - 42y = -18{,}900$
$\underline{42x + 35y = 16{,}520}$
$-7y = -2380$
$y = 340$

$x + 340 = 450$
$x = 110$
450 acres of corn; 340 acres of wheat

6. x = rental cost for compact car
y = rental cost for intermediate car
$25x + 10y = 13750$
$32x + 3y = 12700$

$-75x - 30y = -41250$
$\underline{320x + 30y = 127000}$
$245x = 85750$
$x = 350$

$32(350) + 3y = 12700$
$3y = 1500$
$y = 500$
compact car: \$350; intermediate car: \$500

8. x = number of basic detectors
y = number of advanced detectors
$3x + 5y = 1050$ (1)
$2x + 3y = 660$ (2)
Add 2 times (1) and -3 times (2)
$6x + 10y = 2100$
$\underline{-6x - 9y = -1980}$
$y = 120$
Substitute 120 for y in (1)
$3x + 5(120) = 1050$
$3x + 600 = 1050$
$3x = 450$
$x = 150$
Number of basic detectors = 150.
Number of advanced detectors = 120.

10. x = number of old packages
y = number of new packages
$50x + 65y = 3125$
$60x + 45y = 2925$

$300x + 390y = 18750$
$\underline{-300x - 225y = -14625}$
$165y = 4125$
$y = 25$

$60x + 45(25) = 2925$
$60x = 1800$
$x = 30$
30 old packages; 25 new packages

12. x = cost to set up printing
y = cost to print
$x + 5000y = 1350$
$x + 7000y = 1750$

$-x - 5000y = -1350$
$\underline{x + 7000y = 1750}$
$2000y = 400$
$y = 0.2$

$x + 5000(0.2) = 1350$
$x = 350$
Cost to set up printing = \$350
Cost to print one brochure = \$0.20

14. x = speed of boat in still water
y = speed of the current
$x + y = \dfrac{84}{2} = 42$ (1)
$\underline{x - y = \dfrac{84}{3} = 28}$ (2)
$2x = 70$
$x = 35$
Substitute 35 for x in (1)
$35 + y = 42$
$y = 7$
The speed of the boat in still water = 35 mph
The speed of the current = 7 mph.

16. x = speed of the plane in still air
y = speed of the wind

$$x - y = \frac{630}{3.5} = 180 \quad (1)$$

$$x + y = \frac{630}{3} = 210 \quad (2)$$

$$2x = 390$$
$$x = 195$$

Substitute 195 for x in (2)
$$(195) + y = 210$$
$$y = 15$$

Speed of plane in still air = 195 mph.
Speed of wind = 15 mph.

18. x = number of free throws
y = number of regular shots
$$x + 2y = 32 \quad (1)$$
$$x + y = 21 \quad (2)$$
Add –2 times (2) to (1)
$$x + 2y = 32$$
$$-2x - 2y = -42$$

$$-x = -10$$
Substitute 10 for x in (2)
$$10 + y = 21$$
$$y = 11$$
10 free throws and 11 regular shots

20. x = miles driven on the highway
y = miles driven in the city
$$x + y = 432 \quad (1)$$

$$\frac{x}{32} + \frac{y}{24} = 16 \quad (2)$$
Add – 3 times (1) and 96 times (2)
$$-3x - 3y = -1296$$
$$3x + 4y = 1536$$

$$y = 240$$
Substitute 240 for y in (1)
$$x + 240 = 432$$
$$x = 192$$
Number of highway miles = 192.
Number of city miles = 240.

22. x = number of 10-ton trucks
y = number of 5-ton trucks
z = number of 3-ton trucks
$$10x + 5y + 3z = 78 \quad (1)$$
$$x + y + z = 12 \quad (2)$$
$$y + z = 8 \quad (3)$$

Substitute 8 for $y + z$ in (2)
$$x + 8 = 12$$
$$x = 4$$
Substitute 4 for x in (1)
$$10(4) + 5y + 3z = 78$$
$$5y + 3z = 38 \quad (4)$$
Add –5 times (3) to (4)
$$-5y - 5z = -40$$
$$5y + 3z = 38$$

$$-2z = -2$$
$$z = 1$$
Substitute 1 for z in (3)
$$y + 1 = 8$$
$$y = 7$$
There were (4) 10-ton trucks, (7) 5-ton trucks, and (1) 3-ton truck on the road.

24. number of students: x
number of faculty: y
number of staff: z
$$x + y + z = 400$$
$$2x + 10y + 8z = 2130$$
$$15y + 10z = 2425$$

$$-2x - 2y - 2z = -800$$
$$2x + 10y + 8z = 2130$$

$$8y + 6z = 1330$$
$$4y + 3z = 665$$

$$-45y - 30z = -7275$$
$$40y + 30z = 6650$$

$$-5y = -625$$
$$y = 125$$

$$4(125) + 3z = 665$$
$$3z = 165$$
$$z = 55$$

$$x + 125 + 55 = 400$$
$$x = 220$$
220 students; 125 faculty; 55 staff

26. number of cars: x
number of Windstars: y
number of Explorers: z
$$x + y + z = 520$$
$$100x + 200y + 300z = 87,000$$
$$150x + 250y + 300z = 106,500$$

$100x + 200y + 300z = 87,000$
$\underline{-150x - 250y - 300z = -106,500}$

$-50x - 50y = -19,500$
$-x - y = -390$

$-300x - 300y - 300z = -156,000$
$\underline{100x + 200y + 300z = 87,000}$

$-200x - 100y = -69,000$
$2x + y = 690$

$-x - y = -390$
$\underline{2x + y = 690}$

$x = 300$

$2(300) + y = 690$
$y = 90$

$300 + 90 + z = 520$
$z = 130$
cars: 300, Windstars: 90, Explorers: 130

28. radius of circle A: x
radius of circle B: y
radius of circle C: z
$x - y = 9$
$x - z = 7$
$y + z = 8$

$x - z = 7$
$\underline{y + z = 8}$
$x + y = 15$

$x - y = 9$
$\underline{x + y = 15}$
$2x = 24$
$x = 12$

$12 - y = 9$
$-y = -3$
$y = 3$

$3 + z = 8$
$z = 5$
A: 12 cm; B: 3 cm; C: 5 cm

30. $x =$ number of *B* packages
$y =$ number of *C* packages
$x + y - 3 =$ number of *A* packages
$x + y + (x + y - 3) = 75$ (1)
$0.5(x + y - 3) + 0.25x + y = 42$ (2)
Simplify (1) and (2) then multiply (2) by 100 and divide (1) by 2
$x + y = 39$ (3)
$75x + 150y = 4350$ (4)
Add -75 times (3) to (4)
$-75x - 75y = -2925$
$\underline{75x + 150y = 4350}$
$75y = 1425$
$y = 19$
Substitute 19 for y in (3)
$x + 19 = 39$
$x = 20$
$20 + 19 - 3 = 36$
(36) *A* packages, (20) *B* packages, and (19) *C* packages.

32. $x =$ number of advance tickets
$y =$ number sold at the door
$x + y = 987$ (1)
$9.95x + 12.95y = \$10,738.65$ (2)
Add -995 times (1) and 100 times (2)
$-995x - 995y = -982,065$
$\underline{995x + 1295y = 1,073,865.}$
$300y = 91,800$
$y = 306$
Substitute 306 for y in (1)
$x + 306 = 987$
$x = 681$
681 advanced tickets, 306 tickets at the door.

Cumulative Review Problems

34. $\dfrac{1}{3}(4 - 2x) = \dfrac{1}{2}x - 3$

$6\left[\dfrac{1}{3}(4 - 2x)\right] = 6\left(\dfrac{1}{2}x - 3\right)$
$2(4 - 2x) = 3x - 18$
$8 - 4x = 3x - 18$
$8 = 7x - 18$
$26 = 7x$
$\dfrac{26}{7} = x$

36. $2(y-3)-(2y+4)=-6y$

$2y-6-2y-4=-6y$

$-10=-6y$

$\dfrac{5}{3}=y$

4.4 Exercises

2. $\begin{vmatrix} 3 & 4 \\ 1 & 8 \end{vmatrix} = (3)(8)-(1)(4)$

$= 24-4$

$= 20$

4. $\begin{vmatrix} -4 & 2 \\ 1 & 5 \end{vmatrix} = (-4)(5)-(1)(2)$

$= -20-2$

$= -22$

6. $\begin{vmatrix} 10 & 4 \\ -\dfrac{3}{2} & -\dfrac{2}{5} \end{vmatrix} = (10)\left(-\dfrac{2}{5}\right)-\left(-\dfrac{3}{2}\right)(4)$

$= -4+6$

$= 2$

8. $\begin{vmatrix} 2 & -3 \\ -4 & -6 \end{vmatrix} = (2)(-6)-(-4)(-3)$

$= -12-12$

$= -24$

10. $\begin{vmatrix} -5 & 0 \\ 2 & -7 \end{vmatrix} = (-5)(-7)-(2)(0)$

$= 35-0$

$= 35$

12. $\begin{vmatrix} -3 & 6 \\ 7 & -14 \end{vmatrix} = (-3)(-14)-(7)(6)$

$= 42-42$

$= 0$

14. $\begin{vmatrix} -4 & 0 \\ -3 & 0 \end{vmatrix} = (-4)(0)-(-3)(0)$

$= 0-0$

$= 0$

16. $\begin{vmatrix} 0.1 & 0.7 \\ 0.5 & 0.8 \end{vmatrix} = (0.1)(0.8)-(0.5)(0.7)$

$= 0.08-0.35$

$= -0.27$

18. $\begin{vmatrix} \dfrac{1}{4} & \dfrac{3}{5} \\ \dfrac{2}{3} & \dfrac{1}{5} \end{vmatrix} = \left(\dfrac{1}{4}\right)\left(\dfrac{1}{5}\right)-\left(\dfrac{2}{3}\right)\left(\dfrac{3}{5}\right)$

$= \dfrac{1}{20}-\dfrac{2}{5}$

$= \dfrac{1}{20}-\dfrac{8}{20}$

$= -\dfrac{7}{20}$

20. $\begin{vmatrix} -3 & y \\ -2 & x \end{vmatrix} = (-3)(x)-(-2)(y)$

$= -3x+2y$

22. $\begin{vmatrix} -2 & x \\ 1 & 3 \end{vmatrix} = 2$

$(-2)(3)-(1)(x)=2$

$-6-x=2$

$-x=8$

$x=-8$

24. $\begin{vmatrix} -3 & 1 \\ 4x & x \end{vmatrix} = -21$

$(-3)(x)-(4x)(1)=-21$

$-3x-4x=-21$

$-7x=-21$

$x=3$

26. $\begin{vmatrix} -3 & 4 \\ x-1 & 2x+1 \end{vmatrix} = -3$

$(-3)(2x+1)-(x-1)(4)=-3$

$-6x-3-4x+4=-3$

$-10x+1=-3$

$-10x=-4$

$x=\dfrac{2}{5}$

28. Eliminate row 2 and column 1.

$\begin{vmatrix} -4 & 7 \\ -5 & 9 \end{vmatrix}$

30. Eliminate row 3 and column 3.

$\begin{vmatrix} 3 & -4 \\ -2 & 6 \end{vmatrix}$

32.
$$\begin{vmatrix} 2 & 3 & 1 \\ -3 & 1 & 0 \\ 2 & 1 & 4 \end{vmatrix} = 1\begin{vmatrix} -3 & 1 \\ 2 & 1 \end{vmatrix} - 0 + 4\begin{vmatrix} 2 & 3 \\ -3 & 1 \end{vmatrix}$$
$$= (-3)(1) - (2)(1) + 4[(2)(1) - (-3)(3)]$$
$$= -3 - 2 + 4(2 + 9)$$
$$= -5 + 44$$
$$= 39$$

34.
$$\begin{vmatrix} 3 & -4 & -1 \\ -2 & 1 & 3 \\ 0 & 1 & 4 \end{vmatrix} = 0 - 1\begin{vmatrix} 3 & -1 \\ -2 & 3 \end{vmatrix} + 4\begin{vmatrix} 3 & -4 \\ -2 & 1 \end{vmatrix}$$
$$= -[(3)(3) - (-2)(-1)] + 4[(3)(1) - (-2)(-4)]$$
$$= -(9 - 2) + 4(3 - 8)$$
$$= -7 - 20$$
$$= -27$$

36.
$$\begin{vmatrix} 1 & 2 & 3 \\ 4 & -2 & -1 \\ 5 & -3 & 2 \end{vmatrix}$$
$$= 1\begin{vmatrix} -2 & -1 \\ -3 & 2 \end{vmatrix} - 2\begin{vmatrix} 4 & -1 \\ 5 & 2 \end{vmatrix} + 3\begin{vmatrix} 4 & -2 \\ 5 & -3 \end{vmatrix}$$
$$= (-2)(2) - (-3)(-1) - 2[(4)(2) - (5)(-1)] +$$
$$\quad 3[(4)(-3) - (5)(-2)]$$
$$= -4 - 3 - 2(8 + 5) + 3(-12 + 10)$$
$$= -7 - 2(13) + 3(-2)$$
$$= -39$$

38.
$$\begin{vmatrix} -\frac{1}{2} & 2 & 3 \\ \frac{5}{2} & -2 & -1 \\ \frac{3}{4} & -3 & 2 \end{vmatrix}$$
$$= -\frac{1}{2}\begin{vmatrix} -2 & -1 \\ -3 & 2 \end{vmatrix} - \frac{5}{2}\begin{vmatrix} 2 & 3 \\ -3 & 2 \end{vmatrix} + \frac{3}{4}\begin{vmatrix} 2 & 3 \\ -2 & -1 \end{vmatrix}$$
$$= -\frac{1}{2}(-7) - \frac{5}{2}(13) + \frac{3}{4}(4)$$
$$= \frac{7}{2} - \frac{65}{2} + 3$$
$$= -26$$

40.
$$\begin{vmatrix} 7 & 0 & 2 \\ 1 & 0 & -5 \\ 3 & 0 & 6 \end{vmatrix} = -0 + 0 - 0 = 0$$

42.
$$\begin{vmatrix} 7 & 0 & 3 \\ 1 & 2 & 4 \\ 3 & 0 & -7 \end{vmatrix} = -0 + 2\begin{vmatrix} 7 & 3 \\ 3 & -7 \end{vmatrix} - 0$$
$$= 2[(7)(-7) - (3)(3)]$$
$$= 2(-49 - 9)$$
$$= -116$$

44.
$$\begin{vmatrix} 0.7 & 5.3 & 0.4 \\ 1.6 & 0.3 & 3.7 \\ 0.8 & 6.7 & 4.2 \end{vmatrix} = -32.207$$

46.
$$\begin{vmatrix} 82 & -20 & 56 \\ 93 & -18 & 39 \\ 65 & -27 & 72 \end{vmatrix} = -11,802$$

48. $(-2, 1)$, $(0, 3)$, and $(-1, 6)$
$$A = \frac{1}{2}\begin{vmatrix} -2 & 1 & 1 \\ 0 & 3 & 1 \\ -1 & 6 & 1 \end{vmatrix}$$
$$A = \frac{1}{2}\left[-2\begin{vmatrix} 3 & 1 \\ 6 & 1 \end{vmatrix} - 0\begin{vmatrix} 1 & 1 \\ 6 & 1 \end{vmatrix} - 1\begin{vmatrix} 1 & 1 \\ 3 & 1 \end{vmatrix}\right]$$
$$A = \frac{1}{2}[-2(-3) - 0 - 1(-2)]$$
$$A = \frac{1}{2}(8) = 4$$

50. $(-4, -4)$, $(2, -1)$, $(-2, 3)$
$$A = \frac{1}{2}\begin{vmatrix} -4 & -4 & 1 \\ 2 & -1 & 1 \\ -2 & 3 & 1 \end{vmatrix}$$
$$= \frac{1}{2}\left[-4\begin{vmatrix} -1 & 1 \\ 3 & 1 \end{vmatrix} - 2\begin{vmatrix} -4 & 1 \\ 3 & 1 \end{vmatrix} - 2\begin{vmatrix} -4 & 1 \\ -1 & 1 \end{vmatrix}\right]$$
$$= \frac{1}{2}[-4(-4) - 2(-7) - 2(-3)]$$
$$= \frac{1}{2}(16 + 14 + 6)$$
$$= 18$$

52. $\begin{vmatrix} 1 & 3 & 2 & 4 \\ -2 & 1 & 0 & 3 \\ 3 & 0 & 1 & 6 \\ 5 & 2 & 0 & 0 \end{vmatrix}$

$= -5\begin{vmatrix} 3 & 2 & 4 \\ 1 & 0 & 3 \\ 0 & 1 & 6 \end{vmatrix} + 2\begin{vmatrix} 1 & 2 & 4 \\ -2 & 0 & 3 \\ 3 & 1 & 6 \end{vmatrix} - 0\begin{vmatrix} 1 & 3 & 4 \\ -2 & 1 & 3 \\ 3 & 0 & 6 \end{vmatrix} + 0\begin{vmatrix} 1 & 3 & 2 \\ -2 & 1 & 0 \\ 3 & 0 & 1 \end{vmatrix}$

$= -5\{3[0-3] - 1[12-4] + 0[6-0]\} + 2\{-2[-12-9] + 0[6-12] - 1[3+8]\} + 0 + 0$

$= -5(-9-8) + 2(42-11)$

$= 85 + 62$

$= 147$

54. $\begin{vmatrix} 0.31 & 0.76 & 1.55 & 0.82 \\ 5.31 & 8.05 & 3.72 & 8.91 \\ 4.98 & 5.77 & 4.03 & 9.33 \\ 0.56 & 0.93 & 6.37 & 7.11 \end{vmatrix} = -57.44850824$

Cumulative Review Problems

56. $\frac{1}{2}a - 3y + 5z - \frac{1}{3}a + 5y - 2z$

$= \left(\frac{1}{2} - \frac{1}{3}\right)a + (-3+5)y + (5-2)z$

$= \frac{1}{6}a + 2y + 3z$

58. $\frac{(4x^{-3}y^2)^3}{(3x^2y)^4}$

$= \frac{4^3 x^{-9} y^6}{3^4 x^8 y^4}$

$= \frac{64}{81} x^{-9-8} y^{6-4}$

$= \frac{64}{81} x^{-17} y^2$

$= \frac{64y^2}{81x^{17}}$

60. daily rate for car $= x$
daily rate for insurance $= y$
rate per mile $= z$
$3x + 3y + 400z = 189$
$4x + 4y + 360z = 226$
$5x + 520z = 253$

$12x + 12y + 1600z = 756$
$\underline{-12x - 12y - 1080z = -678}$
$520z = 78$
$z = 0.15$

$5x + 520(0.15) = 253$
$5x = 175$
$x = 35$
$3(35) + 3y + 400(0.15) = 189$
$3y = 24$
$y = 8$
$35 per day car rental
$8 per day collision insurance
$0.15 per mile

4.5 Exercises

2. $x + 3y = 6$
$2x + y = 7$

$D = \begin{vmatrix} 1 & 3 \\ 2 & 1 \end{vmatrix} = (1)(1) - (2)(3) = -5$

$D_x = \begin{vmatrix} 6 & 3 \\ 7 & 1 \end{vmatrix} = (6)(1) - (7)(3) = -15$

$D_y = \begin{vmatrix} 1 & 6 \\ 2 & 7 \end{vmatrix} = (1)(7) - (2)(6) = -5$

$$x = \frac{D_x}{D} = \frac{-15}{-5} = 3$$

$$y = \frac{D_y}{D} = \frac{-5}{-5} = 1$$

$$x = 3, \; y = 1$$

4. $3x + 5y = 11$
$2x + y = -2$

$$D = \begin{vmatrix} 3 & 5 \\ 2 & 1 \end{vmatrix} = 3(1) - 2(5) = -7$$

$$D_x = \begin{vmatrix} 11 & 5 \\ -2 & 1 \end{vmatrix} = 11(1) - (-2)(5) = 21$$

$$D_y = \begin{vmatrix} 3 & 11 \\ 2 & -2 \end{vmatrix} = 3(-2) - 2(11) = -28$$

$$x = \frac{D_x}{D} = \frac{21}{-7} = -3$$

$$y = \frac{D_y}{D} = \frac{-28}{-7} = 4$$

The solution is (–3, 4).

6. $x - 3y = 4$
$-3x + 4y = -12$

$$D = \begin{vmatrix} 1 & -3 \\ -3 & 4 \end{vmatrix} = 1(4) - (-3)(-3) = -5$$

$$D_x = \begin{vmatrix} 4 & -3 \\ -12 & 4 \end{vmatrix} = 4(4) - (-12)(-3) = -20$$

$$D_y = \begin{vmatrix} 1 & 4 \\ -3 & -12 \end{vmatrix} = 1(-12) - (-3)(4) = 0$$

$$x = \frac{D_x}{D} = \frac{-20}{-5} = 4$$

$$y = \frac{D_y}{D} = \frac{0}{-5} = 0$$

The solution is (4, 0).

8. $9x - 7y = 6$
$3x - 2y = 2$

$$D = \begin{vmatrix} 9 & -7 \\ 3 & -2 \end{vmatrix} = -18 + 21 = 3$$

$$D_x = \begin{vmatrix} 6 & -7 \\ 2 & -2 \end{vmatrix} = -12 + 14 = 2$$

$$D_y = \begin{vmatrix} 9 & 6 \\ 3 & 2 \end{vmatrix} = 18 - 18 = 0$$

$$x = \frac{D_x}{D} = \frac{2}{3}$$

$$y = \frac{D_y}{D} = \frac{0}{3} = 0$$

$$x = \frac{2}{3}, \; y = 0$$

10. $-x - 3y = -14$
$5x - 2y = 2$

$$D = \begin{vmatrix} -1 & -3 \\ 5 & -2 \end{vmatrix} = (-1)(-2) - (5)(-3) = 17$$

$$D_x = \begin{vmatrix} -14 & -3 \\ 2 & -2 \end{vmatrix} = (-14)(-2) - (2)(-3) = 34$$

$$D_y = \begin{vmatrix} -1 & -14 \\ 5 & 2 \end{vmatrix} = (-1)(2) - (5)(-14) = 68$$

$$x = \frac{D_x}{D} = \frac{34}{17} = 2$$

$$y = \frac{D_y}{D} = \frac{68}{17} = 4$$

$$x = 2, \; y = 4$$

12. $0.5x + 0.3y = -0.7$
$0.4x + 0.5y \; -0.3$

$$D = \begin{vmatrix} 0.5 & 0.3 \\ 0.4 & 0.5 \end{vmatrix}$$
$$= (0.5)(0.5) - (0.4)(0.3)$$
$$= 0.13$$

$$D_x = \begin{vmatrix} -0.7 & 0.3 \\ -0.3 & 0.5 \end{vmatrix}$$
$$= (-0.7)(0.5) - (-0.3)(0.3)$$
$$= -0.26$$

$$D_y = \begin{vmatrix} 0.5 & -0.7 \\ 0.4 & -0.3 \end{vmatrix}$$
$$= (0.5)(-0.3) - (0.4)(-0.7)$$
$$= 0.13$$

$$x = \frac{D_x}{D} = \frac{-0.26}{0.13} = -2$$

$$y = \frac{D_y}{D} = \frac{0.13}{0.13} = 1$$

$$x = -2, \; y = 1$$

14. $0.0076x + 0.0092y = 0.01237$
$-0.5628x - 0.2374y = -0.7635$

$$D = \begin{vmatrix} 0.0076 & 0.0092 \\ -0.5628 & -0.2374 \end{vmatrix}$$
$$= (0.0076)(-0.2374) - (-0.5628)(0.0092)$$
$$= 0.00337352$$

$$D_x = \begin{vmatrix} 0.01237 & 0.0092 \\ -0.7635 & -0.2374 \end{vmatrix}$$
$$= (0.01237)(-0.2374) - (-0.7635)(0.0092)$$
$$= 0.004087562$$

$$D_y = \begin{vmatrix} 0.0076 & 0.01237 \\ -0.5628 & -0.7635 \end{vmatrix}$$
$$= (0.0076)(-0.7635) - (-0.5628)(0.01237)$$
$$= 0.001159236$$

$$x = \frac{D_x}{D} = \frac{0.004087562}{0.00337352} = 1.2117$$

$$y = \frac{D_y}{D} = \frac{0.001159236}{0.00337352} = 0.3436$$

$$x = 1.2117, \; y = 0.3436$$

16. $3(x+1) = 4 - y$

$5 + 2(y-1) = 3 + x$

$3x + 3 = 4 - y$

$5 + 2y - 2 = 3 + x$

$3x + y = 1$

$-x + 2y = 0$

$$D = \begin{vmatrix} 3 & 1 \\ -1 & 2 \end{vmatrix} = 3(2) - (-1)(1) = 7$$

$$D_x = \begin{vmatrix} 1 & 1 \\ 0 & 2 \end{vmatrix} = 1(2) - 0(1) = 2$$

$$D_y = \begin{vmatrix} 3 & 1 \\ -1 & 0 \end{vmatrix} = 3(0) - (-1)(1) = 1$$

$$x = \frac{D_x}{D} = \frac{2}{7}$$

$$y = \frac{D_y}{D} = \frac{1}{7}$$

The solution is $\left(\dfrac{2}{7}, \dfrac{1}{7} \right)$.

18. $x - \dfrac{5}{4}y = \dfrac{17}{4}$

$\dfrac{3}{10}x - \dfrac{1}{10}y = 1$

$4x - 5y = 17$

$3x - y = 10$

$$D = \begin{vmatrix} 4 & -5 \\ 3 & -1 \end{vmatrix} = 4(-1) - 3(-5) = 11$$

$$D_x = \begin{vmatrix} 17 & -5 \\ 10 & -1 \end{vmatrix} = 17(-1) - 10(-5) = 33$$

$$D_y = \begin{vmatrix} 4 & 17 \\ 3 & 10 \end{vmatrix} = 4(10) - 3(17) = -11$$

$$x = \frac{D_x}{D} = \frac{33}{11} = 3$$

$$y = \frac{D_y}{D} = \frac{-11}{11} = -1$$

The solution is $(3, -1)$.

20. $\dfrac{1}{2}x - \dfrac{3}{8}y + \dfrac{1}{8} = 1$

$2(x+1) - \dfrac{2}{3}y = x + 4$

$4x - 3y + 1 = 8$

$6x + 6 - 2y = 3x + 12$

$4x - 3y = 7$

$3x - 2y = 6$

$$D = \begin{vmatrix} 4 & -3 \\ 3 & -2 \end{vmatrix} = (4)(-2) - (3)(-3) = 1$$

$$D_x = \begin{vmatrix} 7 & -3 \\ 6 & -2 \end{vmatrix} = (7)(-2) - (6)(-3) = 4$$

$$D_y = \begin{vmatrix} 4 & 7 \\ 3 & 6 \end{vmatrix} = (4)(6) - (3)(7) = 3$$

$$x = \frac{D_x}{D} = \frac{4}{1} = 4$$

$$y = \frac{D_y}{D} = \frac{3}{1} = 3$$

$x = 4, \; y = 3$

22. $x + 2y - z = -4$

$x + 4y - 2z = -6$

$2x + 3y + z = 3$

$$D = \begin{vmatrix} 1 & 2 & -1 \\ 1 & 4 & -2 \\ 2 & 3 & 1 \end{vmatrix}$$

$= 1(10) - 2(5) - 1(-5)$

$= 5$

$$D_x = \begin{vmatrix} -4 & 2 & -1 \\ -6 & 4 & -2 \\ 3 & 3 & 1 \end{vmatrix}$$

$= -4(10) - 2(0) - 1(-30)$

$= -10$

$$D_y = \begin{vmatrix} 1 & -4 & -1 \\ 1 & -6 & -2 \\ 2 & 3 & 1 \end{vmatrix}$$

$= 1(0) - (-4)(5) - 1(15) = 5$

$$D_z = \begin{vmatrix} 1 & 2 & -4 \\ 1 & 4 & -6 \\ 2 & 3 & 3 \end{vmatrix}$$

$= 1(30) - 2(15) - 4(-5)$

$= 20$

$$x = \frac{D_x}{D} = \frac{-10}{5} = -2$$

$$y = \frac{D_y}{D} = \frac{5}{5} = 1$$

$$z = \frac{D_z}{D} = \frac{20}{5} = 4$$

$$x = -2, \; y = 1, \; z = 4$$

24. $4x + y + 2z = 6$

$x + y + z = 1$

$-x + 3y - z = -5$

$$D = \begin{vmatrix} 4 & 1 & 2 \\ 1 & 1 & 1 \\ -1 & 3 & -1 \end{vmatrix}$$

$$= 4(-4) - 1(-7) - 1(-1)$$

$$= -8$$

$$D_x = \begin{vmatrix} 6 & 1 & 2 \\ 1 & 1 & 1 \\ -5 & 3 & -1 \end{vmatrix}$$

$$= 6(-4) - 1(-7) - 5(-1)$$

$$= -12$$

$$D_y = \begin{vmatrix} 4 & 6 & 2 \\ 1 & 1 & 1 \\ -1 & -5 & -1 \end{vmatrix}$$

$$= 4(4) - 1(4) - 1(4)$$

$$= 8$$

$$D_z = \begin{vmatrix} 4 & 1 & 6 \\ 1 & 1 & 1 \\ -1 & 3 & -5 \end{vmatrix}$$

$$= 4(-8) - 1(-23) - 1(-5)$$

$$= -4$$

$$x = \frac{D_x}{D} = \frac{-12}{-8} = \frac{3}{2}$$

$$y = \frac{D_y}{D} = \frac{8}{-8} = -1$$

$$z = \frac{D_z}{D} = \frac{-4}{-8} = \frac{1}{2}$$

$$x = \frac{3}{2}, \; y = -1, \; z = \frac{1}{2}$$

26. $3x + y + z = 2$

$2y + 3z = -6$

$2x - y = -1$

$$D = \begin{vmatrix} 3 & 1 & 1 \\ 0 & 2 & 3 \\ 2 & -1 & 0 \end{vmatrix} = 2(1) - (-1)(9) = 11$$

$$D_x = \begin{vmatrix} 2 & 1 & 1 \\ -6 & 2 & 3 \\ -1 & -1 & 0 \end{vmatrix} = -1(1) - (-1)(12) = 11$$

$$D_y = \begin{vmatrix} 3 & 2 & 1 \\ 0 & -6 & 3 \\ 2 & -1 & 0 \end{vmatrix} = 2(12) - (-1)(9) = 33$$

$$D_z = \begin{vmatrix} 3 & 1 & 2 \\ 0 & 2 & -6 \\ 2 & -1 & -1 \end{vmatrix} = 2(-7) - (-6)(-5) = -44$$

$$x = \frac{D_x}{D} = \frac{11}{11} = 1$$

$$y = \frac{D_y}{D} = \frac{33}{11} = 3$$

$$z = \frac{D_z}{D} = \frac{-44}{11} = -4$$

$$x = 1, \; y = 3, \; z = -4$$

28. $2x + 5y + 3z = 1$

$x + 3y = 8$

$4y - z = 5$

$$D = \begin{vmatrix} 2 & 5 & 3 \\ 1 & 3 & 0 \\ 0 & 4 & -1 \end{vmatrix} = -1(-17) + 3(-2) = 11$$

$$D_x = \begin{vmatrix} 1 & 5 & 3 \\ 8 & 3 & 0 \\ 5 & 4 & -1 \end{vmatrix} = 3(17) - 1(-37) = 88$$

$$D_y = \begin{vmatrix} 2 & 1 & 3 \\ 1 & 8 & 0 \\ 0 & 5 & -1 \end{vmatrix} = 2(-8) - 1(-16) = 0$$

$$D_z = \begin{vmatrix} 2 & 5 & 1 \\ 1 & 3 & 8 \\ 0 & 4 & 5 \end{vmatrix} = 2(-17) - 1(21) = -55$$

$$x = \frac{D_x}{D} = \frac{88}{11} = 8$$

$$y = \frac{D_y}{D} = \frac{0}{11} = 0$$

$$z = \frac{D_z}{D} = \frac{-55}{11} = -5$$

$$x = 8, \; y = 0, \; z = -5$$

30. $121x + 134y + 101z = 146$

$315x - 112y - 108z = 426$

$148x + 503y + 516z = -127$

$x = 1.188$

$y = 1.731$

$z = -2.274$

32. $6x - 5y - 3z = -5$
$-2x + y + z = 1$
$3x - 2y + 3z = 1$

$$D = \begin{vmatrix} 6 & -5 & -3 \\ -2 & 1 & 1 \\ 3 & -2 & 3 \end{vmatrix}$$

$= 6(5) + 2(-21) + 3(-2)$
$= -18$

$$D_z = \begin{vmatrix} 6 & -5 & -5 \\ -2 & 1 & 1 \\ 3 & -2 & 1 \end{vmatrix}$$

$= 6(3) + 2(-15) + 3(0)$
$= -12$

$z = \dfrac{D_z}{D} = \dfrac{-12}{-18} = \dfrac{2}{3}$

34. $x + 3y + 2z = 3$
$2x - 5y + z = 7$
$y + z = -3$

$$D = \begin{vmatrix} 1 & 3 & 2 \\ 2 & -5 & 1 \\ 0 & 1 & 1 \end{vmatrix}$$

$= 1(-6) - 2(1)$
$= -8$

$$D_x = \begin{vmatrix} 3 & 3 & 2 \\ 7 & -5 & 1 \\ -3 & 1 & 1 \end{vmatrix}$$

$= -3(13) - 1(-11) + 1(-36)$
$= -64$

$x = \dfrac{D_x}{D} = \dfrac{-64}{-8} = 8$

36. $-16x - 14y = 8$
$8x + 7y = -4$

$$D = \begin{vmatrix} -16 & -14 \\ 8 & 7 \end{vmatrix} = (-16)(7) - (8)(-14) = 0$$

$$D_x = \begin{vmatrix} 8 & -14 \\ -4 & 7 \end{vmatrix} = (8)(7) - (-4)(-14) = 0$$

$$D_y = \begin{vmatrix} -16 & 8 \\ 8 & -4 \end{vmatrix} = (-16)(-4) - (8)(8) = 0$$

Infinite number of solutions; dependent
equations

38. $3x + 2y + z = 7$
$x + y - z = 2$
$3x + 2y + z = 5$

$$D = \begin{vmatrix} 3 & 2 & 1 \\ 1 & 1 & -1 \\ 3 & 2 & 1 \end{vmatrix} = 3(3) - 1(0) + 3(-3) = 0$$

$$D_x = \begin{vmatrix} 7 & 2 & 1 \\ 2 & 1 & -1 \\ 5 & 2 & 1 \end{vmatrix} = 7(3) - 2(0) + 5(-3) = 6$$

$D = 0$ and D_x is nonzero; no solutions;
inconsistent system of equations

40. $28w + 35x - 18y + 40z = 60$
$60w + 32x + 28y = 400$
$30w + 15x + 18y + 66z = 720$
$26w - 18x - 15y + 75z = 125$
$w = -3.105$
$x = 4.402$
$y = 15.909$
$z = 6.981$

Cumulative Review Problems

42. x = number of miles Melinda drove
$31(5) + 0.16x = 185.40$
$0.16x = 185.40 - 155$
$0.16x = 30.40$
$x = \dfrac{30.40}{16} = 190$ miles

44. $y = ax + b$
$22 = a(10) + b$
$-23 = a(-5) + b$

$10a + b = 22$
$\underline{5a - b = 23}$
$15a = 45$
$a = 3$

$b = 22 - 10(3) = -8$
$a = 3,\ b = -8$

4.6 Exercises

2. $y \leq 3x - 3$
$5x + 2y \geq 10$

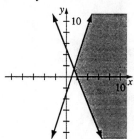

4. $y \geq x$
$y \geq -x$

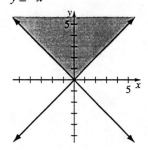

6. $y \leq 3x - 2$
$y \geq \dfrac{1}{2}x$

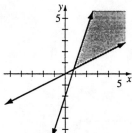

8. $2x + y \leq 3$
$x - 2y \leq 4$

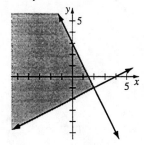

10. $2x + y < 8$
$y < 4$

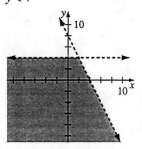

12. $2x - y > 4$
$x < 1$

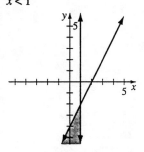

14. $y > -3$
$x < 2$
Test point: $(0, 0)$, True

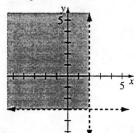

16. $2x - y < 2$
$2x - y > -2$

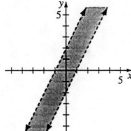

18. $5x - 2y \leq 10$
$x - y \geq -1$
Test point: (0, 0), True

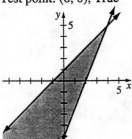

20. $x + y = 3$
$4x + y = 6$

$-x - y = -3$
$\underline{4x + y = 6}$
$3x = 3$
$x = 1$

$1 + y = 3$
$y = 2$
Point of intersection: (1, 2)
$x + y \leq 3$
$4x + y \leq 6$

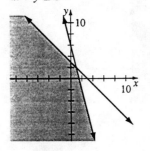

22. $x + 2y = 4$
$y = -x$
$x + 2(-x) = 4$
$-x = 4$
$x = -4$
$y = 4$

Point of intersection: (–4, 4)
$x + 2y \leq 4$
$y < -x$

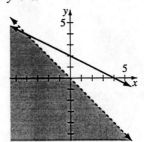

24. $x - y = 2$ $x - y = 2$
$\underline{x + y = 2}$ $x = -2$
$2x = 4$
$x = 2$ $-2 - y = 2$
$2 + y = 2$ $-y = 4$
$y = 0$ $y = -4$
$(2, 0)$ $(-2, -4)$

$x + y = 2$
$x = -2$
$-2 + y = 2$
$y = 4$
$(-2, 4)$

$x - y \leq 2$
$x + y \leq 2$
$x \geq -2$

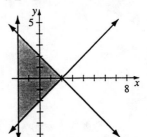

26. $3x + 2y = 4$ $3x + 2y = 4$
$x - y = 3$ $x = 0$

$3x + 2y = 4$ $3(0) + 2y = 4$
$\underline{2x - 2y = 6}$ $2y = 4$
$5x = 10$ $y = 2$
$x = 2$ $(0, 2)$

$2 - y = 3$
$-y = 1$
$y = -1$
$(2, -1)$

$x - y = 3$ $3x + 2y = 4$
$x = 0$ $y = 0$

$0 - y = 3$ $3x + 2(0) = 4$
$y = -3$ $3x = 4$
$(0, -3)$ $x = \dfrac{4}{3}$

$\left(\dfrac{4}{3}, 0\right)$

$x - y = 3$ $x = 0$
$y = 0$ $y = 0$
                     $(0, 0)$

$x - 0 = 3$
$x = 3$
$(3, 0)$
$3x + 2y \geq 4$
$x - y \leq 3$
$x \geq 0$
$y \geq 0$

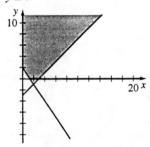

28. $x + y \leq 100$
$x + 3y \leq 150$
$x \geq 0$
$y \geq 20$

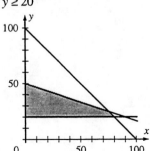

Cumulative Review Problems

30. $3x + 4y = -8$
$4y = -3x - 8$
$y = -\dfrac{3}{4}x - 2$
$m = -\dfrac{3}{4}; \ b = -2$

32. $y + 2x = 8$
$y = -2x + 8$
$m = -2$
$y - y_1 = m(x - x_1)$
$y - 0 = -2(x - 5)$
$y = -2x + 10$

34. volunteer feet per day $= x$
experienced feet per day $= y$
$3x + 4y = 389$
$5x + 7y = 670$

$-15x - 20y = -1945$
$\underline{15x + 21y = 2010}$
$y = 65$

$3x + 4(65) = 389$
$3x = 129$
$x = 43$

The volunteers establish 43 feet of bicycle trails per day. The experienced professionals establish 65 feet of bicycle trails per day.

36. $x =$ roast beef sandwiches
$y =$ french fries orders
$z =$ sodas
$3x + 2y + 3z = 13.85$
$4x + 3y + 5z = 20$
$3x + 3y + 4z = 16.55$

$-12x - 8y - 12z = -55.4$
$\underline{12x + 9y + 15z = 60}$
$y + 3z = 4.6$

$3x + 2y + 3z = 13.85$
$\underline{-3x - 3y - 4z = -16.55}$
$-y - z = -2.7$

$$y + 3z = 4.6$$
$$\underline{-y - z = -2.7}$$
$$2z = 1.9$$
$$z = 0.95$$
$$y + 3(0.95) = 4.6$$
$$y = 1.75$$

$$3x + 2(1.75) + 3(0.95) = 13.85$$
$$x = 2.50$$

One roast beef sandwich costs $2.50.
One order of french fries costs $1.75.
One soda costs $0.95.

Chapter 4 Review Problems

2. $x + y = 2$
    $3x - y = 6$

4. $3x - 2y = -9$
    $2x + y = 1$

$$y = 1 - 2x$$
$$3x - 2(1 - 2x) = -9$$
$$3x - 2 + 4x - 9$$
$$7x - 2 = -9$$
$$7x = -7$$
$$x = -1$$
$$y = 1 - 2(-1) = 3$$
$$x = -1, \; y = 3$$

6. $4x + 3y = 10$
    $5x - y = 3$

$$y = 5x - 3$$
$$4x + 3(5x - 3) = 10$$
$$4x + 15x - 9 = 10$$
$$19x - 9 = 10$$
$$19x = 19$$
$$x = 1$$
$$y = 5(1) - 3 = 2$$
$$x = 1, \; y = 2$$

8. $-2x + 5y = -12$
    $3x + y = 1$

$$-2x + 5y = -12$$
$$\underline{-15x - 5y = -5}$$
$$-17x = -17$$
$$x = 1$$

$$3(1) + y = 1$$
$$y = -2$$
$$x = 1, \; y = -2$$

10. $7x - 4y = 2$
    $6x - 5y = -3$

$$-35x + 20y = -10$$
$$\underline{24x - 20y = -12}$$
$$-11x = -22$$
$$x = 2$$

$$7(2) - 4y = 2$$
$$-4y = -12$$
$$y = 3$$
$$x = 2, \; y = 3$$

12. $2x + 4y = 9$
    $3x + 6y = 8$

$$6x + 12y = 27$$
$$\underline{-6x - 12y = -16}$$
$$0 = 11$$

No solution; inconsistent system of equations

14. $7x + 6y = -10$
    $2x + y = 0$

$$y = -2x$$
$$7x + 6(-2x) = -10$$
$$7x - 12x = -10$$
$$-5x = -10$$
$$x = 2$$

$$y = -2(2) = -4$$
$$x = 2, \; y = -4$$

16. $x + \dfrac{1}{3}y = 1$

$\dfrac{1}{4}x - \dfrac{3}{4}y = -\dfrac{9}{4}$

$3x + y = 3$
$x - 3y = -9$

$9x + 3y = 9$
$\underline{x - 3y = -9}$
$10x = 0$
$x = 0$

$0 - 3y = -9$
$-3y = -9$
$y = 3$
$x = 0,\ y = 3$

18. $9a + 10b = 7$
$6a - 4b = 10$

$18a + 20b = 14$
$\underline{30a - 20b = 50}$
$48a = 64$
$a = \dfrac{4}{3}$

$6\left(\dfrac{4}{3}\right) - 4b = 10$
$8 - 4b = 10$
$-4b = 2$
$b = -\dfrac{1}{2}$

$a = \dfrac{4}{3},\ b = -\dfrac{1}{2}$

20. $x + 3 = 3y + 1$
$1 - 2(x - 2) = 6y + 1$

$x = 3y - 2$

$1 - 2x + 4 = 6y + 1$
$-2x = 6y - 4$
$-2(3y - 2) = 6y - 4$
$-6y + 4 = 6y - 4$
$8 = 12y$
$\dfrac{2}{3} = y$

$x = 3\left(\dfrac{2}{3}\right) - 2 = 0$
$x = 0,\ y = \dfrac{2}{3}$

22. $0.3x - 0.2y = 0.7$
$-0.6x + 0.4y = 0.3$

$3x - 2y = 7$
$-6x + 4y = 3$

$6x - 4y = 14$
$\underline{-6x + 4y = 3}$
$0 = 17$

No solution; inconsistent system of equations

24. $3x - 2y - z = 3$
$2x + y + z = 1$
$-x - y + z = -4$

$3x - 2y - z = 3$ $3x - 2y - z = 3$
$\underline{2x + y + z = 1}$ $\underline{-x - y + z = -4}$
$5x - y = 4$ $2x - 3y = -1$

$-15x + 3y = -12$
$\underline{2x - 3y = -1}$
$-13x = -13$
$x = 1$

$5(1) - y = 4$
$-y = -1$
$y = 1$

$-1 - 1 + z = -4$
$-2 + z = -4$
$z = -2$
$x = 1,\ y = 1,\ z = -2$

26. $2x + 5y + z = 3$
$x + y + 5z = 42$
$2x + y = 7$

$-10x - 25y - 5z = -15$
$\underline{x + y + 5z = 42}$
$-9x - 24y = 27$

$-9x - 24y = 27$
$\underline{48x + 24y = 168}$
$39x = 195$
$x = 5$

$2(5) + y = 7$
$y = -3$

$2(5) + 5(-3) + z = 3$
$10 - 15 + z = 3$
$-5 + z = 3$
$z = 8$
$x = 5, y = -3, z = 8$

28. $2x - 4y + 3z = 0$
$x - 2y - 5z = 13$
$5x + 3y - 2z = 19$

$\begin{array}{l} 2x - 4y + 3z = 0 \\ \underline{-2x + 4y + 10z = -26} \\ 13z = -26 \\ z = -2 \end{array}$ $\begin{array}{l} 3x - 6y - 15z = 39 \\ \underline{10x + 6y - 4z = 38} \\ 13x - 19z = 77 \\ 13x - 19(-2) = 77 \\ 13x = 39 \\ x = 3 \end{array}$

$3 - 2y - 5(-2) = 13$
$3 - 2y + 10 = 13$
$13 - 2y = 13$
$-2y = 0$
$y = 0$
$x = 3, y = 0, z = -2$

30. $3x + 2y = 7$
$2x + 7z = -26$
$5y + z = 6$

$2x + 7z = -26$
$\underline{-35y - 7z = -42}$
$2x - 35y = -68$

$-6x - 4y = -14$
$\underline{6x - 105y = -204}$
$-109y = -218$
$y = 2$

$5(2) + z = 6$
$z = -4$

$2x + 7(-4) = -26$
$2x = 2$
$x = 1$
$x = 1, y = 2, z = -4$

32. speed of plane: x
speed of wind: y
$3(x - y) = 720$
$\dfrac{5}{2}(x + y) = 720$

$x - y = 240$
$\underline{x + y = 288}$
$2x = 528$
$x = 264$
$264 + y = 288$
$y = 24$
plane: 264 mph, wind: 24 mph

34. number of laborers: x
number of mechanics: y
$70x + 90y = 1950$
$80x + 100y = 2200$

$7x + 9y = 195$
$8x + 10y = 220$

$-70x - 90y = -1950$
$\underline{72x + 90y = 1980}$
$2x = 30$
$x = 15$

$7(15) + 9y = 195$
$9y = 90$
$y = 10$
15 laborers; 10 mechanics

36. cost of hat: x
cost of shirt: y
cost of pants: z
$2x + 5y + 4z = 129$
$x + y + 2z = 42$
$2x + 3y + z = 63$

$$2x + 5y + 4z = 129$$
$$\underline{-2x - 2y - 4z = -84}$$
$$3y = 45$$
$$y = 15$$

$$x + 15 + 2(12) = 42$$
$$x + 15 + 24 = 42$$
$$x + 39 = 42$$
$$x = 3$$
hat: $3; shirt: $15; pants: $12

$$2x + 5y + 4z = 129$$
$$\underline{-2x - 3y - z = -63}$$
$$2y + 3z = 66$$
$$2(15) + 3z = 66$$
$$3z = 36$$
$$z = 12$$

38. cost of jelly: x
cost of peanut butter: y
cost of honey: z
$$4x + 3y + 5z = 9.80$$
$$2x + 2y + z = 4.20$$
$$3x + 4y + 2z = 7.70$$

$$4x + 3y + 5z = 9.80$$
$$\underline{-10x - 10y - 5z = -21.00}$$
$$-6x - 7y = -11.20$$

$$-4x - 4y - 2z = -8.40$$
$$\underline{3x + 4y + 2z = 7.70}$$
$$-x = -0.70$$
$$x = 0.70$$

$$-6(0.70) - 7y = -11.20$$
$$-7y = -7$$
$$y = 1$$

$$2(0.70) + 2(1) + z = 4.20$$
$$1.40 + 2 + z = 4.20$$
$$3.40 + z = 4.20$$
$$z = 0.80$$
jelly: $0.70; peanut butter: $1.00; honey: $0.80

40. $\begin{vmatrix} 5 & -7 \\ 2 & -3 \end{vmatrix} = (5)(-3) - (2)(-7)$
$$= -15 + 14$$
$$= -1$$

42. $\begin{vmatrix} -6 & -8 \\ -2 & 3 \end{vmatrix} = (-6)(3) - (-2)(-8)$
$$= -18 - 16$$
$$= -34$$

44. $\begin{vmatrix} 0.8 & -5.3 \\ -0.2 & 1.2 \end{vmatrix} = (0.8)(1.2) - (-0.2)(-5.3)$
$$= 0.96 - 1.06$$
$$= -0.1$$

46. $\begin{vmatrix} 0 & -3 & 2 \\ 1 & 5 & 3 \\ -2 & 1 & 4 \end{vmatrix} = 0 - 1\begin{vmatrix} -3 & 2 \\ 1 & 4 \end{vmatrix} - 2\begin{vmatrix} -3 & 2 \\ 5 & 3 \end{vmatrix}$
$$= -(-12 - 2) - 2(-9 - 10)$$
$$= 14 + 38$$
$$= 52$$

48. $\begin{vmatrix} 6 & 1 & 0 \\ 2 & 3 & 0 \\ 6 & -2 & 1 \end{vmatrix} = 0 - 0 + 1\begin{vmatrix} 6 & 1 \\ 2 & 3 \end{vmatrix}$
$$= 18 - 2$$
$$= 16$$

50. $x + y = 10$
$6x + 9y = 70$

$$D = \begin{vmatrix} 1 & 1 \\ 6 & 9 \end{vmatrix} = (1)(9) - (6)(1) = 3$$

$$D_x = \begin{vmatrix} 10 & 1 \\ 70 & 9 \end{vmatrix} = (10)(9) - (70)(1) = 20$$

$$D_y = \begin{vmatrix} 1 & 10 \\ 6 & 70 \end{vmatrix} = (1)(70) - (6)(10) = 10$$

$$x = \frac{D_x}{D} = \frac{20}{3}$$

$$y = \frac{D_y}{D} = \frac{10}{3}$$

$$x = \frac{20}{3}, \; y = \frac{10}{3}$$

52. $2x - 3y + 2z = 0$
$x + 2y - z = 2$
$2x + y + 3z = -1$

$$D = \begin{vmatrix} 2 & -3 & 2 \\ 1 & 2 & -1 \\ 2 & 1 & 3 \end{vmatrix}$$
$$= 2(6 + 1) - 1(-9 - 2) + 2(3 - 4)$$
$$= 2(7) - (-11) + 2(-1)$$
$$= 23$$

$$D_x = \begin{vmatrix} 0 & -3 & 2 \\ 2 & 2 & -1 \\ -1 & 1 & 3 \end{vmatrix}$$
$$= 0 - 2(-9 - 2) - 1(3 - 4)$$
$$= -2(-11) - (-1)$$
$$= 23$$

$$D_y = \begin{vmatrix} 2 & 0 & 2 \\ 1 & 2 & -1 \\ 2 & -1 & 3 \end{vmatrix}$$
$$= 2(6 - 1) - 0 + 2(-1 - 4)$$
$$= 2(5) + 2(-5)$$
$$= 0$$

$$D_z = \begin{vmatrix} 2 & -3 & 0 \\ 1 & 2 & 2 \\ 2 & 1 & -1 \end{vmatrix}$$
$$= 2(-2 - 2) + 3(-1 - 4) + 0$$
$$= 2(-4) + 3(-5)$$
$$= -23$$

$$x = \frac{D_x}{D} = \frac{23}{23} = 1$$
$$y = \frac{D_y}{D} = \frac{0}{23} = 0$$
$$z = \frac{D_z}{D} = \frac{-23}{23} = -1$$
$$x = 1, y = 0, z = -1$$

54. $x - 2y + z = -5$
$2x + z = -10$
$y - z = 15$

$$D = \begin{vmatrix} 1 & -2 & 1 \\ 2 & 0 & 1 \\ 0 & 1 & -1 \end{vmatrix}$$
$$= 0 - 1(1 - 2) - 1(0 + 4)$$
$$= -(-1) - (4)$$
$$= -3$$

$$D_y = \begin{vmatrix} 1 & -5 & 1 \\ 2 & -10 & 1 \\ 0 & 15 & -1 \end{vmatrix}$$
$$= 1(10 - 15) - 2(5 - 15) + 0$$
$$= -5 - 2(-10)$$
$$= 15$$

$$y = \frac{D_y}{D} = \frac{15}{-3} = -5$$

56. $x - y \le 3$
$$y \le -\frac{1}{4}x + 2$$

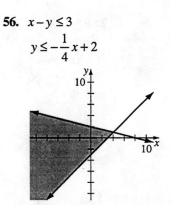

58. $x + y > 1$
$2x - y < 5$

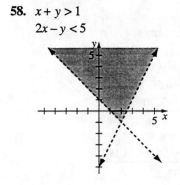

Chapter 4 Test

2. $6x - 2y = -2$
$3x + 4y = 14$

$$12x - 4y = -4$$
$$\underline{3x + 4y = 14}$$
$$15x = 10$$
$$x = \frac{2}{3}$$

$$3\left(\frac{2}{3}\right) + 4y = 14$$
$$2 + 4y = 14$$
$$4y = 12$$
$$y = 3$$
$$x = \frac{2}{3}, y = 3$$

4. $7x - 1 = 3(1 + y)$
$1 - 6y = -7(2x + 1)$

$$7x - 3y = 4$$
$$14x - 6y = -8$$

$$-14x + 6y = -8$$
$$\underline{14x - 6y = -8}$$
$$0 = -16$$

No solution; inconsistent system of equations

6. $3x + 2y = 0$
$2x - y + 3z = 8$
$5x + 3y + z = 4$

$2x - y + 3z = 8$
$\underline{-15x - 9y - 3z = -12}$
$-13x - 10y = -4$

$15x + 10y = 0$
$\underline{-13x - 10y = -4}$
$2x = -4$
$x = -2$

$3(-2) + 2y = 0$
$2y = 6$
$y = 3$

$5(-2) + 3(3) + z = 4$
$-10 + 9 + z = 4$
$z = 5$
$x = -2, y = 3, z = 5$

8. number of station wagons: x
number of 4-door sedans: y
number of 2-door sedans: z
$5x + 4y + 3z = 62$
$4x + 3y + 3z = 52$
$3x + 2y + 2z = 36$

$5x + 4y + 3z = 62$ $-8x - 6y - 6z = -104$
$\underline{-4x - 3y - 3z = -52}$ $\underline{9x + 6y + 6z = 108}$
$x + y = 10$ $x = 4$

$4 + y = 10$
$y = 6$

$3(4) + 2(6) + 2z = 36$
$12 + 12 + 2z = 36$
$2z = 12$
$z = 6$
4 station wagons; 6 4-door sedans; 6 2-door sedans

10. $\dfrac{1}{3}x + \dfrac{5}{6}y = 2$
$\dfrac{3}{5}x - y = -\dfrac{7}{5}$

$2x + 5y = 12$
$3x - 5y = -7$

$D = \begin{vmatrix} 2 & 5 \\ 3 & -5 \end{vmatrix} = (2)(-5) - (3)(5) = -25$

$D_x = \begin{vmatrix} 12 & 5 \\ -7 & -5 \end{vmatrix} = (12)(-5) - (-7)(5) = -25$

$D_y = \begin{vmatrix} 2 & 12 \\ 3 & -7 \end{vmatrix} = (2)(-7) - (3)(12) = -50$

$x = \dfrac{D_x}{D} = \dfrac{-25}{-25} = 1$

$y = \dfrac{D_y}{D} = \dfrac{-50}{-25} = 2$

$x = 1, y = 2$

12. $x + 2y \le 6$
$-2x + y \ge -2$

Cumulative Test For Chapters 1–4

2. $\sqrt{25} + (2 - 3)^3 + 20 \div (-10)$
$= 5 + (-1)^3 + 20 \div (-10)$
$= 5 - 1 + 20 \div (-10)$
$= 5 - 1 - 2$
$= 2$

4. $2x - 4[x - 3(2x + 1)]$
$= 2x - 4(x - 6x - 3)$
$= 2x - 4(-5x - 3)$
$= 2x + 20x + 12$
$= 22x + 12$

6. $\dfrac{1}{4}x + 5 = \dfrac{1}{3}(x - 2)$
$3x + 60 = 4(x - 2)$
$3x + 60 = 4x - 8$
$60 = x - 8$
$68 = x$

8. $m = \dfrac{y_2 - y_1}{x_2 - x_1}$

$= \dfrac{-1 - (-2)}{6 - (-4)}$

$= \dfrac{1}{10}$

10. $\dfrac{2x - 1}{3} \le 7$ and $2(x + 1) \ge 12$

$2x - 1 \le 21$ and $2x + 2 \ge 12$

$2x \le 22$ and $2x \ge 10$

$x \le 11$ and $x \ge 5$

$5 \le x \le 11$

```
<———————•———————•———————>
        5       11
```

12. 1st side: x

2nd side: $x + 7$

3rd side: $2x - 6$

$x + x + 7 + 2x - 6 = 69$

$4x + 1 = 69$

$4x = 68$

$x = 17$

$x + 7 = 17 + 7 = 24$

$2x - 6 = 2(17) - 6 = 28$

1st side: 17 m; 2nd side: 24 m; 3rd side: 28 m

14. $5x + 2y = 2$

$4x + 3y = -4$

$-15x - 6y = -6$

$\underline{8x + 6y = -8}$

$-7x = -14$

$x = 2$

$5(2) + 2y = 2$

$2y = -8$

$y = -4$

$x = 2,\ y = -4$

16. cost of shirt: x

cost of slacks: y

$5x + 8y = 345$

$7x + 3y = 237$

$15x + 24y = 1035$

$\underline{-56x - 24y = -1896}$

$-41x = -861$

$x = 21$

$7(21) + 3y = 237$

$3y = 90$

$y = 30$

shirt: $21; slacks: $30

18. $x + 3y + z = 5$

$2x - 3y - 2z = 0$

$x - 2y + 3z = -9$

$D = \begin{vmatrix} 1 & 3 & 1 \\ 2 & -3 & -2 \\ 1 & -2 & 3 \end{vmatrix} = 1(-13) - 2(11) + 1(-3)$

$= -38$

$D_z = \begin{vmatrix} 1 & 3 & 5 \\ 2 & -3 & 0 \\ 1 & -2 & -9 \end{vmatrix} = -2(-17) - 3(-14)$

$= 76$

$z = \dfrac{D_z}{D} = \dfrac{76}{-38} = -2$

20. $x - y \ge -4$

$x + 2y \ge 2$

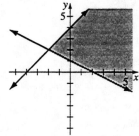

Chapter 5

2. $(x^2 - 3x - 4)(2x - 3)$
$= 2x^3 - 6x^2 - 8x - 3x^2 + 9x + 12$
$= 2x^3 - 9x^2 + x + 12$

4. $(2y - 3)(2y + 3)$
$= (2y)^2 - 3^2$
$= 4y^2 - 9$

6. $(25x^3y^2 - 30x^2y^3 - 50x^2y^2) \div 5x^2y^2$
$= \dfrac{25x^3y^2 - 30x^2y^3 - 50x^2y^2}{5x^2y^2}$
$= \dfrac{25x^3y^2}{5x^2y^2} - \dfrac{30x^2y^3}{5x^2y^2} - \dfrac{50x^2y^2}{5x^2y^2}$
$= 5x - 6y - 10$

8.
$$
\begin{array}{r}
x^3 + 2x^2 - x - 2 \\
2x+5\overline{\smash{)}2x^4 + 9x^3 + 8x^2 - 9x - 10} \\
\underline{2x^4 + 5x^3} \\
4x^3 + 8x^2 \\
\underline{4x^3 + 10x^2} \\
-2x^2 - 9x \\
\underline{-2x^2 - 5x} \\
-4x - 10 \\
\underline{-4x - 10} \\
0
\end{array}
$$

10. $3x(4x - 3y) - 2(4x - 3y) = (4x - 3y)(3x - 2)$

12. $mn = 10;$ $m + n = -7$
$(-5)(-2) = 10$ $-5 - 2 = -7$
$x^2 - 7xy + 10y^2 = (x - 5y)(x - 2y)$

14. $28x^2 - 19xy + 3y^2$
$= 28x^2 - 12xy - 7xy + 3y^2$
$= 4x(7x - 3y) - y(7x - 3y)$
$= (7x - 3y)(4x - y)$

16. $121x^2 - 1$
$= (11x)^2 - 1^2$
$= (11x - 1)(11x + 1)$

18. $64x^3 + 27$
$= (4x)^3 + 3^3$
$= (4x + 3)\left[(4x)^2 - (4x)(3) + 3^2\right]$
$= (4x + 3)(16x^2 - 12x + 9)$

20. $2x^3 - 2x^2 - 24x$
$= 2x(x^2 - x - 12)$
$= 2x(x - 4)(x + 3)$

22. $81a^3 + 126a^2y + 49ay^2$
$= a(81a^2 + 126ay + 49y^2)$
$= a\left[(9a)^2 + 2(9a)(7y) + (7y)^2\right]$
$= a(9a + 7y)^2$

24. $3x^2 + 5x = 7x^2 - 2x$
$0 = 4x^2 - 7x$
$0 = x(4x - 7)$

$x = 0$ or $4x - 7 = 0$
                                  $4x = 7$
                                  $x = \dfrac{7}{4}$

26. width: x
length: $3x + 1$
$x(3x + 1) = 52$
$3x^2 + x = 52$
$3x^2 + x - 52 = 0$
$(3x + 13)(x - 4) = 0$
$3x + 13 = 0$ or $x - 4 = 0$
$3x = -13$ $x = 4$
$x = -\dfrac{13}{3}$
Since $x > 0$, $x = 4$ and $3x + 1 = 3(4) + 1 = 13$
4 m by 13 m

5.1 Exercises

2. Trinomial; 2nd degree

4. Binomial; 7th degree

6. Monomial; 6th degree

8. $(x^2 + 2x - 12) + (7x^2 - 5x - 14)$
$= 8x^2 - 3x - 26$

10. $(2x^2 - 5x - 1) + (3x^2 - 7x + 3) + (-5x^2 + x + 1)$
$= -11x + 3$

12. $(3x^3 + 2x^2 - 8x - 9.2) - (-5x^3 + x^2 - x - 12.7)$
$= 3x^3 + 2x^2 - 8x - 9.2 + 5x^3 - x^2 + x + 12.7$
$= 8x^3 + x^2 - 7x + 3.5$

14. $(7a^2 - 2a + 6) + (-12a^3 - 6a + 5)$
$\quad -(3a^2 - a - 2)$
$= 7a^2 - 2a + 6 - 12a^3 - 6a + 5 - 3a^2 + a + 2$
$= -12a^3 + 4a^2 - 7a + 13$

16. $\left(\dfrac{1}{5}x^2 + 9x\right) + \left(\dfrac{4}{5}x^2 - \dfrac{1}{6}x\right)$
$= x^2 + \dfrac{53}{6}x$
$= x^2 + 8\dfrac{5}{6}x$

18. $(5.9x^3 + 3.4x^2 - 7) - (2.9x^3 - 9.6x^2 + 3)$
$= 5.9x^3 + 3.4x^2 - 7 - 2.9x^3 + 9.6x^2 - 3$
$= 3x^3 + 13x^2 - 10$

20. $-5x(x^2 - 6x - 2) = -5x^3 + 30x^2 + 10x$

22. $4xy^2(x - y + 3) = 4x^2y^2 - 4xy^3 + 12xy^2$

24. $(x + 12)(x + 2)$
$= x^2 + 2x + 12x + 24$
$= x^2 + 14x + 24$

26. $(2x - 1)(x + 5)$
$= 2x^2 + 10x - x - 5$
$= 2x^2 + 9x - 5$

28. $(2x - 4)(9x - 5)$
$= 18x^2 - 10x - 36x + 20$
$= 18x^2 - 46x + 20$

30. $(7a + 8b)(5d - 8w)$
$= 35ad + 40bd - 56aw - 64bw$

32. $(-8x - 3y)(x + 2y)$
$= -8x^2 - 16xy - 3xy - 6y^2$
$= -8x^2 - 19xy - 6y^2$

34. $(-3r - 2s^2)(5r - 6s^2)$
$= -15r^2 + 18rs^2 - 10rs^2 + 12s^4$
$= -15r^2 + 8rs^2 + 12s^4$

36. $(4x + 1)(2x^2 + x + 1)$
$= 8x^3 + 4x^2 + 4x + 2x^2 + x + 1$
$= 8x^3 + 6x^2 + 5x + 1$

38. $(5x^2 + 3xy - 7y^2)(3x - 2y)$
$= 15x^3 + 9x^2y - 21xy^2 - 10x^2y - 6xy^2 + 14y^3$
$= 15x^3 - x^2y - 27xy^2 + 14y^3$

40. $(3x^2 - 2x - 4)(x^2 + 2x + 3)$
$= 3x^4 + 6x^3 + 9x^2 - 2x^3 - 4x^2$
$\quad -6x - 4x^2 - 8x - 12$
$= 3x^4 + 4x^3 + x^2 - 14x - 12$

42. $(2b^3 - 5b^2 - 4b + 1)(2b - 1)$
$= 4b^4 - 10b^3 - 8b^2 + 2b - 2b^3 + 5b^2 + 4b - 1$
$= 4b^4 - 12b^3 - 3b^2 + 6b - 1$

44. $(m^2 - 6mp + 2p^2)(2m^2 - 4mp + 3p^2)$
$= 2m^4 - 4m^3p + 3m^2p^2 - 12m^3p$
$\quad + 24m^2p^2 - 18mp^3 + 4m^2p^2 - 8mp^3 + 6p^4$
$= 2m^4 - 16m^3p + 31m^2p^2 - 26mp^3 + 6p^4$

46. $(2a - 7b)(2a + 7b)$
$= (2a)^2 - (7b)^2$
$= 4a^2 - 49b^2$

48. $(6a + 5b)^2$
$= (6a)^2 + 2(6a)(5b) + (5b)^2$
$= 36a^2 + 60ab + 25b^2$

50. $(5r + 3)^2$
$= (5r)^2 + 2(5r)(3) + 3^2$
$= 25r^2 + 30r + 9$

52. $(1 - 7x^3)(1 + 7x^3)$
$= 1^2 - (7x^3)^2$
$= 1 - 49x^6$

54. $(3x^2 - 5y^2)^2$
$= (3x^2)^2 - 2(3x^2)(5y^2) + (5y^2)^2$
$= 9x^4 - 30x^2y^2 + 25y^4$

56. $(5x + 8y^2)(5x - 8y^2)$

$= (5x)^2 - (8y^2)^2$

$= 25x^2 - 64y^4$

58. $(x - 6)(x + 2)(3x + 2)$

$= (x^2 - 4x - 12)(3x + 2)$

$= 3x^3 - 12x^2 - 36x + 2x^2 - 8x - 24$

$= 3x^3 - 10x^2 - 44x - 24$

60. $(6 - 5a)(a + 1)(2 - 3a)$

$= (6a + 6 - 5a^2 - 5a)(2 - 3a)$

$= (-5a^2 + a + 6)(2 - 3a)$

$= -10a^2 + 2a + 12 + 15a^3 - 3a^2 - 18a$

$= 15a^3 - 13a^2 - 16a + 12$

62. $(52.613x + 49.408y)(34.078x - 28.231y)$

$= 1792.945814x^2 - 1485.317603xy$

$\quad + 1683.725824xy - 1394.837248y^2$

$= 1792.945814x^2 + 198.408221xy$

$\quad - 1394.837248y^2$

64. $(3n^2 + 4n + 7)(2n + 5)$

$= 6n^3 + 8n^2 + 14n + 15n^2 + 20n + 35$

$= 6n^3 + 23n^2 + 34n + 35$ flowers

Cumulative Review Problems

66. $2\{3 - x[4 + x(2 - x)]\}$

$= 2\{3 - x[4 + 2x - x^2]\}$

$= 2\{3 - 4x - 2x^2 + x^3\}$

$= 6 - 8x - 4x^2 + 2x^3$

$= 2x^3 - 4x^2 - 8x + 6$

68. $-0.03t^2 + 78$

$= -0.03(30)^2 + 78 = 51$

51 parts per million

70. $-0.03t^2 + 78$

$= -0.03(50.9)^2 + 78 = 0.2757$

Approximately 0.28 parts per million

5.2 Exercises

2. $(14x^2 - 28x - 35) \div 7$

$= \dfrac{14x^2 - 28x - 35}{7}$

$= \dfrac{14x^2}{7} - \dfrac{28x}{7} - \dfrac{35}{7}$

$= 2x^2 - 4x - 5$

4. $(22x^4 + 33x^3 - 121x^2) \div 11x$

$= \dfrac{22x^4 + 33x^3 - 121x^2}{11x}$

$= \dfrac{22x^4}{11x} + \dfrac{33x^3}{11x} - \dfrac{121x^2}{11x}$

$= 2x^3 + 3x^2 - 11x$

6. $\dfrac{4w^3 + 8w^2 - w}{4w}$

$= \dfrac{4w^3}{4w} + \dfrac{8w^2}{4w} - \dfrac{w}{4w}$

$= w^2 + 2w - \dfrac{1}{4}$

8. $\dfrac{25m^5n - 10m^4n + 15m^3n}{5m^3n}$

$= \dfrac{25m^5n}{5m^3n} - \dfrac{10m^4n}{5m^3n} + \dfrac{15m^3n}{5m^3n}$

$= 5m^2 - 2m + 3$

10.

$$
\begin{array}{r}
3x + 2 \\
4x + 1 \overline{\smash{)}\,12x^2 + 11x + 2} \\
\underline{12x^2 + 3x} \\
8x + 2 \\
\underline{8x + 2} \\
\end{array}
$$

$= 3x + 2$

Check: $(3x + 2)(4x + 1)$

$= 12x^2 + 3x + 8x + 2$

$= 12x^2 + 11x + 2$

12.

$$5x-2 \overline{)\,30x^2-17x+2\,}$$

quotient: $6x-1$

$$\underline{30x^2-12x}$$
$$-5x+2$$
$$\underline{-5x+2}$$

$= 6x - 1$

Check: $(6x-1)(5x-2)$

$= 30x^2 - 12x - 5x + 2$

$= 30x^2 - 17x + 2$

14.

$$3a+4 \overline{)\,18a^2+9a-17\,}$$

quotient: $6a-5+\frac{3}{3a+4}$

$$\underline{18a^2+24a}$$
$$-15a-17$$
$$\underline{-15a-20}$$
$$3$$

$= 6a - 5 + \dfrac{3}{3a+4}$

16.

$$x+1 \overline{)\,x^3+2x^2-3x+2\,}$$

quotient: $x^2+x-4+\frac{6}{x+1}$

$$\underline{x^3+\;x^2}$$
$$x^2-3x$$
$$\underline{x^2+\;x}$$
$$-4x+2$$
$$\underline{-4x-4}$$
$$6$$

$= x^2 + x - 4 + \dfrac{6}{x+1}$

18.

$$2x-4 \overline{)\,4x^3+0x^2-6x-11\,}$$

quotient: $2x^2+4x+5+\frac{9}{2x-4}$

$$\underline{4x^3-8x^2}$$
$$8x^2-\;6x$$
$$\underline{8x^2-16x}$$
$$10x-11$$
$$\underline{10x-20}$$
$$9$$

$= 2x^2 + 4x + 5 + \dfrac{9}{2x-4}$

20.

$$x-5 \overline{)\,x^3-7x^2+13x-15\,}$$

quotient: x^2-2x+3

$$\underline{x^3-5x^2}$$
$$-2x^2+13x$$
$$\underline{-2x^2+10x}$$
$$3x-15$$
$$\underline{3x-15}$$

$= x^2 - 2x + 3$

22.

$$x-4 \overline{)\,x^3+0x^2+0x-64\,}$$

quotient: $x^2+4x+16$

$$\underline{x^3-4x^2}$$
$$4x^2+\;0x$$
$$\underline{4x^2-16x}$$
$$16x-64$$
$$\underline{16x-64}$$

$= x^2 + 4x + 16$

24.

$$2x-3 \overline{)\,4x^4+0x^3-17x^2+14x-3\,}$$

quotient: $2x^3+3x^2-4x+1$

$$\underline{4x^4-6x^3}$$
$$6x^3-17x^2$$
$$\underline{6x^3-\;9x^2}$$
$$-8x^2+14x$$
$$\underline{-8x^2+12x}$$
$$2x-3$$
$$\underline{2x-3}$$

$= 2x^3 + 3x^2 - 4x + 1$

26.

$$a^2+3 \overline{)\,2a^4+3a^3+4a^2+9a-6\,}$$

quotient: $2a^2+3a-2$

$$\underline{2a^4\qquad+6a^2}$$
$$3a^3-2a^2+9a$$
$$\underline{3a^3\qquad+9a}$$
$$-2a^2\qquad-6$$
$$\underline{-2a^2\qquad-6}$$

$= 2a^2 + 3a - 2$

28.

$$\begin{array}{r} 2t^2+3t-2 \\ t^2+t-6\overline{)2t^4+5t^3-11t^2-20t+12} \\ \underline{2t^4+2t^3-12t^2} \\ 3t^3+\;\;t^2-20t \\ \underline{3t^3+\;3t^2-18t} \\ -2t^2-2t+12 \\ \underline{-2t^2-2t+12} \\ =2t^2+3t-2 \end{array}$$

30.

$$\begin{array}{r} 5x-3.122137405+\frac{1.34748092}{2.62x+3.50} \\ 2.62x+3.50\overline{)13.1x^2+\;9.32x-9.58} \\ \underline{13.1x^2+17.50x} \\ -8.18x-\;9.58 \\ \underline{-8.18x-10.92748092} \\ 1.34748092 \end{array}$$

32. $\dfrac{4x^3+12x^2+7x-3}{2x+3}=2x^2+3x-1$

The graphs of

$y_1=\dfrac{4x^3+12x^2+7x-3}{2x+3}$

and $y_2=2x^2+3x-1$ coincide.

Cumulative Review Problems

34. $9x-2x+8=4x+38$

$7x+8=4x+38$

$3x+8=38$

$3x=30$

$x=10$

36. $5-\dfrac{x}{4}=x-1$

$20-x=4x-4$

$20=5x-4$

$24=5x$

$\dfrac{24}{5}=x$

5.3 Exercises

2.

$$\begin{array}{r} 8\;\underline{}\;\;1\quad\;2\quad-80 \\ \underline{\quad\quad\;\;8\quad\;\;80} \\ 1\quad10\;\boxed{\;0} \end{array}$$

$(x^2+2x-80)\div(x-8)=x+10$

4.

$$\begin{array}{r} 9\;\underline{}\;\;2\quad-15\quad-23 \\ \underline{\quad\quad\;18\quad\;\;27} \\ 2\quad\;\;3\;\boxed{\;4} \end{array}$$

$(2x^2-15x-23)\div(x-9)=2x+3+\dfrac{4}{x-9}$

6.

$$\begin{array}{r} -2\;\underline{}\;\;3\quad10\quad\;6\quad-4 \\ \underline{\quad\quad\;-6\quad-8\quad\;4} \\ 3\quad\;4\quad-2\;\boxed{\;0} \end{array}$$

$(3x^3+10x^2+6x-4)\div(x+2)$

$=3x^2+4x-2$

8.

$$\begin{array}{r} -2\;\underline{}\;\;3\quad-1\quad\;4\quad\;8 \\ \underline{\quad\quad\;-6\quad14\quad-36} \\ 3\quad-7\quad18\;\boxed{-28} \end{array}$$

$(3x^3-x^2+4x+8)\div(x+2)$

$=3x^2-7x+18-\dfrac{28}{x+2}$

10.

$$\begin{array}{r} 1\;\underline{}\;\;4\quad\;1\quad-3\quad-1 \\ \underline{\quad\quad\;\;4\quad\;5\quad\;2} \\ 4\quad\;5\quad\;2\;\boxed{\;1} \end{array}$$

$(4x^3+x^2-3x-1)\div(x-1)$

$=4x^2+5x+2+\dfrac{1}{x-1}$

12.

$$\begin{array}{r} -3\;\underline{}\;\;2\quad\;7\quad\;0\quad-5 \\ \underline{\quad\quad\;-6\quad-3\quad\;9} \\ 2\quad\;1\quad-3\;\boxed{\;4} \end{array}$$

$(2x^3+7x^2-5)\div(x+3)$

$=2x^2+x-3+\dfrac{4}{x+3}$

14.

$$\begin{array}{r} 3\;\underline{}\;\;3\quad\;0\quad-25\quad\;0\quad-18 \\ \underline{\quad\quad\;\;9\quad27\quad\;6\quad18} \\ 3\quad\;9\quad\;2\quad\;6\;\boxed{\;0} \end{array}$$

$(3x^4-25x^2-18)\div(x-3)$

$=3x^3+9x^2+2x+6$

16.

$$\begin{array}{r|rrrrr} 5 & 1 & -3 & -11 & 3 & 10 \\ & & 5 & 10 & -5 & -10 \\ \hline & 1 & 2 & -1 & -2 & 0 \end{array}$$

$(x^4 - 3x^3 - 11x^2 + 3x + 10) \div (x - 5)$
$= x^3 + 2x^2 - x - 2$

18.

$$\begin{array}{r|rrrrr} 2 & 2 & 0 & 0 & -1 & 3 \\ & & 4 & 8 & 16 & 30 \\ \hline & 2 & 4 & 8 & 15 & 33 \end{array}$$

$(2x^4 - x + 3) \div (x - 2)$
$= 2x^3 + 4x^2 + 8x + 15 + \dfrac{33}{x - 2}$

20.

$$\begin{array}{r|rrrrrr} -2 & 2 & -3 & 1 & -1 & 2 & -1 \\ & & -4 & 14 & -30 & 62 & -128 \\ \hline & 2 & -7 & 15 & -31 & 64 & -129 \end{array}$$

$(2x^5 - 3x^4 + x^3 - x^2 + 2x - 1) \div (x + 2)$
$= 2x^4 - 7x^3 + 15x^2 - 31x + 64 - \dfrac{129}{x + 2}$

22.

$$\begin{array}{r|rrrrrrr} 2 & 1 & 0 & 2 & 0 & 0 & -5 & 11 \\ & & 2 & 4 & 12 & 24 & 48 & 86 \\ \hline & 1 & 2 & 6 & 12 & 24 & 43 & 97 \end{array}$$

$(x^6 + 2x^4 - 5x + 11) \div (x - 2)$
$= x^5 + 2x^4 + 6x^3 + 12x^2 + 24x + 43 + \dfrac{97}{x - 2}$

24.

$$\begin{array}{r|rrrr} -1.8 & 1 & -4.2 & -8.8 & 3.7 \\ & & -1.8 & 10.8 & -3.6 \\ \hline & 1 & -6.0 & 2.0 & 0.1 \end{array}$$

$(x^3 - 4.2x^2 - 8.8x + 3.7) \div (x + 1.8)$
$= x^2 - 6x + 2 + \dfrac{0.1}{x + 1.8}$

26.

$$\begin{array}{r|rrrrr} -5 & 2 & 12 & a & -5 & 75 \\ & & -10 & -10 & -5a + 50 & 25a - 225 \\ \hline & 2 & 2 & a - 10 & -5a + 45 & 25a - 150 \end{array}$$

$25a - 150 = 0$
$25a = 150$
$a = 6$

28.

$$\begin{array}{r|rrrr} -\frac{3}{2} & 4 & -6 & 0 & 6 \\ & & -6 & 18 & -27 \\ \hline & 4 & -12 & 18 & -21 \end{array}$$

$(4x^3 - 6x^2 + 6) \div (2x + 3)$
$= \dfrac{4x^2 - 12x + 18}{2} - \dfrac{21}{2x + 3}$
$= 2x^2 - 6x + 9 - \dfrac{21}{2x + 3}$

30. To have an equivalent fraction, you must divide both the numerator and the denominator by the same value. However, in the case of the remainder, the denominator has not changed. When we write the remainder in fraction form, the denominator is still $ax + b$.

Cumulative Review Problems

32. Volume $= \pi r^2 h$
$268,000 = 3.14(200)^2 h$
$h = \dfrac{268,000}{3.14(200)^2}$
$h = 2.1$
2.1 feet deep

5.4 Exercises

2. $16x - 16 = 16 \cdot x - 16 \cdot 1$
$= 16(x - 1)$

4. $7a^2 - 14a = 7a \cdot a + 7a \cdot (-2)$
$= 7a(a - 2)$

6. $a^3 b^2 + a^2 b^3 + a^2 b^2$
$= a^2 b^2 \cdot a + a^2 b^2 \cdot b + a^2 b^2 \cdot 1$
$= a^2 b^2 (a + b + 1)$

8. $3x^4 - 6x^3 + 9x^2$
$$= 3x^2 \cdot x^2 - 3x^2 \cdot 2x + 3x^2 \cdot 3$$
$$= 3x^2(x^2 - 2x + 3)$$

10. $14x^2y - 35xy - 63x$
$$= 7x \cdot 2xy - 7x \cdot 5y - 7x \cdot 9$$
$$= 7x(2xy - 5y - 9)$$

12. $20x^2y^2z^2 - 30x^3y^3z^2 + 25x^2yz^2$
$$= 5x^2yz^2 \cdot 4y - 5x^2yz^2 \cdot 6xy^2 + 5x^2yz^2 \cdot 5$$
$$= 5x^2yz^2(4y - 6xy^2 + 5)$$

14. There is no common factor.

16. $15a^3b^3 + 6a^4b^3 - 9a^2b^3 + 30a^5b^3$
$$= 3a^2b^3 \cdot 5a + 3a^2b^3 \cdot 2a^2 - 3a^2b^3 \cdot 3$$
$$\quad + 3a^2b^3 \cdot 10a^3$$
$$= 3a^2b^3(5a + 2a^2 - 3 + 10a^3)$$

18. $5a(a + 3b) + 4(a + 3b)$
$$= (a + 3b)(5a + 4)$$

20. $4y(x - 5y) - 3(-5y + x)$
$$= 4y(x - 5y) - 3(x - 5y)$$
$$= (x - 5y)(4y - 3)$$

22. $2w(s - 3t) - (s - 3t) = (s - 3t)(2w - 1)$

24. $7a^3(5a + 4) - 2(5a + 4)$
$$= (5a + 4)(7a^3 - 2)$$

26. $4w(y - 8x) + 5z(y - 8x) + (y - 8x)$
$$= (y - 8x)(4w + 5z + 1)$$

28. $x^3 + 8x^2 + 2x + 16$
$$= x^2(x + 8) + 2(x + 8)$$
$$= (x + 8)(x^2 + 2)$$

30. $ax + a - 7bx - 7b$
$$= a(x + 1) - 7b(x + 1) = (x + 1)(a - 7b)$$

32. $6xy - 3x - 2py + p$
$$= 3x(2y - 1) - p(2y - 1) = (2y - 1)(3x - p)$$

34. $4ax - 10ay - 2bx + 5by$
$$= 2a(2x - 5y) - b(2x - 5y)$$
$$= (2x - 5y)(2a - b)$$

36. $5bc - a^3 - b + 5a^3c$
$$= 5bc - b + 5a^3c - a^3$$
$$= b(5c - 1) + a^3(5c - 1)$$
$$= (5c - 1)(b + a^3)$$

38. $18ax - 6bx + 9ay^2 - 3by^2$
$$= 3(6ax - 2bx + 3ay^2 - by^2)$$
$$= 3[2x(3a - b) + y^2(3a - b)]$$
$$= 3(3a - b)(2x + y^2)$$

40. $6x^3 + 35wy - 14x^2y - 15xw$
$$= 6x^3 - 14x^2y - 15xw + 35wy$$
$$= 2x^2(3x - 7y) - 5w(3x - 7y)$$
$$= (3x - 7y)(2x^2 - 5w)$$

42. $19.62x^2 - 29.43w + 147.15z^2$
$$= 9.81(2x^2 - 3w + 15z^2)$$

Cumulative Review Problems

44. $y = \dfrac{2}{3}x - 2$
$$m = \dfrac{2}{3}, \quad b = -2$$

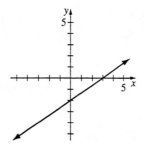

46. $2y + 6x = -3$
$$2y = -6x - 3$$
$$y = -3x - \dfrac{3}{2}$$
$$m = -3, \quad b = -\dfrac{3}{2}$$

48. x = number of multiple choice
y = number of fill-in
$$4x + 5y = 102$$
$$x + y = 22$$

$4x + 5y = 102$

$-4x - 4y = -88$

$y = 14$

$x = 8$

Let z = number of multiple choice correct

$82 = 5(14 - 4) + 4z$

$z = 7.75$

He answered 8 multiple choice questions correctly.

5.5 Exercises

2. $mn = 7;\ m + n = 8$

$x^2 + 8x + 7 = (x + 7)(x + 1)$

4. $mn = -20;\ m + n = 8$

$x^2 + 8x - 20 = (x + 10)(x - 2)$

6. $mn = -6;\ m + n = -1$

$x^2 - x - 6 = (x + 2)(x - 3)$

8. $mn = 35;\ m + n = 12$

$x^2 + 12x + 35 = (x + 5)(x + 7)$

10. $mn = -16;\ m + n = -6$

$a^2 - 6a - 16 = (a - 8)(a + 2)$

12. $mn = 60;\ m + n = 17$

$a^2 + 17a + 60 = (a + 5)(a + 12)$

14. $mn = -27;\ m + n = -6$

$x^2 - 6xy - 27y^2 = (x - 9y)(x + 3y)$

16. $mn = 10;\ m + n = 7$

$x^2 + 7xy + 10y^2 = (x + 2y)(x + 5y)$

18. $mn = 5;\ m + n = 6$

$x^4 + 6x^2 + 5 = (x^2 + 5)(x^2 + 1)$

20. $mn = -55;\ m + n = -6$

$x^4 - 6x^2 - 55 = (x^2 - 11)(x^2 + 5)$

22. $2x^2 + 30x + 52$

$= 2(x^2 + 15x + 26)$

$= 2(x + 2)(x + 13)$

24. $x^3 + 11x^2 - 42x$

$= x(x^2 + 11x - 42)$

$= x(x + 14)(x - 3)$

26. $3x^2 + 22x + 7$

$= 3x^2 + 21x + x + 7$

$= 3x(x + 7) + 1(x + 7)$

$= (x + 7)(3x + 1)$

28. $6x^2 + x - 1$

$= 6x^2 + 3x - 2x - 1$

$= 3x(2x + 1) - 1(2x + 1)$

$= (2x + 1)(3x - 1)$

30. $5x^2 - 13x - 28$

$= 5x^2 + 7x - 20x - 28$

$= x(5x + 7) - 4(5x + 7)$

$= (5x + 7)(x - 4)$

32. $6a^2 + 11a + 3$

$= 6a^2 + 2a + 9a + 3$

$= 2a(3a + 1) + 3(3a + 1)$

$= (3a + 1)(2a + 3)$

34. $3a^2 - 20a + 12$

$= 3a^2 - 2a - 18a + 12$

$= a(3a - 2) - 6(3a - 2)$

$= (3a - 2)(a - 6)$

36. $4x^2 + 4x - 15$

$= 4x^2 + 10x - 6x - 15$

$= 2x(2x + 5) - 3(2x + 5)$

$= (2x + 5)(2x - 3)$

38. $5x^2 - 8x - 4$

$= 5x^2 + 2x - 10x - 4$

$= x(5x + 2) - 2(5x + 2)$

$= (5x + 2)(x - 2)$

40. $6x^4 + 7x^2 - 5$

$= 6x^4 + 10x^2 - 3x^2 - 5$

$= 2x^2(3x^2 + 5) - 1(3x^2 + 5)$

$= (3x^2 + 5)(2x^2 - 1)$

42. $5x^2 + 12xy + 7y^2$

$= 5x^2 + 7xy + 5xy + 7y^2$

$= x(5x + 7y) + y(5x + 7y)$

$= (5x + 7y)(x + y)$

44. $9x^2 - 13xy + 4y^2$
$= 9x^2 - 9xy - 4xy + 4y^2$
$= 9x(x - y) - 4y(x - y)$
$= (x - y)(9x - 4y)$

46. $8x^3 + 6x^2 - 9x$
$= x(8x^2 + 6x - 9)$
$= x(8x^2 - 6x + 12x - 9)$
$= x[2x(4x - 3) + 3(4x - 3)]$
$= x(4x - 3)(2x + 3)$

48. $9x^3 + 30x^2 + 9x$
$= 3x(3x^2 + 10x + 3)$
$= 3x(3x^2 + 9x + x + 3)$
$= 3x[3x(x + 3) + 1(x + 3)]$
$= 3x(x + 3)(3x + 1)$

50. $mn = -40;\ m + n = 6$
$x^2 + 6x - 40 = (x + 10)(x - 4)$

52. $5x^2 + 17x + 6$
$= 5x^2 + 2x + 15x + 6$
$= x(5x + 2) + 3(5x + 2)$
$= (5x + 2)(x + 3)$

54. $mn = 99;\ m + n = -20$
$x^2 - 20x + 99 = (x - 9)(x - 11)$

56. $12x^2 - 5x - 3$
$= 12x^2 - 9x + 4x - 3$
$= 3x(4x - 3) + 1(4x - 3)$
$= (4x - 3)(3x + 1)$

58. $3x^2 + 9x - 84$
$= 3(x^2 + 3x - 28)$
$= 3(x + 7)(x - 4)$

60. $24x^2 + 26x + 6$
$= 2(12x^2 + 13x + 3)$
$= 2(12x^2 + 9x + 4x + 3)$
$= 2[3x(4x + 3) + 1(4x + 3)]$
$= 2(4x + 3)(3x + 1)$

62. $2x^3 - 6x^2 - 20x$
$= 2x(x^2 - 3x - 10)$
$= 2x(x - 5)(x + 2)$

64. $12x^3 - 14x^2 + 4x$
$= 2x(6x^2 - 7x + 2)$
$= 2x(6x^2 - 4x - 3x + 2)$
$= 2x[2x(3x - 2) - 1(3x - 2)]$
$= 2x(3x - 2)(2x - 1)$

66. $6x^4 - 13x^2 - 5$
$= 6x^4 + 2x^2 - 15x^2 - 5$
$= 2x^2(3x^2 + 1) - 5(3x^2 + 1)$
$= (3x^2 + 1)(2x^2 - 5)$

68. $10x^2 - 17xy + 6y^2$
$= 10x^2 - 12xy - 5xy + 6y^2$
$= 2x(5x - 6y) - y(5x - 6y)$
$= (5x - 6y)(2x - y)$

70. $x^6 - 3x^3 - 70 = (x^3 - 10)(x^3 + 7)$

72. $4x^3 + 4x^2 - 3x$
$= x(4x^2 + 4x - 3)$
$= x(4x^2 - 2x + 6x - 3)$
$= x[2x(2x - 1) + 3(2x - 1)]$
$= x(2x - 1)(2x + 3)$

Cumulative Review Problems

74. $A = \dfrac{1}{2}(2a + 5b)$
$2A = 2a + 5b$
$2A - 2a = 5b$
$\dfrac{2A - 2a}{5} = b$

76. $6x + 4y = -12$
$(0, -3);\ (-2, 0)$

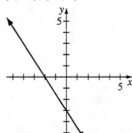

78. $\dfrac{0.2}{8} = \dfrac{x}{8 - 0.2}$

$0.2(8 - 0.2) = 8x$

$\dfrac{1.56}{8} = x$

$0.195 = x$

She should add 0.195 ounces of milk.

5.6 Exercises

2. $x^2 - 36 = x^2 - 6^2 = (x - 6)(x + 6)$

4. $100x^2 - 9$

$= (10x)^2 - 3^2$

$= (10x - 3)(10x + 3)$

6. $81x^2 - 1$

$= (9x)^2 - 1^2$

$= (9x - 1)(9x + 1)$

8. $w^4 - z^4$

$= (w^2)^2 - (z^2)^2$

$= (w^2 - z^2)(w^2 + z^2)$

$(w - z)(w + z)(w^2 + z^2)$

10. $16x^4 - 1$

$= (4x^2)^2 - 1^2$

$= (4x^2 - 1)(4x^2 + 1)$

$= \left[(2x)^2 - 1^2\right](4x^2 + 1)$

$= (2x - 1)(2x + 1)(4x^2 + 1)$

12. $36x^2 - 25y^2$

$= (6x)^2 - (5y)^2$

$= (6x - 5y)(6x + 5y)$

14. $1 - 49x^2y^2$

$= 1^2 - (7xy)^2$

$= (1 - 7xy)(1 + 7xy)$

16. $144x^2 - 9$

$= 9(16x^2 - 1)$

$= 9\left[(4x)^2 - 1^2\right]$

$= 9(4x - 1)(4x + 1)$

18. $50x^2 - 8$

$= 2(25x^2 - 4)$

$= 2\left[(5x)^2 - 2^2\right]$

$= 2(5x - 2)(5x + 2)$

20. $49x^3 - 36x$

$= x(49x^2 - 36)$

$= x\left[(7x)^2 - 6^2\right]$

$= x(7x - 6)(7x + 6)$

22. $9x^2 - 6x + 1$

$= (3x)^2 - 2(3x)(1) + 1^2$

$= (3x - 1)^2$

24. $w^2 - 12w + 36$

$= w^2 - 2(w)(6) + 6^2$

$= (w - 6)^2$

26. $4x^2 - 4x + 1$

$= (2x)^2 - 2(2x)(1) + 1^2$

$= (2x - 1)^2$

28. $z^2 + 18z + 81$

$= z^2 + 2(z)(9) + 9^2$

$= (z + 9)^2$

30. $25w^2 + 20wt + 4t^2$

$= (5w)^2 + 2(5w)(2t) + (2t)^2$

$= (5w + 2t)^2$

32. $49x^2 - 70xy + 25y^2$

$= (7x)^2 - 2(7x)(5y) + (5y)^2$

$= (7x - 5y)^2$

34. $128x^2 + 32x + 2$

$= 2(64x^2 + 16x + 1)$

$= 2\left[(8x)^2 + 2(8x)(1) + 1^2\right]$

$= 2(8x + 1)^2$

36. $50x^3 - 20x^2 + 2x$

$= 2x(25x^2 - 10x + 1)$

$= 2x\left[(5x)^2 - 2(5x)(1) + 1^2\right]$

$= 2x(5x - 1)^2$

38. $64x^3 + 27$
$$= (4x)^3 + 3^3$$
$$= (4x+3)\left[(4x)^2 - (4x)(3) + 3^2\right]$$
$$= (4x+3)(16x^2 - 12x + 9)$$

40. $x^3 + 64$
$$= x^3 + 4^3$$
$$= (x+4)(x^2 - 4x + 4^2)$$
$$= (x+4)(x^2 - 4x + 16)$$

42. $125x^3 - 1$
$$= (5x)^3 - 1^3$$
$$= (5x-1)\left[(5x)^2 + (5x)(1) + 1^2\right]$$
$$= (5x-1)(25x^2 + 5x + 1)$$

44. $27x^3 - 64$
$$= (3x)^3 - 4^3$$
$$= (3x-4)\left[(3x)^2 + (3x)(4) + 4^2\right]$$
$$= (3x-4)(9x^2 + 12x + 16)$$

46. $1 - 8x^3$
$$= 1 - (2x)^3$$
$$= (1-2x)\left[1^2 + 1(2x) + (2x)^2\right]$$
$$= (1-2x)(1 + 2x + 4x^2)$$

48. $27x^3 + 216$
$$= 27(x^3 + 8)$$
$$= 27(x^3 + 2^3)$$
$$= 27(x+2)(x^2 - 2x + 2^2)$$
$$= 27(x+2)(x^2 - 2x + 4)$$

50. $125s^6 + t^6$
$$(5s^2)^3 + (t^2)^3$$
$$= (5s^2 + t^2)\left[(5s^2)^2 - (5s^2)(t^2) + (t^2)^2\right]$$
$$= (5s^2 + t^2)(25s^4 - 5s^2t^2 + t^4)$$

52. $80y^3 - 10$
$$= 10(8y^3 - 1)$$
$$= 10\left[(2y)^3 - 1^3\right]$$
$$= 10(2y-1)(4y^2 + 2y + 1)$$

54. $64x^4 + 125x$
$$= x(64x^3 + 125)$$
$$= x\left[(4x)^3 + 5^3\right]$$
$$= x(4x+5)\left[(4x)^2 - (4x)(5) + 5^2\right]$$
$$= x(4x+5)(16x^2 - 20x + 25)$$

56. $x^6 - 27x^2y^3$
$$= x^2(x^3 - 27y^3)$$
$$= x^2\left[x^3 - (3y)^3\right]$$
$$= x^2(x-3y)\left[x^2 + (x)(3y) + (3y)^2\right]$$
$$= x^2(x-3y)(x^2 + 3xy + 9y^2)$$

58. $x^8 - 1$
$$= (x^4)^2 - 1^2$$
$$= (x^4 - 1)(x^4 + 1)$$
$$= \left[(x^2)^2 - 1^2\right](x^4 + 1)$$
$$= (x^2 - 1)(x^2 + 1)(x^4 + 1)$$
$$= (x-1)(x+1)(x^2 + 1)(x^4 + 1)$$

60. $9w^4 + 12w^2 + 4$
$$= (3w^2)^2 + 2(3w^2)(2) + 2^2$$
$$= (3w^2 + 2)^2$$

62. $27w^3 + 125$
$$= (3w)^3 + 5^3$$
$$= (3w+5)\left[(3w)^2 - (3w)(5) + 5^2\right]$$
$$= (3w+5)(9w^2 - 15w + 25)$$

64. $64z^3 - 27w^3$
$$= (4z)^3 - (3w)^3$$
$$= (4z-3w)\left[(4z)^2 + (4z)(3w) + (3w)^2\right]$$
$$= (4z-3w)(16z^2 + 12zw + 9w^2)$$

66. $49 - 64a^2b^2$
$$= 7^2 - (8ab)^2$$
$$= (7 - 8ab)(7 + 8ab)$$

68. $9x^2y^2 + 24xy + 16$
$$= (3xy)^2 + 2(3xy)(4) + 4^2$$
$$= (3xy + 4)^2$$

70. $121x^4 - 4y^2 = (11x^2)^2 - (2y)^2$
$$= (11x^2 - 2y)(11x^2 + 2y)$$

72. $w^3z^3 - 8y^3$
$$= (wz)^3 - (2y)^3$$
$$= (wz - 2y)[(wz)^2 + (wz)(2y) + (2y)^2]$$
$$= (wz - 2y)(w^2z^2 + 2wyz + 4y^2)$$

74. $121 + 66y^2 + 9y^4$
$$= 11^2 + 2(11)(3y^2) + (3y^2)^2$$
$$= (11 + 3y^2)^2$$

76. $256x^4 - 1$
$$= (16x^2)^2 - 1^2$$
$$= (16x^2 - 1)(16x^2 + 1)$$
$$= \left[(4x)^2 - 1^2\right](16x^2 + 1)$$
$$= (4x - 1)(4x + 1)(16x^2 + 1)$$

78. $16x^2 + 40x + 9$
$$2(4x)(3) = 24x \neq 40x$$
$$16x^2 + 40x + 9$$
$$= 16x^2 + 4x + 36x + 9$$
$$= 4x(4x + 1) + 9(4x + 1)$$
$$= (4x + 1)(4x + 9)$$

80. $36x^2 - 65x + 25$
$$2(6x)(5) = 60x \neq 65x$$
$$36x^2 - 65x + 25$$
$$= 36x^2 - 45x - 20x + 25$$
$$= 9x(4x - 5) - 5(4x - 5)$$
$$= (4x - 5)(9x - 5)$$

82. $8x^{15} + 343y^{21}$
$$= (2x^5)^3 + (7y^7)^3$$
$$= (2x^5 + 7y^7)\left[(2x^5)^2 - (2x^5)(7y^7) + (7y^7)^2\right]$$
$$= (2x^5 + 7y^7)(4x^{10} - 14x^5y^7 + 49y^{14})$$

84. $m^6 - 64n^6$
$$= (m^3)^2 - (8n^3)^2$$
$$= (m^3 - 8n^3)(m^3 + 8n^3)$$
$$= \left[m^3 - (2n)^3\right]\left[m^3 + (2n)^3\right]$$
$$= (m - 2n)\left[m^2 + m(2n) + (2n)^2\right](m + 2n)\left[m^2 - m(2n) + (2n)^2\right]$$
$$= (m - 2n)(m^2 + 2mn + 4n^2)(m + 2n)(m^2 - 2mn + 4n^2)$$

Cumulative Review Problems

86. x = amount invested at 14%

y = amount invested at 11%

$x + y = 4000$ (1)

$0.14x + 0.11y = 482$ (2)

Add -14 times (1) and 100 times (2)

$$
\begin{array}{r}
-14x - 14y = -56,000 \\
\underline{14x + 11y = \ 48,200} \\
-3y = -\ 7,800 \\
y = \ \ 2,600
\end{array}
$$

Substitute 2600 for y in (1)

$x + 2600 = 4000$

$x = 1400$

$2600 at 11% and $1400 at 14%

88. x = amount Hector paid

y = amount Melinda paid

z = amount Alice paid

$x + y + z = 858$ (1)

$y = x + 110$ (2)

$z = x - 86$ (3)

Substitute $x - 86$ for z in (1)

$x + y + (x - 86) = 858$

$2x + y = 944$ (4)

Substitute $x + 110$ for y in (4)

$2x + (x + 110) = 944$

$3x = 834$

$x = 278$

Substitute 278 for x in (2) and (3)

$y = 278 + 110 = 388$

$z = 278 - 86 = 192$

Hector paid $278, Melinda paid $388, and Alice paid $192.

5.7 Exercises

2. e and f must be negative

4. $x^2 - x - 56 = (x - 8)(x + 7)$

6. $ax - 2xy + 3aw - 6wy$

$= x(a - 2y) + 3w(a - 2y)$

$= (a - 2y)(x + 3w)$

8. $27x^3 + 64y^3$

$= (3x)^3 + (4y)^3$

$= (3x + 4y)\left[(3x)^2 - (3x)(4y) + (4y)^2\right]$

$= (3x + 4y)(9x^2 - 12xy + 16y^2)$

10. Prime

12. $x^3 - 11x^2 + 30x$

$= x(x^2 - 11x + 30)$

$= x(x - 5)(x - 6)$

14. $12y^3 - 36y^2 + 27y$

$= 3y(4y^2 - 12y + 9)$

$= 3y\left[(2y)^2 - 2(2y)(3) + 3^2\right]$

$= 3y(2y - 3)^2$

16. $25x^2 - 40x + 16$

$= (5x)^2 - 2(5x)(4) + 4^2$

$= (5x - 4)^2$

18. $ac + bc - a - b$

$= c(a + b) - 1(a + b)$

$= (a + b)(c - 1)$

20. $1 - 16x^4$

$= 1^2 - (4x^2)^2$

$= (1 - 4x^2)(1 + 4x^2)$

$= \left[1^2 - (2x)^2\right](1 + 4x^2)$

$= (1 - 2x)(1 + 2x)(1 + 4x^2)$

22. $8a^3b - 50ab^3$

$= 2ab(4a^2 - 25b^2)$

$= 2ab\left[(2a)^2 - (5b)^2\right]$

$= 2ab(2a - 5b)(2a + 5b)$

24. $12x^3 + 3xy^2$

$= 3x(4x^2 + y^2)$

26. Prime

28. $8x^2 + 10x - 12$

$= 2(4x^2 + 5x - 6)$

$= 2(4x^2 + 8x - 3x - 6)$

$= 2[4x(x + 2) - 3(x + 2)]$

$= 2(x + 2)(4x - 3)$

30. $2a^6 + 20a^5 b + 50a^4 b^2$

$= 2a^4 (a^2 + 10ab + 25b^2)$

$= 2a^4 \left[a^2 + 2(a)(5b) + (5b)^2 \right]$

$= 2a^4 (a + 5b)^2$

32. $7a^2 + 14a - 168$

$= 7(a^2 + 2a - 24)$

$= 7(a + 6)(a - 4)$

34. $8w^3 + awx + 4aw^2 + 2w^2 x$

$= w(8w^2 + ax + 4aw + 2wx)$

$= w(8w^2 + 2wx + ax + 4aw)$

$= w[2w(4w + x) + a(x + 4w)]$

$= w(4w + x)(2w + a)$

36. $x^4 + 13x^3 + 36x^2$

$= x^2 (x^2 + 13x + 36)$

$= x^2 (x + 9)(x + 4)$

38. $50x^2 y^2 - 32y^2$

$= 2y^2 (25x^2 - 16)$

$= 2y^2 (5x + 4)(5x - 4)$

40. $2x^5 - 3x^4 + x^3$

$= x^3 (2x^2 - 3x + 1)$

$= x^3 (2x^2 - 2x - x + 1)$

$x^3 [2x(x - 1) - 1(x - 1)]$

$= x^3 (x - 1)(2x - 1)$

42. $3x^6 + 7x^3 + 2$

$= 3x^6 + 6x^3 + x^3 + 2$

$= 3x^3 (x^3 + 2) + 1(x^3 + 2)$

$(x^3 + 2)(3x^3 + 1)$

44. $81x^4 z^6 - 25y^8$

$= (9x^2 z^3)^2 - (5y^4)^2$

$= (9x^2 z^3 - 5y^4)(9x^2 z^3 + 5y^4)$

46. $25x^2 + ax + 169 = (5x - 13)^2$

$25x^2 + ax + 169 = 25x^2 - 130x + 169$

$ax = -130x$

$a = -130$

Cumulative Review Problems

48. $|2 + 5x - 3| < 2$

$|5x - 1| < 2$

$-2 < 5x - 1 < 2$

$-1 < 5x < 3$

$-\dfrac{1}{5} < x < \dfrac{3}{5}$

50. $x - 4 \geq 7$　　or　　$4x + 1 \leq 17$

　　$x \geq 11$　　or　　$4x \leq 16$

　　　　　　　　　　　　$x \leq 4$

52. $\dfrac{86 - 65}{65} \approx 0.323$

$\dfrac{143 - 86}{86} \approx 0.663$

$\dfrac{0.323 + 0.663}{2} = 0.493$

Approximately 49.3%

54. $1.663(143) \approx 237.8$

Approximately \$237.8 million

5.8 Exercises

The answer checks in this section are left to the reader.

2. $x^2 - 8x + 15 = 0$

$(x - 5)(x - 3) = 0$

$x - 5 = 0$　　or　　$x - 3 = 0$

$x = 5$　　　　　　　$x = 3$

4. $x^2 - x = 2$

　　$x^2 - x - 2 = 0$

　　$(x - 2)(x + 1) = 0$

　　$x - 2 = 0$　　or　　$x + 1 = 0$

　　$x = 2$　　　　　　　$x = -1$

6. $3x^2 + 5x = 0$

$x(3x + 5) = 0$

$x = 0$　　　　or　　$3x + 5 = 0$

　　　　　　　　　　$3x = -5$

　　　　　　　　　　$x = -\dfrac{5}{3}$

8. $2x^2 + 3x - 5 = 0$
$(2x + 5)(x - 1) = 0$
$2x + 5 = 0 \quad$ or $\quad x - 1 = 0$
$2x = -5 \qquad\qquad x = 1$
$x = -\dfrac{5}{2}$

10. $4x^2 - 13x + 3 = 0$
$(4x - 1)(x - 3) = 0$
$4x - 1 = 0 \quad$ or $\quad x - 3 = 0$
$4x = 1 \qquad\qquad x = 3$
$x = \dfrac{1}{4}$

12. $9x^2 + 9x = -2$
$9x^2 + 9x + 2 = 0$
$(3x + 2)(3x + 1) = 0$
$3x + 2 = 0 \quad$ or $\quad 3x + 1 = 0$
$3x = -2 \quad$ or $\quad 3x = -1$
$x = -\dfrac{2}{3} \qquad\qquad x = -\dfrac{1}{3}$

14. $5x^2 = 11x - 2$
$5x^2 - 11x + 2 = 0$
$(5x - 1)(x - 2) = 0$
$5x - 1 = 0 \quad$ or $\quad x - 2 = 0$
$5x = 1 \quad$ or $\quad x = 2$
$x = \dfrac{1}{5}$

16. $x(x - 21) = 22$
$x^2 - 21x = 22$
$x^2 - 21 - 22 = 0$
$(x - 22)(x + 1) = 0$
$x - 22 = 0 \quad$ or $\quad x + 1 = 0$
$x = 22 \qquad\qquad x = -1$

18. $8(1 - x) = -1(4 + x^2)$
$8 - 8x = -4 - x^2$
$x^2 - 8x + 12 = 0$
$(x - 6)(x - 2) = 0$
$x - 6 = 0 \quad$ or $\quad x - 2 = 0$
$x = 6 \qquad\qquad x = 2$

20. $x^2 - \dfrac{5}{2}x = \dfrac{x}{2}$
$2x^2 - 5x = x$
$2x^2 - 6x = 0$
$2x(x - 3) = 0$
$2x = 0 \quad$ or $\quad x - 3 = 0$
$x = 0 \qquad\qquad x = 3$

22. $5x^2 - 2x = x^2 - 8x$
$4x^2 + 6x = 0$
$2x(2x + 3) = 0$
$2x = 0 \quad$ or $\quad 2x + 3 = 0$
$x = 0 \qquad\qquad 2x = -3$
$\qquad\qquad\qquad x = -\dfrac{3}{2}$

24. $x^3 + 11x^2 + 18x = 0$
$x(x^2 + 11x + 18) = 0$
$x(x + 9)(x + 2) = 0$
$x = 0 \quad$ or $\quad x + 9 = 0 \quad$ or $\quad x + 2 = 0$
$\qquad\qquad\quad x = -9 \qquad\qquad x = -2$

26. $x^3 = 2x^2 + 24x$
$x^3 - 2x^2 - 24x = 0$
$x(x^2 - 2x - 24) = 0$
$x(x - 6)(x + 4) = 0$
$x = 0 \quad$ or $\quad x - 6 = 0 \quad$ or $\quad x + 4 = 0$
$\qquad\qquad\quad x = 6 \qquad\qquad x = -4$

28. $2x^3 - 32x = 0$
$2x(x^2 - 16) = 0$
$2x(x + 4)(x - 4) = 0$
$2x = 0 \quad$ or $\quad x + 4 = 0 \quad$ or $\quad x - 4 = 0$
$x = 0 \qquad\qquad x = -4 \qquad\qquad x = 4$

30. $2x^3 + 6x^2 = 20x$
$2x^3 + 6x^2 - 20x = 0$
$2x(x^2 + 3x - 10) = 0$
$2x(x + 5)(x - 2) = 0$
$2x = 0 \quad$ or $\quad x + 5 = 0 \quad$ or $\quad x - 2 = 0$
$x = 0 \qquad\qquad x = -5 \qquad\qquad x = 2$

32. $\dfrac{5}{2}x^2 - 8x = -\dfrac{3}{2}$
$5x^2 - 16x = -3$
$5x^2 - 16x + 3 = 0$
$(5x - 1)(x - 3) = 0$

$5x - 1 = 0$ or $x - 3 = 0$
$5x = 1$ $\qquad x = 3$

$x = \dfrac{1}{5}$

34. $2(x^2 - 4) - 3x = 4x - 11$

$2x^2 - 8 - 3x = 4x - 11$

$2x^2 - 7x + 3 = 0$

$(2x - 1)(x - 3) = 0$

$2x - 1 = 0$ or $x - 3 = 0$
$2x = 1$ $\qquad x = 3$

$x = \dfrac{1}{2}$

36. $20x^2 = 5x$

$20x^2 - 5x = 0$

$5x(4x - 1) = 0$

$5x = 0$ or $4x - 1 = 0$
$x = 0$ $\qquad 4x = 1$

$\qquad\qquad x = \dfrac{1}{4}$

38. $4x^2 + 5x - 2 = 3x^2 - 2$

$x^2 + 5x = 0$

$x(x + 5) = 0$

$x = 0$ or $x + 5 = 0$
$\qquad\qquad x = -5$

40. $2x(x - 1) = 2(3 + x)$

$2x^2 - 2x = 6 + 2x$

$2x^2 - 4x - 6 = 0$

$x^2 - 2x - 3 = 0$

$(x - 3)(x + 1) = 0$

$x - 3 = 0$ or $x + 1 = 0$
$x = 3$ $\qquad x = -1$

42. $2x^2 - 3x + c = 0$

$2\left(-\dfrac{1}{2}\right)^2 - 3\left(-\dfrac{1}{2}\right) + c = 0$

$\dfrac{1}{2} + \dfrac{3}{2} + c = 0$

$2 + c = 0$

$c = -2$

$2x^2 - 3x - 2 = 0$

$(2x + 1)(x - 2) = 0$

The other solution:

$x - 2 = 0$

$x = 2$ or $x + \dfrac{1}{2}$ is a factor, so

$(2x + 1)(x + c) = 0$

$x + 2xc = -3x$

$x(1 + 2c) = -3x$

$1 + 2c = -3$

$c = -2$

$x = 2$ is the other solution.

44. $A = \dfrac{1}{2} bh$

$87 = \dfrac{1}{2} b(4b + 5)$

$174 = 4b^2 + 5b$

$4b^2 + 5b - 174 = 0$

$(2b - 12)(2b + 14.5) = 0$

$b = 6$ or $b = -7.25$

$h = 4(6) + 5 = 29$

The base is 6 mm and the altitude is 29 mm.

46. a. $A = \dfrac{1}{2} bh$

$104 = \dfrac{1}{2}(3h + 2)h$

$208 = 3h^2 + 2h$

$3h^2 + 2h - 208 = 0$

$(3h + 26)(h - 8) = 0$

$h = -\dfrac{26}{3}$ or $h = 8$

$b = 3(8) + 2 = 26$

The altitude is 8 feet and the base is 26 feet.

b. altitude $= \dfrac{8}{3} = 2\dfrac{2}{3}$ yards

base $= \dfrac{26}{3} = 8\dfrac{2}{3}$ yards

48. a. $A = lw$

$896 = (w + 4)w$

$w^2 + 4w - 896 = 0$

$(w - 28)(w + 32) = 0$

$w = 28$ or $w = -32$

$l = 28 + 4 = 32$

The width is 28 cm and the length is 32 cm.

b. width $28(10) = 280$ mm

length $= 32(10) = 320$ mm

50. $A = s^2$
$P = 4s$
$s^2 = 4s + 165$
$s^2 - 4s - 165 = 0$
$(s - 15)(s + 11) = 0$
$s = 15 \qquad$ or $\qquad s = -11$
Each side of the room is 15 feet.

52. Width $= x$
Length $= 2x + 3$
$V = x(2x + 3)6 = 390$
$12x^2 + 18x = 390$
$12x^2 + 18x - 390 = 0$
$6(2x^2 + 3x - 65) = 0$
$6(2x + 13)(x - 5) = 0$
$x = -\dfrac{13}{2}$ or $x = 5$
The width is 5 meters.
The length is 13 meters.

54. width: x
length: $2x - 3$
$A = wl$
$54 = x(2x - 3)$
$54 = 2x^2 - 3x$
$0 = 2x^2 - 3x - 54$
$0 = (2x + 9)(x - 6)$
$2x + 9 = 0 \quad$ or $x - 6 = 0$
$2x = -9 \qquad\qquad x = 6$
$x = -\dfrac{9}{2}$
Since $x > 0$, $x = 6$, and $2x - 3 = 2(6) - 3 = 9$.
width: 6 mi; length: 9 mi

56. Old side $= x$
New side $= 2x + 2$
$(2x + 2)^2 = 84 + x^2$
$4x^2 + 8x + 4 = x^2 + 84$
$3x^2 + 8x - 80 = 0$
$(3x + 20)(x - 4) = 0$
$x = -\dfrac{20}{3}, \ x = 4$
The dimensions of the old garden were 4 ft by
4 ft. The dimensions of the new garden are
$2(4) + 2 = 10$ ft by 10 ft.

58. $2n^2 - 19n - 10 = 0$
$(2n + 1)(n - 10) = 0$
$n = -\dfrac{1}{2}$ or $n = 10$
Since $n > 0$, $n = 10$.
10 units

60. $2n^2 - 19n - 10 = -34$
$2n^2 - 19n + 24 = 0$
$(2n - 3)(n - 8) = 0$
$n = \dfrac{3}{2}$ or $n = 8$
8 units

Cumulative Review Problems

62. $\dfrac{(2a^3b^2)^3}{16a^5b^8}$

$= \dfrac{8a^9b^6}{16a^5b^8}$

$= \dfrac{a^4}{2b^2}$

64. $\left(\dfrac{5xy^{-2}}{2x^{-3}y}\right)^3$

$= \dfrac{125x^3y^{-6}}{8x^{-9}y^3}$

$= \dfrac{125}{8}x^{3-(-9)}y^{-6-3}$

$= \dfrac{125}{8}x^{12}y^{-9}$

$= \dfrac{125x^{12}}{8y^9}$

Putting Your Skills to Work

2. $\dfrac{1}{6}x^3 + \dfrac{1}{2}x^2 + \dfrac{1}{3}x$

$= \dfrac{1}{6}x(x^2 + 3x + 2)$

$= \dfrac{1}{6}x(x + 2)(x + 1)$

$= x\left(\dfrac{1}{2}x + 1\right)\left(\dfrac{1}{3}x + \dfrac{1}{3}\right)$

4. Each row is a square number: 1, 4, 9, 16, ...
The polynomial is $\dfrac{1}{3}x^3 + \dfrac{1}{2}x^2 + \dfrac{1}{6}x$.

Chapter 5 Review Problems

2. $(-4x^2y - 7xy + y) + (5x^2y + 2xy - 9y)$
   $= x^2y - 5xy - 8y$

4. $(-13x^2 + 9x - 14) - (-2x^2 - 6x + 1)$
   $= -13x^2 + 9x - 14 + 2x^2 + 6x - 1$
   $= -11x^2 + 15x - 15$

6. $(5x - 2x^2 - x^3) - (2x - 3 + 5x^2)$
   $= 5x - 2x^2 - x^3 - 2x + 3 - 5x^2$
   $= -x^3 - 7x^2 + 3x + 3$

8. $(3x^2 + 1)(2x - 1) = 6x^3 - 3x^2 + 2x - 1$

10. $(x - 3)(2x - 5)(x + 2)$
    $= (2x^2 - 11x + 15)(x + 2)$
    $= 2x^3 - 11x^2 + 15x + 4x^2 - 22x + 30$
    $= 2x^3 - 7x^2 - 7x + 30$

12. $(3x - 5)(3x^2 + 2x - 4)$
    $= 9x^3 + 6x^2 - 12x - 15x^2 - 10x + 20$
    $= 9x^3 - 9x^2 - 22x + 20$

14. $$3x + 2 \overline{) 12x^2 - 16x - 4} \quad \Rightarrow \quad 4x - 8 + \frac{12}{3x+2}$$

$$\begin{array}{r} 4x - 8 + \dfrac{12}{3x+2} \\ 3x+2 \overline{\smash{)}12x^2 - 16x - 4} \\ \underline{12x^2 + 8x} \\ -24x - 4 \\ \underline{-24x - 16} \\ 12 \end{array}$$

16.
$$\begin{array}{r|rrrr} 3 & 3 & 0 & -2 & 5 \\ & & 9 & 27 & 75 \\ \hline & 3 & 9 & 25 & \boxed{80} \end{array}$$

$(3y^3 - 2y + 5) \div (y - 3)$

$= 3y^2 + 9y + 25 + \dfrac{80}{y - 3}$

18.
$$\begin{array}{r} x^2 + 2x + 1 \\ x^2 - 3x - 2 \overline{\smash{)}x^4 - x^3 - 7x^2 - 7x - 2} \\ \underline{x^4 - 3x^3 - 2x^2} \\ 2x^3 - 5x^2 - 7x \\ \underline{2x^3 - 6x^2 - 4x} \\ x^2 - 3x - 2 \\ \underline{x^2 - 3x - 2} \end{array}$$

20.
$$\begin{array}{r|rrrrr} -2 & 3 & 5 & -1 & 1 & -2 \\ & & -6 & 2 & -2 & 2 \\ \hline & 3 & -1 & 1 & -1 & 0 \end{array}$$

$(3x^4 + 5x^3 - x^2 + x - 2) \div (x + 2)$
$= 3x^3 - x^2 + x - 1$

22.
$$\begin{array}{r|rrrrr} 3 & 2 & -9 & 5 & 13 & -3 \\ & & 6 & -9 & -12 & 3 \\ \hline & 2 & -3 & -4 & 1 & \boxed{0} \end{array}$$

$(2x^4 - 9x^3 + 5x^2 + 13x - 3) \div (x - 3)$
$= 2x^3 - 3x^2 - 4x + 1$

24. $5x^2 - 11x + 2$
    $= 5x^2 - 10x - x + 2$
    $= 5x(x - 2) - 1(x - 2)$
    $= (x - 2)(5x - 1)$

26. Prime

28. $x^3 + 8x^2 + 12x$
    $= x(x^2 + 8x + 12)$
    $= x(x + 6)(x + 2)$

30. $x^2 + 6xy - 27y^2 = (x + 9y)(x - 3y)$

32. $21a^2 + 20ab + 4b^2$
    $= 21a^2 + 6ab + 14ab + 4b^2$
    $= 3a(7a + 2b) + 2b(7a + 2b)$
    $= (7a + 2b)(3a + 2b)$

34. $a^4b^4 + a^3b^4 - 6a^2b^4$
    $= a^2b^4(a^2 + a - 6)$
    $= a^2b^4(a + 3)(a - 2)$

36. $2x^4 + 20x^2 - 48$
$= 2(x^4 + 10x^2 - 24)$
$= 2(x^2 + 12)(x^2 - 2)$

38. Prime

40. $4y^4 - 13y^3 + 9y^2$
$= y^2(4y^2 - 13y + 9)$
$= y^2(4y^2 - 4y - 9y + 9)$
$y^2[4y(y-1) - 9(y-1)]$
$= y^2(y-1)(4y-9)$

42. $4x^2y^2 - 12x^2y - 8x^2 = 4x^2(y^2 - 3y - 2)$

44. $a^2 + 5ab^3 + 4b^6 = (a + 4b^3)(a + b^3)$

46. $2x^4 - 12x^2 - 54$
$= 2(x^4 - 6x^2 - 27)$
$= 2(x^2 - 9)(x^2 + 3)$
$= 2(x - 3)(x + 3)(x^2 + 3)$

48. $8x^4 + 34x^2y^2 + 21y^4$
$= 8x^4 + 6x^2y^2 + 28x^2y^2 + 21y^4$
$= 2x^2(4x^2 + 3y^2) + 7y^2(4x^2 + 3y^2)$
$= (4x^2 + 3y^2)(2x^2 + 7y^2)$

50. $2a^2x - 15ax + 7x$
$= x(2a^2 - 15a + 7)$
$= x(2a^2 - 14a - a + 7)$
$= x[2a(a - 7) - 1(a - 7)]$
$= x(a - 7)(2a - 1)$

52. $128x^3y - 2xy$
$= 2xy(64x^2 - 1)$
$= 2xy[(8x)^2 - 1^2]$
$2xy(8x - 1)(8x + 1)$

54. $5xb - 28y + 4by - 35x$
$= 5xb - 35x + 4by - 28y$
$= 5x(b - 7) + 4y(b - 7)$
$= (b - 7)(5x + 4y)$

56. $5a^6 + 40a^3b^3$
$= 5a^3(a^3 + 8b^3)$
$= 5a^3[a^3 + (2b)^3]$
$= 5a^3(a + 2b)[a^2 - a(2b) + (2b)^2]$
$= 5a^3(a + 2b)(a^2 - 2ab + 4b^2)$

58. $60x^2 - 100xy + 15y^2$
$= 5(12x^2 - 20xy + 3y^2)$
$= 5(12x^2 - 2xy - 18xy + 3y^2)$
$= 5[2x(6x - y) - 3y(6x - y)]$
$= 5(6x - y)(2x - 3y)$

60. $2x^2 - 11x + 12 = 0$
$(2x - 3)(x - 4) = 0$
$2x - 3 = 0$ or $x - 4 = 0$
$2x = 3$ $x = 4$
$x = \dfrac{3}{2}$

62. $7x^2 = 21x$
$7x^2 - 21x = 0$
$7x(x - 3) = 0$
$7x = 0$ or $x - 3 = 0$
$x = 0$ $x = 3$

64. $3x^2 + 14x + 3 = -1 + 4(x + 1)$
$3x^2 + 14x + 3 = -1 + 4x + 4$
$3x^2 + 10x = 0$
$x(3x + 10) = 0$
$x = 0$ or $3x + 10 = 0$
                    $3x = -10$
                    $x = -\dfrac{10}{3}$

66. width: x
length: $3x - 2$
$A = wl$
$40 = x(3x - 2)$
$40 = 3x^2 - 2x$
$0 = 3x^2 - 2x - 40$
$0 = (3x + 10)(x - 4)$
$3x + 10 = 0$ or $x - 4 = 0$
$3x = -10$ $x = 4$
$x = -\dfrac{10}{3}$
Since $x > 0$, $x = 4$ and $3x - 2 = 3(4) - 2 = 10$.
width: 4 mi; length: 10 mi

68. $P = 3x^2 - 7x - 10$

$30 = 3x^2 - 7x - 10$

$0 = 3x^2 - 7x - 40$

$0 = (3x + 8)(x - 5)$

$3x + 8 = 0$ or $x - 5 = 0$

$3x = -8$ $x = 5$

$x = -\dfrac{8}{3}$

Since $x > 0$, $x = 5$.

5 calculators

Chapter 5 Test

2. $(5a^2 - 3) - (2 + 5a) - (4a - 3)$

$= 5a^2 - 3 - 2 - 5a - 4a + 3$

$= 5a^2 - 9a - 2$

4. $(2x - 3y^2)^2$

$= (2x)^2 - 2(2x)(3y^2) + (3y^2)^2$

$= 4x^2 - 12xy^2 + 9y^4$

6. $(-15x^3 - 12x^2 + 21x) \div (-3x)$

$= \dfrac{-15x^3 - 12x^2 + 21x}{-3x}$

$= \dfrac{-15x^3}{-3x} - \dfrac{12x^2}{-3x} + \dfrac{21x}{-3x}$

$= 5x^2 + 4x - 7$

8.

$$
\begin{array}{r|rrrr}
-2 & 1 & -1 & -5 & 2 \\
   &   & -2 & 6 & -2 \\
\hline
   & 1 & -3 & 1 & 0 \\
\end{array}
$$

$(x^3 - x^2 - 5x + 2) \div (x + 2)$

$= x^2 - 3x + 1$

10.

$$
\begin{array}{r|rrrrrr}
4 & 2 & -7 & 0 & -15 & -1 & 5 \\
  &   & 8 & 4 & 16 & 4 & 12 \\
\hline
  & 2 & 1 & 4 & 1   & 3 & 17 \\
\end{array}
$$

$(2x^5 - 7x^4 - 15x^2 - x + 5) \div (x - 4)$

$= 2x^4 + x^3 + 4x^2 + x + 3 + \dfrac{17}{x - 4}$

12. $9x^2 + 30xy + 25y^2$

$= (3x)^2 + 2(3x)(5y) + (5y)^2$

$= (3x + 5y)^2$

14. $24x^2 + 10x - 4$

$= 2(12x^2 + 5x - 2)$

$= 2(12x^2 + 8x - 3x - 2)$

$= 2[4x(3x + 2) - 1(3x + 2)]$

$= 2(3x + 2)(4x - 1)$

16. $x^2 - 6wy + 3xy - 2wx$

$= x^2 - 2wx + 3xy - 6wy$

$= x(x - 2w) + 3y(x - 2w)$

$= (x - 2w)(x + 3y)$

18. $3x^4 + 36x^3 + 60x^2$

$= 3x^2(x^2 + 12x + 20)$

$= 3x^2(x + 10)(x + 2)$

20. $25x^2y^4 - 16y^4$

$y^4(25x^2 - 16)$

$= y^4[(5x)^2 - 4^2]$

$= y^4(5x - 4)(5x + 4)$

22. $9x^5 - 6x^3y + xy^2$

$= x(9x^4 - 6x^2y + y^2)$

$= x[(3x^2)^2 - 2(3x^2)(y) + y^2]$

$= x(3x^2 - y)^2$

24. $x^2 - 8xy + 12y^2$

$= (x - 6y)(x - 2y)$

26. $16x^4 - 1$

$= (4x^2)^2 - 1^2$

$= (4x^2 - 1)(4x^2 + 1)$

$= [(2x)^2 - 1^2](4x^2 + 1)$

$(2x - 1)(2x + 1)(4x^2 + 1)$

28. $3x^2 - 11x - 4 = 0$

$(3x + 1)(x - 4) = 0$

$3x + 1 = 0$ or $x - 4 = 0$

$3x = -1$ $x = 4$

$x = -\dfrac{1}{3}$

30. base: x

altitude: $x - 4$

$A = \dfrac{1}{2}bh$

$70 = \dfrac{1}{2}x(x-4)$

$140 = x(x-4)$

$140 = x^2 - 4x$

$0 = x^2 - 4x - 140$

$0 = (x-14)(x+10)$

$x - 14 = 0 \quad$ or $\quad x + 10 = 0$

$x = 14 \qquad\qquad x = -10$

Since $x > 0$, $x = 14$ and $x - 4 = 14 - 4 = 10$.

base: 14 in.; altitude: 10 in.

Cumulative Test for Chapters 1–5

2. $\dfrac{2 + 6(-2)}{(2-4)^3 + 3}$

$= \dfrac{2 - 12}{(-2)^3 + 3}$

$= \dfrac{-10}{-8 + 3}$

$= \dfrac{-10}{-5}$

$= 2$

4. $5x + 7y = 2$

$5x = 2 - 7y$

$x = \dfrac{2 - 7y}{5}$

6. $m = \dfrac{y_2 - y_1}{x_2 - x_1}$

$= \dfrac{-3 - 5}{-2 - 1}$

$= \dfrac{8}{3}$

8. $3x - 4y \geq -12$ (solid line)

Test point: $(0, 0)$

$3(0) - 4(0) \geq -12$

$0 \geq -12$

True; shade the half–plane containing $(0, 0)$.

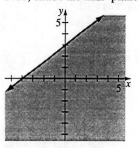

10. width: x

length: $2x + 5$

$2w + 2l = P$

$2(x) + 2(2x + 5) = 46$

$2x + 4x + 10 = 46$

$6x + 10 = 46$

$6x = 36$

$x = 6$

$2x + 5 = 2(6) + 5 = 17$

width: 6 m; length: 17 m

12. $-3xy^2(2x + 3y - 5xy)$

$= -6x^2y^2 - 9xy^3 + 15x^2y^3$

14. $(-21x^3 + 14x^2 - 28x) \div (7x)$

$= \dfrac{-21x^3 + 14x^2 - 28x}{7x}$

$= -\dfrac{21x^3}{7x} + \dfrac{14x^2}{7x} - \dfrac{28x}{7x}$

$= -3x^2 + 2x - 4$

16. $2x^3 - 10x^2$

$= 2x^2(x - 5)$

18. $9x^3 - 24x^2 + 16x$

$= x(9x^2 - 24x + 16)$

$= x[(3x)^2 - 2(3x)(4) + 4^2]$

$= x(3x - 4)^2$

20. $3x^2 - 15x - 42$

$= 3(x^2 - 5x - 14)$

$= 3(x - 7)(x + 2)$

22. Prime

24. $27x^4 + 64x$

$= x(27x^3 + 64)$

$= x[(3x)^3 + 4^3]$

$x(3x+4)[(3x)^2 - (3x)(4) + 4^2]$

$= x(3x+4)(9x^2 - 12x + 16)$

26. $3x^2 - 4x - 4 = 0$

$(3x + 2)(x - 2) = 0$

$3x + 2 = 0 \qquad$ or $\quad x - 2 = 0$

$x = -\dfrac{2}{3} \qquad\qquad\qquad x = 2$

28. base: x

altitude: $2x + 1$

$A = \dfrac{1}{2}bh$

$68 = \dfrac{1}{2}x(2x+1)$

$136 = x(2x+1)$

$136 = 2x^2 + x$

$0 = 2x^2 + x - 136$

$0 = (2x+17)(x-8)$

$2x + 17 = 0 \quad$ or $\qquad x - 8 = 0$

$2x = -17 \qquad\qquad x = 8$

$x = -\dfrac{17}{2}$

Since $x > 0$, $x = 8$ and $2x + 1 = 2(8) + 1 = 17$.

base: 8 m; altitude: 17 m

Chapter 6

2. $\dfrac{2x^3 + 3x^2 - x}{x - 5x^2 - 6x^3}$

$= \dfrac{x(2x^2 + 3x - 1)}{x(1 - 5x - 6x^2)}$

$= \dfrac{2x^2 + 3x - 1}{1 - 5x - 6x^2}$

4. $\dfrac{5x^3 y^2}{x^2 y + 10xy^2 + 25y^3} \div \dfrac{2x^4 y^5}{3x^3 - 75xy^2}$

$= \dfrac{5x^3 y^2}{x^2 y + 10xy^2 + 25y^3} \cdot \dfrac{3x^3 - 75xy^2}{2x^4 y^5}$

$= \dfrac{5x^3 y^2}{y(x + 5y)^2} \cdot \dfrac{3x(x + 5y)(x - 5y)}{2x^4 y^5}$

$= \dfrac{15(x - 5y)}{2y^4(x + 5y)}$

6. $\dfrac{2}{x + 5} + \dfrac{3}{x - 5} + \dfrac{7x}{x^2 - 25}$

$= \dfrac{2}{x + 5} + \dfrac{3}{x - 5} + \dfrac{7x}{(x + 5)(x - 5)}$

$= \dfrac{2}{x + 5} \cdot \dfrac{x - 5}{x - 5} + \dfrac{3}{x - 5} \cdot \dfrac{x + 5}{x + 5} + \dfrac{7x}{(x + 5)(x - 5)}$

$= \dfrac{2x - 10 + 3x + 15 + 7x}{(x + 5)(x - 5)}$

$= \dfrac{12x + 5}{(x + 5)(x - 5)}$

8. $\dfrac{\frac{1}{12x} + \frac{5}{3x}}{\frac{2}{3x^2}} = \dfrac{\frac{1}{12x} + \frac{5}{3x}}{\frac{2}{3x^2}} \cdot \dfrac{12x^2}{12x^2}$

$= \dfrac{x + 20x}{8}$

$= \dfrac{21x}{8}$

10. $\dfrac{3}{y + 5} - \dfrac{1}{y - 5} = \dfrac{5}{y^2 - 25}$

$\dfrac{3}{y + 5} - \dfrac{1}{y - 5} = \dfrac{5}{(y + 5)(y - 5)}$

$(y + 5)(y - 5)\left(\dfrac{3}{y + 5}\right) - (y + 5)(y - 5)\left(\dfrac{1}{y - 5}\right)$

$\quad = (y + 5)(y - 5)\left[\dfrac{5}{(y + 5)(y - 5)}\right]$

$3(y - 5) - (y + 5) = 5$

$3y - 15 - y - 5 = 5$

$2y - 20 = 5$

$2y = 25$

$y = \dfrac{25}{2}$

12. $\dfrac{d_1}{d_2} = \dfrac{w_1}{w_2}$

$d_1 w_2 = w_1 d_2$

$\dfrac{d_1 w_2}{w_1} = d_2$

14. $\dfrac{\text{height}}{\text{shadow}}: \dfrac{49}{14} = \dfrac{x}{9}$

$14x = 441$

$x = 31.5$

31.5 ft

6.1 Exercises

2. $4x + 20 \neq 0$

$4x \neq -20$

$x \neq -5$

All real numbers except -5.

4. $x^2 + 10x - 24 \neq 0$

$(x - 2)(x + 12) \neq 0$

$x - 2 \neq 0 \qquad \text{or} \qquad x + 12 \neq 0$

$x \neq 2 \qquad\qquad\qquad x \neq -12$

All real numbers except -12 and 2.

6. $\dfrac{5ab^3}{25a^2 b^2} = \dfrac{5ab^2 \cdot b}{5ab^2 \cdot 5a} = \dfrac{b}{5a}$

8. $\dfrac{10x^2 + 15x}{35x^2 - 5x} = \dfrac{5x(2x + 3)}{5x(7x - 1)} = \dfrac{2x + 3}{7x - 1}$

10. $\dfrac{12x^2}{24x^2-18x} = \dfrac{6x \cdot 2x}{6x(4x-3)} = \dfrac{2x}{4x-3}$

12. $\dfrac{25x^3+20x^2}{-5x^2} = \dfrac{5x^2(x+4)}{-5x^2} = -x-4$

14. $\dfrac{x^2y^3+4xy^3}{x^2y^3-3xy^2} = \dfrac{xy^3(x+4)}{xy^2(xy-3)} = \dfrac{y(x+4)}{xy-3}$

16. $\dfrac{x^2-16}{2x-8} = \dfrac{(x-4)(x+4)}{2(x-4)} = \dfrac{x+4}{2}$

18. $\dfrac{9x-9y}{11x-11y} = \dfrac{9(x-y)}{11(x-y)} = \dfrac{9}{11}$

20. $\dfrac{4y-2y^2}{5y-10} = \dfrac{-2y(-2+y)}{5(y-2)} = \dfrac{-2y}{5}$

22. $\dfrac{x+2}{7x^2-28} = \dfrac{x+2}{7(x^2-4)}$

$\qquad = \dfrac{x+2}{7(x+2)(x-2)}$

$\qquad = \dfrac{1}{7(x-2)}$

24. $\dfrac{2x^2-x^3-x^4}{x^4-x^3} = \dfrac{-x^2(-2+x+x^2)}{x^3(x-1)}$

$\qquad = \dfrac{-x^2(x+2)(x-1)}{x^3(x-1)}$

$\qquad = -\dfrac{x+2}{x}$

26. $\dfrac{y^2+6y+9}{2y^2+y-15} = \dfrac{(y+3)^2}{(2y-5)(y+3)} = \dfrac{y+3}{2y-5}$

28. $\dfrac{25-a^2}{3a^2-13a-10} = \dfrac{-(a-5)(a+5)}{(3a+2)(a-5)} = -\dfrac{a+5}{3a+2}$

30. $\dfrac{25ab^4}{125ab^3} \cdot \dfrac{10a^5b^4}{14a^3b} = \dfrac{b}{5} \cdot \dfrac{5a^2b^3}{7} = \dfrac{a^2b^4}{7}$

32. $\dfrac{5x^2}{x^2-4} \cdot \dfrac{x^2+4x+4}{10x^3}$

$\qquad = \dfrac{5x^2}{(x+2)(x-2)} \cdot \dfrac{(x+2)^2}{10x^3}$

$\qquad = \dfrac{x+2}{2x(x-2)}$

34. $\dfrac{x-5}{10x-2} \cdot \dfrac{25x^2-1}{x^2-10x+25}$

$\qquad = \dfrac{x-5}{2(5x-1)} \cdot \dfrac{(5x-1)(5x+1)}{(x-5)^2}$

$\qquad = \dfrac{5x+1}{2(x-5)}$

36. $\dfrac{x-3y}{x^2+3xy-18y^2} \cdot \dfrac{x^2+xy-30y^2}{x-5y}$

$\qquad = \dfrac{x-3y}{(x+6y)(x-3y)} \cdot \dfrac{(x+6y)(x-5y)}{x-5y}$

$\qquad = 1$

38. $\dfrac{6y^2+y-1}{6y^2+5y+1} \cdot \dfrac{3y^2+4y+1}{3y^2+2y-1}$

$\qquad = \dfrac{(3y-1)(2y+1)}{(3y+1)(2y+1)} \cdot \dfrac{(3y+1)(y+1)}{(3y-1)(y+1)}$

$\qquad = 1$

40. $\dfrac{3a^3b^2}{8a^3-b^3} \cdot \dfrac{4a^2+2ab+b^2}{12ab^4}$

$\qquad = \dfrac{3a^3b^2}{(2a-b)(4a^2+2ab+b^2)} \cdot \dfrac{4a^2+2ab+b^2}{12ab^4}$

$\qquad = \dfrac{a^2}{4b^2(2a-b)}$

42. $\dfrac{3y+12}{8y^3} \div \dfrac{9y+36}{16y^3}$

$\qquad = \dfrac{3y+12}{8y^3} \cdot \dfrac{16y^3}{9y+36}$

$\qquad = \dfrac{3(y+4)}{8y^3} \cdot \dfrac{16y^3}{9(y+4)}$

$\qquad = \dfrac{2}{3}$

44. $\dfrac{2a^2 - 7a - 15}{(a+4)^2} \div \dfrac{(a-5)^2}{a+4}$

$= \dfrac{2a^2 - 7a - 15}{(a+4)^2} \cdot \dfrac{a+4}{(a-5)^2}$

$= \dfrac{(2a+3)(a-5)}{(a+4)^2} \cdot \dfrac{a+4}{(a-5)^2}$

$= \dfrac{2a+3}{(a+4)(a-5)}$

46. $\dfrac{x^2 - 5x + 4}{2x - 8} \div (3x^2 - 3x)$

$= \dfrac{x^2 - 5x + 4}{2x - 8} \cdot \dfrac{1}{3x^2 - 3x}$

$= \dfrac{(x-4)(x-1)}{2(x-4)} \cdot \dfrac{1}{3x(x-1)} = \dfrac{1}{6x}$

48. $\dfrac{4 - 2y}{2y + y^2} \div \dfrac{3y^2 - 12}{2y^2 + 8y + 8}$

$= \dfrac{4 - 2y}{2y + y^2} \cdot \dfrac{2y^2 + 8y + 8}{3y^2 - 12}$

$= \dfrac{-2(y-2)}{y(2+y)} \cdot \dfrac{2(y+2)^2}{3(y+2)(y-2)}$

$= -\dfrac{4}{3y}$

50. $\dfrac{4a^2 - 9b^2}{6a^2 - 5ab - 6b^2} \div \dfrac{4a^2 + 12ab + 9b^2}{2a^2 + ab - 3b^2}$

$= \dfrac{4a^2 - 9b^2}{6a^2 - 5ab - 6b^2} \cdot \dfrac{2a^2 + ab - 3b^2}{4a^2 + 12ab + 9b^2}$

$= \dfrac{(2a-3b)(2a+3b)}{(3a+2b)(2a-3b)} \cdot \dfrac{(2a+3b)(a-b)}{(2a+3b)^2}$

$= \dfrac{a-b}{3a+2b}$

52. $\dfrac{2y^4}{10x^2} \cdot \dfrac{5x^3}{4y^3}$

$= \dfrac{xy}{4}$

54. $\dfrac{-28x^5y}{35x^6y^2} = \dfrac{7x^5y \cdot (-4)}{7x^5y \cdot 5xy} = -\dfrac{4}{5xy}$

56. $\dfrac{x^2 + 6x + 9}{2x^2y - 18y} \div \dfrac{6xy + 18y}{3x^2y - 27y}$

$= \dfrac{x^2 + 6x + 9}{2x^2y - 18y} \cdot \dfrac{3x^2y - 27y}{6xy + 18y}$

$= \dfrac{(x+3)^2}{2y(x+3)(x-3)} \cdot \dfrac{3y(x+3)(x-3)}{6y(x+3)}$

$= \dfrac{x+3}{4y}$

58. $\dfrac{x^2 - 7x + 10}{xy^6} \div \dfrac{x^2 - 11x + 30}{x^2y^5}$

$= \dfrac{x^2 - 7x + 10}{xy^6} \cdot \dfrac{x^2y^5}{x^2 - 11x + 30}$

$= \dfrac{(x-5)(x-2)}{xy^6} \cdot \dfrac{x^2y^5}{(x-6)(x-5)}$

$= \dfrac{x(x-2)}{y(x-6)}$

60. $\dfrac{5y^3 - 45y}{6 - y - y^2} = \dfrac{5y(y+3)(y-3)}{-(y+3)(y-2)} = -\dfrac{5y(y-3)}{y-2}$

62. $\dfrac{3x^2 + 3x - 60}{2x - 8} \cdot \dfrac{25x^3}{x^3 + 3x^2 - 10x} \cdot \dfrac{x^2 - 7x + 10}{30x^2}$

$= \dfrac{3(x+5)(x-4)}{2(x-4)} \cdot \dfrac{25x^3}{x(x+5)(x-2)} \cdot \dfrac{(x-5)(x-2)}{30x^2}$

$= \dfrac{5(x-5)}{4}$

64. Domain of $\dfrac{5x - 4}{1.6x^2 - 1.3x - 5.9}$ is all real numbers except $x \approx 2.4$ and $x \approx -1.6$

Cumulative Review Problems

66. $6x - 3y = -12$

x	y
0	4
-2	0
-1	2

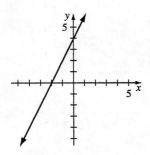

68. $3x + 4y = 12$

$4y = -3x + 12$

$y = -\dfrac{3}{4}x + 3$

$m = -\dfrac{3}{4}$

A perpendicular line has slope $m = \dfrac{4}{3}$.

$y - y_1 = m(x - x_1)$

$y - 4 = \dfrac{4}{3}[x - (-4)]$

$3y - 12 = 4(x + 4)$

$3y - 12 = 4x + 16$

$4x - 3y = -28$

70. minutes per cut $= \dfrac{7 \times 60}{21} = 20$

minutes per cut and color $= \dfrac{7 \times 60}{14} = 30$

minutes per color $= \dfrac{7 \times 60}{18} = 23\dfrac{1}{3}$

Minutes needed to service 12 cuts, 13 cuts and color, and 5 colors is $12(20) + 13(30) +$

$5\left(23\dfrac{1}{3}\right) = 746\dfrac{2}{3}$

hours $= \dfrac{746\frac{2}{3}}{60} = 12\dfrac{4}{9}$ hours

No; he cannot service all of these in a 7-hour shift.

6.2 Exercises

2. $2x^3 y$

4. $3y(y - 3)$

6. $4x^2 - 8x + 3 = (2x - 1)(2x - 3)$

$2x - 1$

LCD: $(2x - 1)(2x - 3)$

8. $(x + 5)^4 (x - 2)$

10. $3x^2 + 2x = x(3x + 2)$

$6x^2 - 5x - 6 = (3x + 2)(2x - 3)$

LCD: $x(3x + 2)(2x - 3)$

12. $16y^2 - 25 = (4y + 5)(4y - 5)$

$16y^2 + 40y + 25 = (4y + 5)^2$

LCD: $(4y - 5)(4y + 5)^2$

14. $2x^2 - 50 = 2(x + 5)(x - 5)$

$x^2 - 2x - 35 = (x - 7)(x + 5)$

$4x^2$

LCD: $4x^2(x + 5)(x - 5)(x - 7)$

16. $\dfrac{5}{3x + y} + \dfrac{2}{3xy}$

$= \dfrac{5}{3x + y} \cdot \dfrac{3xy}{3xy} + \dfrac{2}{3xy} \cdot \dfrac{3x + y}{3x + y}$

$= \dfrac{15xy + 2(3x + y)}{3xy(3x + y)}$

$= \dfrac{15xy + 6x + 2y}{3xy(3x + y)}$

18. $\dfrac{7}{4ab} + \dfrac{3}{4b^2} = \dfrac{7}{4ab} \cdot \dfrac{b}{b} + \dfrac{3}{4b^2} \cdot \dfrac{a}{a} = \dfrac{7b + 3a}{4ab^2}$

20. $\dfrac{2}{x^2 - 9} + \dfrac{3}{x - 3} = \dfrac{2}{(x + 3)(x - 3)} + \dfrac{3}{x - 3}$

$= \dfrac{2}{(x + 3)(x - 3)} + \dfrac{3}{x - 3} \cdot \dfrac{x + 3}{x + 3}$

$= \dfrac{2 + 3(x + 3)}{(x + 3)(x - 3)}$

$= \dfrac{2 + 3x + 9}{(x + 3)(x - 3)}$

$= \dfrac{3x + 11}{(x + 3)(x - 3)}$

22. $\dfrac{3}{x^2 - 3xy + 2y^2} + \dfrac{5x}{x - 2y}$

$= \dfrac{3}{(x - 2y)(x - y)} + \dfrac{5x}{x - 2y}$

$= \dfrac{3}{(x - 2y)(x - y)} + \dfrac{5x}{x - 2y} \cdot \dfrac{x - y}{x - y}$

$$= \frac{3+5x(x-y)}{(x-2y)(x-y)}$$

$$= \frac{3+5x^2-5xy}{(x-2y)(x-y)}$$

24. $\dfrac{2y}{y^2-7y+10}+\dfrac{3y}{y^2-8y+15}$

$$= \frac{2y}{(y-5)(y-2)}+\frac{3y}{(y-5)(y-3)}$$

$$= \frac{2y}{(y-5)(y-2)}\cdot\frac{y-3}{y-3}+\frac{3y}{(y-5)(y-3)}\cdot\frac{y-2}{y-2}$$

$$= \frac{2y(y-3)+3y(y-2)}{(y-5)(y-2)(y-3)}$$

$$= \frac{2y^2-6y+3y^2-6y}{(y-5)(y-2)(y-3)}$$

$$= \frac{5y^2-12y}{(y-5)(y-2)(y-3)}$$

26. $\dfrac{2b}{3b^2-48}+\dfrac{2}{4b+b^2}$

$$= \frac{2b}{3(b+4)(b-4)}+\frac{2}{b(4+b)}$$

$$= \frac{2b}{3(b+4)(b-4)}\cdot\frac{b}{b}+\frac{2}{b(b+4)}\cdot\frac{3(b-4)}{3(b-4)}$$

$$= \frac{2b^2+6(b-4)}{3b(b+4)(b-4)}$$

$$= \frac{2b^2+6b-24}{3b(b+4)(b-4)}$$

28. $\dfrac{y-5}{y+2}-\dfrac{2y}{4y-1}$

$$= \frac{y-5}{y+2}\cdot\frac{4y-1}{4y-1}-\frac{2y}{4y-1}\cdot\frac{y+2}{y+2}$$

$$= \frac{(y-5)(4y-1)-2y(y+2)}{(y+2)(4y-1)}$$

$$= \frac{4y^2-21y+5-2y^2-4y}{(y+2)(4y-1)}$$

$$= \frac{2y^2-25y+5}{(y+2)(4y-1)}$$

30. $\dfrac{8x+3}{2x-1}-3$

$$= \frac{8x+3-3(2x-1)}{2x-1}$$

$$= \frac{8x+3-6x+3}{2x-1}$$

$$= \frac{2x+6}{2x-1}$$

32. $\dfrac{1}{x^2-x-2}-\dfrac{3}{x^2+2x+1}$

$$= \frac{1}{(x-2)(x+1)}-\frac{3}{(x+1)^2}$$

$$= \frac{1}{(x-2)(x+1)}\cdot\frac{x+1}{x+1}-\frac{3}{(x+1)^2}\cdot\frac{x-2}{x-2}$$

$$= \frac{x+1-3(x-2)}{(x-2)(x+1)^2}$$

$$= \frac{x+1-3x+6}{(x-2)(x+1)^2}$$

$$= \frac{-2x+7}{(x-2)(x+1)^2}$$

34. $\dfrac{5x-2}{x^2-9}-\dfrac{2}{x^2-2x-3}$

$$= \frac{5x-2}{(x+3)(x-3)}-\frac{2}{(x-3)(x+1)}$$

$$= \frac{5x-2}{(x+3)(x-3)}\cdot\frac{x+1}{x+1}-\frac{2}{(x-3)(x+1)}\cdot\frac{x+3}{x+3}$$

$$= \frac{(5x-2)(x+1)-2(x+3)}{(x+3)(x-3)(x+1)}$$

$$= \frac{5x^2+3x-2-2x-6}{(x+3)(x-3)(x+1)}$$

$$= \frac{5x^2+x-8}{(x+3)(x-3)(x+1)}$$

36. $\dfrac{2y-46}{2y^2-2y-40}+\dfrac{4}{2y-10}$

$$= \frac{2(y-23)}{2(y-5)(y+4)}+\frac{4}{2(y-5)}$$

$$= \frac{y-23}{(y-5)(y+4)}+\frac{2}{y-5}$$

$$= \frac{y-23}{(y-5)(y+4)}+\frac{2}{y-5}\cdot\frac{y+4}{y+4}$$

$$= \frac{y-23+2(y+4)}{(y-5)(y+4)}$$

$$= \frac{y-23+2y+8}{(y-5)(y+4)}$$

$$= \frac{3y-15}{(y-5)(y+4)}$$

$$= \frac{3(y-5)}{(y-5)(y+4)}$$

$$= \frac{3}{y+4}$$

38. $a-2+\dfrac{3}{2a+1}$

$$= \frac{a-2}{1} \cdot \frac{2a+1}{2a+1} + \frac{3}{2a+1}$$

$$= \frac{(a-2)(2a+1)+3}{2a+1}$$

$$= \frac{2a^2 - 3a - 2 + 3}{2a+1}$$

$$= \frac{2a^2 - 3a + 1}{2a+1}$$

40. $\dfrac{2}{x^2 - 5xy + 6y^2} + \dfrac{1}{x^2 - 7xy + 12y^2}$

$$-\frac{3}{x^2 - 6xy + 8y^2}$$

$$= \frac{2}{(x-2y)(x-3y)} + \frac{1}{(x-4y)(x-3y)}$$

$$-\frac{3}{(x-4y)(x-2y)}$$

$$= \frac{2}{(x-2y)(x-3y)} \cdot \frac{x-4y}{x-4y} + \frac{1}{(x-4y)(x-3y)}$$

$$\cdot \frac{x-2y}{x-2y} - \frac{3}{(x-4y)(x-2y)} \cdot \frac{x-3y}{x-3y}$$

$$= \frac{2(x-4y)+x-2y-3(x-3y)}{(x-2y)(x-3y)(x-4y)}$$

$$= \frac{2x-8y+x-2y-3x+9y}{(x-2y)(x-3y)(x-4y)}$$

$$= \frac{-y}{(x-2y)(x-3y)(x-4y)}$$

42. $\left[x+1+\dfrac{1}{x-1}\right] \div \left[\dfrac{1}{x} + \dfrac{1}{x-1}\right]$

$$= \left[\frac{x+1}{1} \cdot \frac{x-1}{x-1} + \frac{1}{x-1}\right] \div \left[\frac{1}{x} \cdot \frac{x-1}{x-1} + \frac{1}{x-1} \cdot \frac{x}{x}\right]$$

$$= \left[\frac{(x+1)(x-1)+1}{x-1}\right] \div \left[\frac{x-1+x}{x(x-1)}\right]$$

$$= \left[\frac{x^2 - 1 + 1}{x-1}\right] \div \left[\frac{2x-1}{x(x-1)}\right]$$

$$= \left[\frac{x^2}{x-1}\right] \div \left[\frac{2x-1}{x(x-1)}\right]$$

$$= \frac{x^2}{x-1} \cdot \frac{x(x-1)}{2x-1}$$

$$= \frac{x^3}{2x-1}$$

Cumulative Review Problems

44. (a) $\dfrac{630}{985} \approx 0.6396$

63.96% originated in the United States.

(b) $0.07 \cdot 985 = 68.95$

Approximately 69 actual medications came from Switzerland.

46. $x = $ number of liters of 15% acid

$60 - x = $ number of liters of 30% acid

$0.15x + 0.3(60-x) = 0.2(60)$

$15x + 1800 - 30x = 1200$

$600 = 15x$

$x = 40$

$60 - x = 20$

40 liters of 15% acid, 20 liters of 30% acid.

48. $x = $ amount invested at 7%

$3000 - x = $ amount invested at 9%

$0.07x + 0.09(3000-x) = 236$

$7x + 27,000 - 9x = 23,600$

$3400 = 2x$

$x = 1700$

$3000 - x = 1300$

$1700 invested at 7%, $1300 invested at 9%

6.3 Exercises

2. $\dfrac{\frac{8}{x} + \frac{8}{y}}{\frac{2}{x^2}} = \dfrac{\frac{8}{x} + \frac{8}{y}}{\frac{2}{x^2}} \cdot \dfrac{x^2 y}{x^2 y}$

$$= \frac{8xy + 8x^2}{2y}$$

$$= \frac{8x(y+x)}{2y}$$

$$= \frac{4x(x+y)}{y}$$

4.
$$\frac{x^2-4}{x+2} \div \frac{3x+6}{x+2} = \frac{x^2-4}{x+2} \cdot \frac{x+2}{3x+6}$$
$$= \frac{(x+2)(x-2)}{x+2} \cdot \frac{x+2}{3(x+2)}$$
$$= \frac{x-2}{3}$$

6.
$$\frac{1-\frac{9}{y^2}}{1+\frac{3}{y}} = \frac{1-\frac{9}{y^2}}{1+\frac{3}{y}} \cdot \frac{y^2}{y^2}$$
$$= \frac{y^2-9}{y^2+3y}$$
$$= \frac{(y+3)(y-3)}{y(y+3)}$$
$$= \frac{y-3}{y}$$

8.
$$\frac{\frac{1}{3y}+\frac{1}{6y}}{\frac{1}{2y}+\frac{3}{4y}} = \frac{\frac{1}{3y}+\frac{1}{6y}}{\frac{1}{2y}+\frac{3}{4y}} \cdot \frac{12y}{12y}$$
$$= \frac{4+2}{6+9}$$
$$= \frac{6}{15}$$
$$= \frac{2}{5}$$

10.
$$\frac{\frac{2}{y+4}}{\frac{3}{y-4}-\frac{1}{y^2-16}} = \frac{\frac{2}{y+4}}{\frac{3}{y-4}-\frac{1}{(y+4)(y-4)}}$$
$$= \frac{\frac{2}{y+4}}{\frac{3}{y-4}-\frac{1}{(y+4)(y-4)}} \cdot \frac{(y+4)(y-4)}{(y+4)(y-4)}$$
$$= \frac{2(y-4)}{3(y+4)-1}$$
$$= \frac{2y-8}{3y+12-1}$$
$$= \frac{2y-8}{3y+11}$$

12.
$$\frac{\frac{3}{x}+x}{\frac{x^2+2}{3}} = \frac{\frac{3}{x}+x}{\frac{x^2+2}{3}} \cdot \frac{3x}{3x}$$
$$= \frac{9+3x^2}{x^3+2x}$$

14.
$$\frac{-8}{\frac{6x}{x-1}-4} = \frac{-8}{\frac{6x-4(x-1)}{x-1}}$$
$$= \frac{-8}{\frac{6x-4x+4}{x-1}}$$
$$= \frac{-8}{1} \cdot \frac{x-1}{2(x+2)}$$
$$= -\frac{4(x-1)}{x+2}$$

16.
$$\frac{\frac{3}{5x-2}-\frac{2}{25x^2-4}}{\frac{7x}{5x^2-2x}} = \frac{\frac{3}{5x-2}-\frac{2}{(5x+2)(5x-2)}}{\frac{7x}{x(5x-2)}}$$
$$= \frac{\frac{3}{5x-2}-\frac{2}{(5x+2)(5x-2)}}{\frac{7}{5x-2}} \cdot \frac{(5x+2)(5x-2)}{(5x+2)(5x-2)}$$
$$= \frac{3(5x+2)-2}{7(5x+2)}$$
$$= \frac{15x+6-2}{35x+14}$$
$$= \frac{15x+4}{35x+14}$$

18.
$$\frac{\frac{7}{a+3b}+\frac{2}{a-3b}}{\frac{b}{3a}+\frac{a}{2b}}$$
$$= \frac{\frac{7}{a+3b}+\frac{2}{a-3b}}{\frac{b}{3a}+\frac{a}{2b}} \cdot \frac{6ab(a+3b)(a-3b)}{6ab(a+3b)(a-3b)}$$
$$= \frac{42ab(a-3b)+12ab(a+3b)}{2b^2(a+3b)(a-3b)+3a^2(a+3b)(a-3b)}$$
$$= \frac{42a^2b-126ab^2+12a^2b+36ab^2}{(2b^2+3a^2)(a+3b)(a-3b)}$$
$$= \frac{54a^2b-90ab^2}{(3a^2+2b^2)(a+3b)(a-3b)}$$

20.
$$\frac{\frac{1}{x-a}-\frac{1}{x}}{a} = \frac{\frac{1}{x-a}-\frac{1}{x}}{a} \cdot \frac{x(x-a)}{x(x-a)}$$
$$= \frac{x-(x-a)}{ax(x-a)}$$
$$= \frac{x-x+a}{ax(x-a)}$$
$$= \frac{a}{ax(x-a)}$$
$$= \frac{1}{x(x-a)}$$

22.

$$\frac{1+\frac{1}{y-2}}{\frac{6}{y^2+3y-10}-\frac{1}{y-2}} = \frac{1+\frac{1}{y-2}}{\frac{6}{(y+5)(y-2)}-\frac{1}{y-2}}$$

$$= \frac{1+\frac{1}{y-2}}{\frac{6}{(y+5)(y-2)}-\frac{1}{y-2}} \cdot \frac{(y+5)(y-2)}{(y+5)(y-2)}$$

$$= \frac{(y+5)(y-2)+y+5}{6-(y+5)}$$

$$= \frac{y^2+3y-10+y+5}{6-y-5}$$

$$= \frac{y^2+4y-5}{-y+1}$$

$$= \frac{(y+5)(y-1)}{-(y-1)}$$

$$= -(y+5)$$

24.

$$\frac{x}{1+\frac{1}{x}}+\frac{2x}{2+\frac{2}{x}} = \frac{x}{1+\frac{1}{x}}\cdot\frac{x}{x}+\frac{2x}{2+\frac{2}{x}}\cdot\frac{x}{x}$$

$$= \frac{x^2}{x+1}+\frac{2x^2}{2x+2}$$

$$= \frac{x^2}{x+1}+\frac{2x^2}{2(x+1)}$$

$$= \frac{x^2}{x+1}+\frac{x^2}{x+1}$$

$$= \frac{x^2+x^2}{x+1}$$

$$= \frac{2x^2}{x+1}$$

Cumulative Review Problems

26. $\left|\frac{1}{2}(5-x)\right|=5$

$\frac{1}{2}(5-x)=5$ or $\frac{1}{2}(5-x)=-5$

$5-x=10$ or $5-x=-10$

$-x=5$ or $-x=-15$

$x=-5$ or $x=15$

28. $|0.6x+0.3|\geq1.2$

  $0.6x+0.3\geq1.2$ or $0.6x+0.3\leq-1.2$

  $6x+3\geq12$ or $6x+3\leq-12$

  $6x\geq9$ or $6x\leq-15$

  $x\geq1.5$ or $x\leq-2.5$

30. Let $x=$ kg of airfreight

$y=$ kg of ocean freighter

$x+y=5600$

$2.5x+1.3y=9380$

$2.5x+1.3(5600-x)=9380$

$2.5x+7280-1.3x=9380$

$1.2x=2100$

$x=1750$

$y=5600-1750=3850$

Ship 1750 kg by airfreight and 3850 kg by ocean freighter.

6.4 Exercises

2. $\dfrac{1}{x}+\dfrac{2}{3x}=\dfrac{1}{3}$

$3x\left(\dfrac{1}{x}+\dfrac{2}{3x}\right)=\dfrac{1}{3}(3x)$

$3+2=x$

$5=x$

Check:

$\dfrac{1}{5}+\dfrac{2}{3\cdot5}\overset{?}{=}\dfrac{1}{3}$

$\dfrac{3}{15}+\dfrac{2}{15}\overset{?}{=}\dfrac{1}{3}$

$\dfrac{1}{3}=\dfrac{1}{3}$

4. $\dfrac{5}{3x}+2=\dfrac{1}{x}$

$3x\left(\dfrac{5}{3x}\right)+3x(2)=3x\left(\dfrac{1}{x}\right)$

$5+6x=3$

$6x=-2$

$x=-\dfrac{1}{3}$

Check:

$\dfrac{5}{3\left(-\frac{1}{3}\right)}+2\overset{?}{=}\dfrac{1}{-\frac{1}{3}}$

$-5+2\overset{?}{=}-3$

$-3=-3$

6. $\dfrac{1}{y}+2=\dfrac{3}{y}$

$y\left(\dfrac{1}{y}\right)+y(2)=y\left(\dfrac{3}{y}\right)$

$1+2y=3$

$2y=2$

$y=1$

Check:

$$1\left(\frac{1}{1}\right)+2 \overset{?}{=} \frac{3}{1}$$
$$3=3$$

8. $\dfrac{2}{x}-\dfrac{3}{5}=1$

$$5x\left(\frac{2}{x}-\frac{3}{5}\right)=(1)5x$$
$$10-3x=5x$$
$$-8x=-10$$
$$x=\frac{10}{8}=\frac{5}{4}$$

Check:

$$\frac{2}{\frac{5}{4}}-\frac{3}{5}\overset{?}{=}1$$
$$\frac{8}{5}-\frac{3}{5}\overset{?}{=}1$$
$$1=1$$

10. $\dfrac{5}{y}=\dfrac{9}{2y+1}$

$$y(2y+1)\left(\frac{5}{y}\right)=y(2y+1)\left(\frac{9}{2y+1}\right)$$
$$5(2y+1)=9y$$
$$10y+5=9y$$
$$5=-y$$
$$-5=y$$

Check:

$$\frac{5}{-5}\overset{?}{=}\frac{9}{2(-5)+1}$$
$$-1=-1$$

12. $4-\dfrac{8x}{x+1}=\dfrac{8}{x+1}$

$$(x+1)(4)-(x+1)\left(\frac{8x}{x+1}\right)=(x+1)\left(\frac{8}{x+1}\right)$$
$$4x+4-8x=8$$
$$4-4x=8$$
$$-4x=4$$
$$x=-1$$

Since $x=-1$ causes a denominator in the original equation to equal 0, there is no solution.

14. $\dfrac{1}{2x}+\dfrac{5}{x}=\dfrac{3}{x-1}$

$$2x(x-1)\left(\frac{1}{2x}\right)+2x(x-1)\left(\frac{5}{x}\right)=2x(x-1)\left(\frac{3}{x-1}\right)$$
$$x-1+10(x-1)=6x$$
$$x-1+10x-10=6x$$
$$11x-11=6x$$
$$-11=-5x$$
$$\frac{11}{5}=x$$

Check:

$$\frac{1}{2\left(\frac{11}{5}\right)}+\frac{5}{\frac{11}{5}}\overset{?}{=}\frac{3}{\frac{11}{5}-1}$$
$$\frac{5}{22}+\frac{25}{11}\overset{?}{=}\frac{15}{6}$$
$$\frac{55}{22}\overset{?}{=}\frac{5}{2}$$
$$\frac{5}{2}=\frac{5}{2}$$

16. $\dfrac{2}{x+4}=\dfrac{-7}{x-5}$

$$(x+4)(x-5)\left(\frac{2}{x+4}\right)=\frac{-7}{x-5}(x+4)(x-5)$$
$$2(x-5)=-7(x+4)$$
$$2x-10=-7x-28$$
$$9x=-18$$
$$x=-2$$

Check:

$$\frac{2}{-2+4}\overset{?}{=}\frac{-7}{-2-5}$$
$$\frac{2}{2}\overset{?}{=}\frac{-7}{-7}$$
$$1=1$$

18. $\dfrac{x-2}{x+4}=\dfrac{x+1}{x+10}$

$$(x+10)(x+4)\left(\frac{x-2}{x+4}\right)=\left(\frac{x+1}{x+10}\right)(x+10)(x+4)$$
$$(x+10)(x-2)=(x+1)(x+4)$$
$$x^2+8x-20=x^2+5x+4$$
$$3x=24$$
$$x=8$$

Check:

$$\frac{8-2}{8+4}\overset{?}{=}\frac{8+1}{8+10}$$
$$\frac{6}{12}\overset{?}{=}\frac{9}{18}$$
$$\frac{1}{2}=\frac{1}{2}$$

20. $\dfrac{4y}{y+2} + \dfrac{2}{y-1} = 4$

$(y+2)(y-1)\left(\dfrac{4y}{y+2}\right) + (y+2)(y-1)\left(\dfrac{2}{y-1}\right) = (y+2)(y-1)(4)$

$4y(y-1) + 2(y+2) = 4(y^2 + y - 2)$

$4y^2 - 4y + 2y + 4 = 4y^2 + 4y - 8$

$4y^2 - 2y + 4 = 4y^2 + 4y - 8$

$-2y + 4 = 4y - 8$

$4 = 6y - 8$

$12 = 6y$

$2 = y$

Check:

$\dfrac{4(2)}{2+2} + \dfrac{2}{2-1} \overset{?}{=} 4$

$\dfrac{8}{4} + 2 \overset{?}{=} 4$

$2 + 2 = 4$

22. $\dfrac{3}{2x-1} + \dfrac{3}{2x+1} = \dfrac{8x}{4x^2-1}$

$\dfrac{3}{2x-1} + \dfrac{3}{2x+1} = \dfrac{8x}{(2x+1)(2x-1)}$

$(2x+1)(2x-1)\left(\dfrac{3}{2x-1}\right) + (2x+1)(2x-1)\left(\dfrac{3}{2x+1}\right) = (2x+1)(2x-1)\left[\dfrac{8x}{(2x+1)(2x-1)}\right]$

$3(2x+1) + 3(2x-1) = 8x$

$6x + 3 + 6x - 3 = 8x$

$12x = 8x$

$4x = 0$

$x = 0$

Check:

$\dfrac{3}{2(0)-1} + \dfrac{3}{2(0)+1} \overset{?}{=} \dfrac{8(0)}{4(0^2)-1}$

$\dfrac{3}{-1} + \dfrac{3}{1} \overset{?}{=} 0$

$-3 + 3 = 0$

24. $\dfrac{5-x}{x^2-1} + \dfrac{7}{x+1} = \dfrac{6}{x}$

$\dfrac{5-x}{(x+1)(x-1)} + \dfrac{7}{x+1} = \dfrac{6}{x}$

$x(x+1)(x-1)\left[\dfrac{5-x}{(x+1)(x-1)}\right] + x(x+1)(x-1)\left(\dfrac{7}{x+1}\right) = x(x+1)(x-1)\left(\dfrac{6}{x}\right)$

$x(5-x) + 7x(x-1) = 6(x^2-1)$

$5x - x^2 + 7x^2 - 7x = 6x^2 - 6$

$6x^2 - 2x = 6x^2 - 6$

$-2x = -6$

$x = 3$

Check:

$$\frac{5-3}{3^2-1}+\frac{7}{3+1} \stackrel{?}{=} \frac{6}{3}$$

$$\frac{2}{8}+\frac{7}{4} \stackrel{?}{=} 2$$

$$\frac{1}{4}+\frac{7}{4} \stackrel{?}{=} 2$$

$$\frac{8}{4}=2$$

26. $\dfrac{2}{3}+\dfrac{5}{y-4}=\dfrac{y+6}{3y-12}$

$$3(y-4)\left[\frac{2}{3}+\frac{5}{y-4}\right]=3(y-4)\left[\frac{y+6}{3(y-4)}\right]$$

$$2(y-4)+15=y+6$$

$$2y-8+15=y+6$$

$$2y+7=y+6$$

$$y=-1$$

Check:

$$\frac{2}{3}+\frac{5}{-1-4} \stackrel{?}{=} \frac{-1+6}{3(-1)-12}$$

$$\frac{2}{3}+\frac{5}{-5} \stackrel{?}{=} \frac{5}{-15}$$

$$\frac{2}{3}-1 \stackrel{?}{=} -\frac{1}{3}$$

$$-\frac{1}{3}=-\frac{1}{3}$$

28. $\dfrac{3}{2}+\dfrac{2}{2z-8}=\dfrac{1}{z-4}$

$$\frac{3}{2}+\frac{2}{2(z-4)}=\frac{1}{z-4}$$

$$2(z-4)\left(\frac{3}{2}\right)+2(z-4)\left[\frac{2}{2(z-4)}\right]=2(z-4)\left(\frac{1}{z-4}\right)$$

$$3(z-4)+2=2$$

$$3z-12+2=2$$

$$3z-10=2$$

$$3z=12$$

$$z=4$$

Since $z = 4$ causes a denominator in the original equation to equal zero, there is no solution.

30. $\dfrac{-12}{y^2-9}-\dfrac{1}{y+3}=\dfrac{1}{y-3}$

$$\frac{-12}{(y+3)(y-3)}-\frac{1}{y+3}=\frac{1}{y-3}$$

$$(y+3)(y-3)\left[\frac{-12}{(y+3)(y-3)}\right]-(y+3)(y-3)\left(\frac{1}{y+3}\right)=(y+3)(y-3)\left(\frac{1}{y-3}\right)$$

$$-12-(y-3)=y+3$$

$$-12-y+3=y+3$$

$$-y - 9 = y + 3$$
$$-9 = 2y + 3$$
$$-12 = 2y$$
$$-6 = y$$

Check:

$$\frac{-12}{(-6)^2 - 9} - \frac{1}{-6 + 3} \overset{?}{=} \frac{1}{-6 - 3}$$

$$\frac{-12}{27} - \frac{1}{-3} \overset{?}{=} \frac{1}{-9}$$

$$-\frac{4}{9} + \frac{3}{9} \overset{?}{=} -\frac{1}{9}$$

$$-\frac{1}{9} = -\frac{1}{9}$$

32. $\dfrac{z^2 + 16}{z^2 - 16} = \dfrac{z}{z + 4} - \dfrac{4}{z - 4}$

$$\frac{z^2 + 16}{(z + 4)(z - 4)} = \frac{z}{z + 4} - \frac{4}{z - 4}$$

$$(z + 4)(z - 4)\left[\frac{z^2 + 16}{(z + 4)(z - 4)}\right] = (z + 4)(z - 4)\left(\frac{z}{z + 4}\right) - (z + 4)(z - 4)\left(\frac{4}{z - 4}\right)$$

$$z^2 + 16 = z(z - 4) - 4(z + 4)$$
$$z^2 + 16 = z^2 - 4z - 4z - 16$$
$$z^2 + 16 = z^2 - 8z - 16$$
$$16 = -8z - 16$$
$$32 = -8z$$
$$-4 = z$$

Since $z = -4$ causes a denominator in the original equation to equal zero, there is no solution.

34. $\dfrac{5}{2x + 3} + \dfrac{-4}{3x - 4} = \dfrac{3x}{6x^2 + x - 12}$

$$\frac{5}{2x + 3} + \frac{-4}{3x - 4} = \frac{3x}{(2x + 3)(3x - 4)}$$

$$(2x + 3)(3x - 4)\left(\frac{5}{2x + 3}\right) + (2x + 3)(3x - 4)\left(\frac{-4}{3x - 4}\right) = (2x + 3)(3x - 4)\left[\frac{3x}{(2x + 3)(3x - 4)}\right]$$

$$5(3x - 4) - 4(2x + 3) = 3x$$
$$15x - 20 - 8x - 12 = 3x$$
$$7x - 32 = 3x$$
$$-32 = -4x$$
$$8 = x$$

Check:

$$\frac{5}{2(8) + 3} + \frac{-4}{3(8) - 4} \overset{?}{=} \frac{3(8)}{6(8)^2 + 8 - 12}$$

$$\frac{5}{19} - \frac{4}{20} \overset{?}{=} \frac{24}{380}$$

$$\frac{24}{380} = \frac{24}{380}$$

36. $\dfrac{2}{2x+3} + \dfrac{12}{4x^2 - 4x - 15} = \dfrac{2}{2x-5}$

$\dfrac{2}{2x+3} + \dfrac{12}{(2x+3)(2x-5)} = \dfrac{2}{2x-5}$

$(2x+3)(2x-5)\left(\dfrac{2}{2x+3}\right) + (2x+3)(2x-5)\left[\dfrac{12}{(2x+3)(2x-5)}\right] = (2x+3)(2x-5)\left(\dfrac{2}{2x-5}\right)$

$2(2x-5) + 12 = 2(2x+3)$

$4x - 10 + 12 = 4x + 6$

$4x + 2 = 4x + 6$

$2 \neq 6$

No solution

38. An extraneous solution is an apparent solution that, when substituted into the original equation, does not make the equation a true statement.

40. $\dfrac{153.8}{x^2 + 4.9 - 39.56} = \dfrac{75.3}{x+9.2} + \dfrac{84.2}{x-4.3}$

$x \approx -1.9$

Cumulative Review Problems

42. $2x^2 + 20x + 50$

$= 2(x^2 + 10x + 25)$

$= 2\left[x^2 + 2(x)(5) + 5^2\right]$

$= 2(x+5)^2$

44. $3x^2 - 13x + 14$

$= 3x^2 - 7x - 6x + 14$

$= x(3x-7) - 2(3x-7)$

$= (3x-7)(x-2)$

6.5 Exercises

2. $I = \dfrac{E}{R}$

$RI = E$

$R = \dfrac{E}{I}$

4. $P = \dfrac{A}{1+rt}$

$P(1+rt) = A$

$P + Prt = A$

$Prt = A - P$

$r = \dfrac{A-P}{Pt}$

6. $\dfrac{1}{f} = \dfrac{1}{a} + \dfrac{1}{b}$

$abf\left(\dfrac{1}{f}\right) = abf\left(\dfrac{1}{a}\right) + abf\left(\dfrac{1}{b}\right)$

$ab = bf + af$

$ab = f(b+a)$

$\dfrac{ab}{b+a} = f$

8. $A^2 = \dfrac{Q}{5M}$

$5A^2 M = Q$

$M = \dfrac{Q}{5A^2}$

10. $A = \dfrac{ha + hb}{2}$

$2A = 2\left(\dfrac{ha + hb}{2}\right)$

$2A = ha + hb$

$2A = h(a+b)$

$\dfrac{2A}{a+b} = h$

12. $T = \dfrac{24I}{B + Bn}$

$T(B + Bn) = 24I$

$TB(1 + n) = 24I$

$B = \dfrac{24I}{T(1 + n)}$

14. $\dfrac{3V}{\pi h} = r^2$

$3V = r^2 \pi h$

$\dfrac{3V}{\pi r^2} = h$

16. $\dfrac{E}{e} = \dfrac{Re\, r}{r}$

$Er = Re^2 r$

$\dfrac{Er}{e^2 r} = R$

$\dfrac{E}{e^2} = R$

18. $\dfrac{P_1 V_1}{T_1} = \dfrac{P_2 V_2}{T_2}$

$P_1 V_1 T_2 = P_2 V_2 T_1$

$T_2 = \dfrac{P_2 V_2 T_1}{P_1 V_1}$

20. $F = \dfrac{Gm_1 m_2}{d^2}$

$Fd^2 = Gm_1 m_2$

$\dfrac{Fd^2}{m_1 m_2} = G$

22. $E = T_1 - \dfrac{T_1}{T_2}$

$ET_2 = T_1 T_2 - T_1$

$ET_2 - T_1 T_2 = -T_1$

$T_2(E - T_1) = -T_1$

$T_2 = \dfrac{-T_1}{E - T_1}$

$T_2 = \dfrac{T_1}{T_1 - E}$

24. $m = \dfrac{y_2 - y_1}{x_2 - x_1}$

$m(x_2 - x_1) = y_2 - y_1$

$mx_2 - mx_1 = y_2 - y_1$

$mx_2 = mx_1 + y_2 - y_1$

$x_2 = \dfrac{mx_1 + y_2 - y_1}{m}$

26. $S = \dfrac{V_1 t + V_2 t}{2}$

$2S = V_1 t + V_2 t$

$2S - V_2 t = V_1 t$

$\dfrac{2S - V_2 t}{t} = V_1$

28. $Q = \dfrac{kA(t_1 - t_2)}{L}$

$QL = kA(t_1 - t_2)$

$\dfrac{QL}{k(t_1 - t_2)} = A$

30. $d = \dfrac{LR_2}{R_2 + R_1}$

$d(R_2 + R_1) = LR_2$

$dR_2 + dR_1 = LR_2$

$dR_1 = LR_2 - dR_2$

$R_1 = \dfrac{LR_2 - dR_2}{d}$

32. $V = \dfrac{mv}{m + M}$

$V(m + M) = mv$

$Vm + VM = mv$

$VM = mv - Vm$

$M = \dfrac{mv - Vm}{V}$

34. $\dfrac{1}{R} = \dfrac{1}{r_1} + \dfrac{1}{0.368} + \dfrac{1}{0.736}$

$0.736 r_1 R\left(\dfrac{1}{R}\right) = 0.736 r_1 R\left(\dfrac{1}{r_1}\right)$

$\qquad + 0.736 r_1 R\left(\dfrac{1}{0.368}\right) + 0.736 r_1 R\left(\dfrac{1}{0.736}\right)$

$0.736 r_1 = 0.736 R + 2 r_1 R + r_1 R$

$0.736 r_1 = 0.736 R + 3 r_1 R$

$0.736 r_1 - 3 r_1 R = 0.736 R$

$r_1(0.736 - 3R) = 0.736 R$

$r_1 = \dfrac{0.736 R}{0.736 - 3R}$

36. $\dfrac{5}{100} = \dfrac{7}{x}$ and $\dfrac{5}{100} = \dfrac{11}{x}$

$5x = 700$ $5x = 1100$

$x = 140$ $x = 220$

140 inches by 220 inches or $11\dfrac{2}{3}$ feet by $18\dfrac{1}{3}$ feet

38. $\dfrac{40}{2.5} = \dfrac{140}{x}$

$40x = 350$

$x = 8.75$

8.75 minutes

40. $\dfrac{450}{156} = \dfrac{x}{320}$

$156x = 144,000$

$x \approx 923.08$

923 pounds

42. $\dfrac{30}{x} = \dfrac{18}{50}$

$18x = 1500$

$x = 83.\overline{3}$

83 alligators

44. $\dfrac{3.75}{148} = \dfrac{7}{x}$

$3.75x = 1036$

$x = 276.2\overline{6}$

276.27 kilograms

46. $\dfrac{\text{width}}{\text{length}} : \dfrac{500}{800} = \dfrac{1200}{x}$

$500x = 960,000$

$x = 1920$

1920 yards

48. $\dfrac{\text{pressure}}{\text{depth}} : \dfrac{52}{120} = \dfrac{x}{300}$

$120x = 15,600$

$x = 130$

130 pounds per square inch

50. $x =$ number of detectives

$187 - x =$ number of patrol officers

$\dfrac{2}{9} = \dfrac{x}{187 - x}$

$374 - 2x = 9x$

$11x = 374$

$x = 34$

$187 - x = 153$

34 detectives and 153 patrol officers

52. $x =$ number of powerboats

$78 - x =$ number of sailboats

$\dfrac{4}{9} = \dfrac{x}{78 - x}$

$312 - 4x = 9x$

$312 = 13x$

$24 = x$

$54 = 78 - x$

24 powerboats and 54 sailboats

54. $\dfrac{3}{4.8} = \dfrac{x}{177}$

$4.8x = 531$

$x = 110.625$

Approximately, 110.63 feet tall

56. $x =$ number of cars

$2128 - x =$ number of trucks

$\dfrac{5}{11} = \dfrac{x}{2128 - x}$

$10,640 - 5x = 11x$

$10,640 = 16x$

$665 = x$

$2128 - 665 = 1463$

665 cars and 1463 trucks

58. $x =$ hours to do the work together

$\dfrac{x}{4} + \dfrac{x}{6} = 1$

$3x + 2x = 12$

$5x = 12$

$x = 2.4$

2.4 hours

60. $\dfrac{x}{8} + \dfrac{x}{11} = 1$

$11x + 8x = 88$

$19x = 88$

$x \approx 4.63$

4.63 minutes

62. $\dfrac{x}{4} + \dfrac{x}{7} = 1$

$7x + 4x = 28$

$11x = 28$

$x \approx 2.55$

2.55 hours per garden

64. $\dfrac{2}{3}+\dfrac{2}{x}=1$

$2x+6=3x$

$x=6$

6 hours

66. $\dfrac{3}{8}=\dfrac{297}{8+x}$

$3(8+x)=8(297)$

$24+3x=2376$

$3x=2352$

$x=784$

784 ft

Cumulative Review Problems

68. $x^2-2x-120=(x-12)(x+10)$

70. $5yx^2-20y$

$=5y(x^2-4)$

$=5y(x-2)(x+2)$

Putting Your Skills to Work

2. $I=\dfrac{108}{d^2}$

d	I
2	27
3	12
4	6.75
6	3
8	1.69
10	1.08

Based on the graph of $I=\dfrac{108}{d^2}$, the value of d for the intensity to be 4 watts is approximately 5.2 miles.

4. 1.09 yd ≈ 1 m

1 yd ≈ 0.914 m

$I=\dfrac{108(0.914)^2}{(0.62k)^2}$

or $I=\dfrac{234.71}{k^2}$

Chapter 6 Review Problems

2. $\dfrac{12x^4}{3x^5-15x^2}=\dfrac{12x^4}{3x^2(x^3-5)}$

$=\dfrac{4x^2}{x^3-5}$

4. $\dfrac{a^2-a-20}{a^2-2a-15}=\dfrac{(a+4)(a-5)}{(a-5)(a+3)}$

$=\dfrac{a+4}{a+3}$

6. $\dfrac{ax+2a-bx-2b}{3x^2-12}=\dfrac{(x+2)(a-b)}{3(x+2)(x-2)}$

$=\dfrac{a-b}{3(x-2)}$

8. $\dfrac{6x^2y+6xy-36y}{3x^2y-15xy+18y}=\dfrac{6y(x+3)(x-2)}{3y(x-3)(x-2)}$

$=\dfrac{2(x+3)}{x-3}$

10. $\dfrac{3y}{4xy-6y^2}\cdot\dfrac{2x-3y}{12xy}$

$=\dfrac{3y}{2y(2x-3y)}\cdot\dfrac{2x-3y}{12xy}$

$=\dfrac{1}{8xy}$

12. $\dfrac{3x^3y}{x^2+7x+12}\cdot\dfrac{x^2+8x+15}{6xy^2}$

$=\dfrac{3x^3y}{(x+4)(x+3)}\cdot\dfrac{(x+5)(x+3)}{6xy^2}$

$=\dfrac{x^2(x+5)}{2y(x+4)}$

14. $\dfrac{6x^2-6a^2}{3x^2+3}\div\dfrac{x^4-a^4}{a^2x^2+a^2}$

$=\dfrac{6x^2-6a^2}{3x^2+3}\cdot\dfrac{a^2x^2+a^2}{x^4-a^4}$

$=\dfrac{6(x+a)(x-a)}{3(x^2+1)}\cdot\dfrac{a^2(x^2+1)}{(x+a)(x-a)(x^2+a^2)}$

$=\dfrac{2a^2}{x^2+a^2}$

16. $\dfrac{y^2+y-20}{y^2-4y+4}\cdot\dfrac{y^2+y-6}{12+y-y^2}\cdot\dfrac{10-5y}{2y+10}$

$=\dfrac{(y+5)(y-4)}{(y-2)^2}\cdot\dfrac{(y+3)(y-2)}{-(y-4)(y+3)}\cdot\dfrac{-5(y-2)}{2(y+5)}$

$=\dfrac{5}{2}$

18. $\dfrac{4a^2+12a+5}{2a^2-7a-13}\div(4a^2+2a)$

$=\dfrac{4a^2+12a+5}{2a^2-7a-13}\cdot\dfrac{1}{4a^2+2a}$

$=\dfrac{(2a+1)(2a+5)}{2a^2-7a-13}\cdot\dfrac{1}{2a(2a+1)}$

$=\dfrac{2a+5}{2a(2a^2-7a-13)}$

20. $\dfrac{5}{x-3}+\dfrac{2}{3x+1}$

$=\dfrac{5}{x-3}\cdot\dfrac{3x+1}{3x+1}+\dfrac{2}{3x+1}\cdot\dfrac{x-3}{x-3}$

$=\dfrac{5(3x+1)+2(x-3)}{(x-3)(3x+1)}$

$=\dfrac{15x+5+2x-6}{(x-3)(3x+1)}$

$=\dfrac{17x-1}{(x-3)(3x+1)}$

22. $\dfrac{x-5}{2x+1}-\dfrac{x+1}{x-2}$

$=\dfrac{x-5}{2x+1}\cdot\dfrac{x-2}{x-2}-\dfrac{x+1}{x-2}\cdot\dfrac{2x+1}{2x+1}$

$=\dfrac{(x-5)(x-2)-(x+1)(2x+1)}{(2x+1)(x-2)}$

$=\dfrac{x^2-7x+10-(2x^2+3x+1)}{(2x+1)(x-2)}$

$=\dfrac{x^2-7x+10-2x^2-3x-1}{(2x+1)(x-2)}$

$=\dfrac{-x^2-10x+9}{(2x+1)(x-2)}$

24. $\dfrac{2y-1}{12y}-\dfrac{3y+2}{9y}$

$=\dfrac{2y-1}{12y}\cdot\dfrac{3}{3}-\dfrac{3y+2}{9y}\cdot\dfrac{4}{4}$

$=\dfrac{3(2y-1)-4(3y+2)}{36y}$

$=\dfrac{6y-3-12y-8}{36y}$

$=\dfrac{-6y-11}{36y}$

26. $\dfrac{4y}{y^2+2y+1}+\dfrac{3}{y^2-1}$

$=\dfrac{4y}{(y+1)^2}+\dfrac{3}{(y+1)(y-1)}$

$=\dfrac{4y}{(y+1)^2}\cdot\dfrac{y-1}{y-1}+\dfrac{3}{(y+1)(y-1)}\cdot\dfrac{y+1}{y+1}$

$=\dfrac{4y(y-1)+3(y+1)}{(y-1)(y+1)^2}$

$=\dfrac{4y^2-4y+3y+3}{(y-1)(y+1)^2}$

$=\dfrac{4y^2-y+3}{(y-1)(y+1)^2}$

28. $\dfrac{5}{a^2+3a+2}+\dfrac{6}{a^2+4a+3}-\dfrac{7}{a^2+5a+6}$

$=\dfrac{5}{(a+2)(a+1)}+\dfrac{6}{(a+3)(a+1)}-\dfrac{7}{(a+2)(a+3)}$

$=\dfrac{5}{(a+2)(a+1)}\cdot\dfrac{a+3}{a+3}+\dfrac{6}{(a+3)(a+1)}\cdot$

$\dfrac{a+2}{a+2}-\dfrac{7}{(a+2)(a+3)}\cdot\dfrac{a+1}{a+1}$

$=\dfrac{5(a+3)+6(a+2)-7(a+1)}{(a+1)(a+2)(a+3)}$

$=\dfrac{5a+15+6a+12-7a-7}{(a+1)(a+2)(a+3)}$

$=\dfrac{4a+20}{(a+1)(a+2)(a+3)}$

30. $\dfrac{1}{a}+\dfrac{1}{3a}+3a+2 = \dfrac{1}{a}\cdot\dfrac{3}{3}+\dfrac{1}{3a}+\dfrac{3a+2}{1}\cdot\dfrac{3a}{3a}$

$= \dfrac{3+1+3a(3a+2)}{3a}$

$= \dfrac{4+9a^2+6a}{3a}$

$= \dfrac{9a^2+6a+4}{3a}$

32. $\dfrac{\frac{1}{x}+\frac{3}{2y}}{\frac{1}{4y}+\frac{7}{2y}} = \dfrac{\frac{1}{x}+\frac{3}{2y}}{\frac{1}{4y}+\frac{7}{2y}}\cdot\dfrac{4xy}{4xy}$

$= \dfrac{4y+6x}{x+14x}$

$= \dfrac{4y+6x}{15x}$

34. $\dfrac{\frac{4}{x+3}}{\frac{2}{x-2}-\frac{1}{x^2+x-6}}$

$= \dfrac{\frac{4}{x+3}}{\frac{2}{x-2}-\frac{1}{(x+3)(x-2)}}$

$= \dfrac{\frac{4}{x+3}}{\frac{2}{x-2}-\frac{1}{(x+3)(x-2)}}\cdot\dfrac{(x-2)(x+3)}{(x-2)(x+3)}$

$= \dfrac{4(x-2)}{2(x+3)-1}$

$= \dfrac{4x-8}{2x+6-1}$

$= \dfrac{4x-8}{2x+5}$

36. $\dfrac{\frac{10}{a+2}-5}{\frac{4}{a+2}-2} = \dfrac{\frac{10}{a+2}-5}{\frac{4}{a+2}-2}\cdot\dfrac{a+2}{a+2}$

$= \dfrac{10-5(a+2)}{4-2(a+2)}$

$= \dfrac{10-5a-10}{4-2a-4}$

$= \dfrac{-5a}{-2a}$

$= \dfrac{5}{2}$

38. $\dfrac{\frac{y^2}{y^2-x^2}-1}{x+\frac{xy}{x-y}} = \dfrac{\frac{y^2}{-(x-y)(x+y)}-1}{x+\frac{xy}{x-y}}$

$= \dfrac{\frac{y^2}{-(x-y)(x+y)}-1}{x+\frac{xy}{x-y}}\cdot\dfrac{(x-y)(x+y)}{(x-y)(x+y)}$

$= \dfrac{-y^2-(x-y)(x+y)}{x(x-y)(x+y)+xy(x+y)}$

$= \dfrac{-y^2-(x^2-y^2)}{x(x+y)(x-y+y)}$

$= \dfrac{-y^2-x^2+y^2}{x(x+y)(x)}$

$= \dfrac{-x^2}{x^2(x+y)}$

$= -\dfrac{1}{x+y}$

40. $\dfrac{\frac{3}{x}-\frac{2}{x+1}}{\frac{5}{x^2+5x+4}-\frac{1}{x+4}} = \dfrac{\frac{3}{x}-\frac{2}{x+1}}{\frac{5}{(x+4)(x+1)}-\frac{1}{x+4}}$

$= \dfrac{\frac{3}{x}-\frac{2}{x+1}}{\frac{5}{(x+4)(x+1)}-\frac{1}{x+4}}\cdot\dfrac{x(x+1)(x+4)}{x(x+1)(x+4)}$

$= \dfrac{3(x+1)(x+4)-2x(x+4)}{5x-x(x+1)}$

$= \dfrac{3x^2+15x+12-2x^2-8x}{5x-x^2-x}$

$= \dfrac{x^2+7x+12}{-x^2+4x}$ or $\dfrac{-(x^2+7x+12)}{x^2-4x}$

In exercises 42–52, the check is left to the reader.

42. $\dfrac{3}{2}=1-\dfrac{1}{x-1}$

$2(x-1)\left(\dfrac{3}{2}\right)=2(x-1)(1)-2(x-1)\left(\dfrac{1}{x-1}\right)$

$3(x-1)=2x-2-2$

$3x-3=2x-4$

$x-3=-4$

$x=-1$

44. $\dfrac{3}{x-2}+\dfrac{8}{x+3}=\dfrac{6}{x-2}$

$(x-2)(x+3)\left(\dfrac{3}{x-2}\right)+(x-2)(x+3)\left(\dfrac{8}{x+3}\right)$

$=(x-2)(x+3)\left(\dfrac{6}{x-2}\right)$

$3(x+3)+8(x-2)=6(x+3)$

$3x+9+8x-16=6x+18$

$11x-7=6x+18$

$5x-7=18$

$5x=25$

$x=5$

46. $\dfrac{1}{2a} = \dfrac{2}{a} - \dfrac{3}{8}$

$8a\left(\dfrac{1}{2a}\right) = 8a\left(\dfrac{2}{a}\right) - 8a\left(\dfrac{3}{8}\right)$

$4 = 16 - 3a$

$-12 = -3a$

$4 = a$

48. $\dfrac{5}{y^2} + \dfrac{7}{y} = \dfrac{6}{y^2}$

$y^2\left(\dfrac{5}{y^2}\right) + y^2\left(\dfrac{7}{y}\right) = y^2\left(\dfrac{6}{y^2}\right)$

$5 + 7y = 6$

$7y = 1$

$y = \dfrac{1}{7}$

50. $\dfrac{5}{a+5} + \dfrac{a+4}{2a+10} = \dfrac{3}{2}$

$\dfrac{5}{a+5} + \dfrac{a+4}{2(a+5)} = \dfrac{3}{2}$

$2(a+5)\left(\dfrac{5}{a+5}\right) + 2(a+5)\left[\dfrac{a+4}{2(a+5)}\right] = 2(a+5)\left(\dfrac{3}{2}\right)$

$10 + a + 4 = 3a + 15$

$a + 14 = 3a + 15$

$14 = 2a + 15$

$-1 = 2a$

$-\dfrac{1}{2} = a$

52. $\dfrac{y+1}{y^2+2y-3} - \dfrac{1}{y+3} = \dfrac{1}{y-1}$

$\dfrac{y+1}{(y+3)(y-1)} - \dfrac{1}{y+3} = \dfrac{1}{y-1}$

$(y+3)(y-1)\left[\dfrac{y+1}{(y+3)(y-1)}\right] - (y+3)(y-1)\left(\dfrac{1}{y+3}\right)$

$\qquad = (y+3)(y-1)\left(\dfrac{1}{y-1}\right)$

$y + 1 - (y - 1) = y + 3$

$y + 1 - y + 1 = y + 3$

$2 = y + 3$

$-1 = y$

54. $m = \dfrac{y - y_0}{x - x_0}$

$m(x - x_0) = y - y_0$

$mx - mx_0 = y - y_0$

$mx = mx_0 + y - y_0$

$x = \dfrac{mx_0 + y - y_0}{m}$

56. $\dfrac{1}{f} = \dfrac{1}{a} + \dfrac{1}{b}$

$fab\left(\dfrac{1}{f}\right) = fab\left(\dfrac{1}{a}\right) + fab\left(\dfrac{1}{b}\right)$

$ab = fb + fa$

$ab - fa = fb$

$a(b - f) = fb$

$a = \dfrac{fb}{b - f}$

58. $A = \dfrac{12I}{p + 3pr}$

$A(p + 3pr) = 12I$

$Ap(1 + 3r) = 12I$

$p = \dfrac{12I}{A(1 + 3r)}$

60. $\dfrac{S - P}{Pr} = t$

$S - P = tPr$

$\dfrac{S - P}{tP} = r$

62. $\dfrac{\text{kg}}{\text{lb}}: \ \dfrac{5}{11} = \dfrac{x}{143}$

$11x = 5(143)$

$11x = 715$

$x = 65$

65 kg

64. $\dfrac{\text{number}}{\text{tagged}}: \ \dfrac{x}{100} = \dfrac{40}{8}$

$8x = 40(100)$

$8x = 4000$

$x = 500$

500 rabbits

66. $\dfrac{\text{officers}}{\text{troopers}}: \ \dfrac{2}{9} = \dfrac{x}{154 - x}$

$2(154 - x) = 9x$

$308 - 2x = 9x$

$308 = 11x$

$28 = x$

28 officers

68. $\dfrac{\text{height}}{\text{shadow}}:\ \dfrac{7}{6}=\dfrac{x}{156}$

$6x=7(156)$

$6x=1092$

$x=182$

182 ft

70. $x=$ time working together

$\dfrac{x}{3}+\dfrac{x}{7}=1$

$7x+3x=21$

$10x=21$

$x=2.1$

2.1 hours

72. $x=$ time working together

$\dfrac{x}{12}+\dfrac{x}{18}=1$

$3x+2x=36$

$5x=36$

$x=7.2$

7.2 hours

Chapter 6 Test

2. $\dfrac{y^2-4}{y^3+8}=\dfrac{(y-2)(y+2)}{(y+2)(y^2-2y+4)}$

$\quad=\dfrac{y-2}{y^2-2y+4}$

4. $\dfrac{4-2x}{3x^2-2x-8}\div\dfrac{2x^2+x-1}{9x+12}$

$\quad=\dfrac{4-2x}{3x^2-2x-8}\cdot\dfrac{9x+12}{2x^2+x-1}$

$\quad=\dfrac{-2(x-2)}{(3x+4)(x-2)}\cdot\dfrac{3(3x+4)}{(2x-1)(x+1)}$

$\quad=-\dfrac{6}{(2x-1)(x+1)}$

6. $\dfrac{2}{x^2+5x+6}+\dfrac{3x}{x^2+6x+9}$

$\quad=\dfrac{2}{(x+2)(x+3)}+\dfrac{3x}{(x+3)^2}$

$\quad=\dfrac{2}{(x+2)(x+3)}\cdot\dfrac{x+3}{x+3}+\dfrac{3x}{(x+3)^2}\cdot\dfrac{x+2}{x+2}$

$\quad=\dfrac{2(x+3)+3x(x+2)}{(x+2)(x+3)^2}$

$\quad=\dfrac{2x+6+3x^2+6x}{(x+2)(x+3)^2}$

$\quad=\dfrac{3x^2+8x+6}{(x+2)(x+3)^2}$

8. $\dfrac{\frac{1}{x}-\frac{3}{x+2}}{\frac{2}{x^2+2x}}=\dfrac{\frac{1}{x}-\frac{3}{x+2}}{\frac{2}{x(x+2)}}$

$\quad=\dfrac{\frac{1}{x}-\frac{3}{x+2}}{\frac{2}{x(x+2)}}\cdot\dfrac{x(x+2)}{x(x+2)}$

$\quad=\dfrac{x+2-3x}{2}$

$\quad=\dfrac{2-2x}{2}$

$\quad=1-x$

10. $2+\dfrac{x}{x+4}=\dfrac{3x}{x-4}$

$(x+4)(x-4)(2)+(x+4)(x-4)\left(\dfrac{x}{x+4}\right)$

$\quad=(x+4)(x-4)\left(\dfrac{3x}{x-4}\right)$

$(x^2-16)2+x(x-4)=3x(x+4)$

$2x^2-32+x^2-4x=3x^2+12x$

$3x^2-4x-32=3x^2+12x$

$-4x-32=12x$

$-32=16x$

$-2=x$

Check:

$2+\dfrac{-2}{-2+4}\overset{?}{=}\dfrac{3(-2)}{-2-4}$

$2+\dfrac{-2}{2}\overset{?}{=}\dfrac{-6}{-6}$

$2-1=1$

12.

$$\frac{3}{2x+3} - \frac{1}{2x-3} = \frac{2}{4x^2-9}$$

$$\frac{3}{2x+3} - \frac{1}{2x-3} = \frac{2}{(2x+3)(2x-3)}$$

$$(2x+3)(2x-3)\left(\frac{3}{2x+3}\right) - (2x+3)(2x-3)\left(\frac{1}{2x-3}\right) = (2x+3)(2x-3)\left[\frac{2}{(2x+3)(2x-3)}\right]$$

$$3(2x-3) - (2x+3) = 2$$

$$6x - 9 - 2x - 3 = 2$$

$$4x - 12 = 2$$

$$4x = 14$$

$$x = \frac{7}{2}$$

Check:

$$\frac{3}{2\left(\frac{7}{2}\right)+3} - \frac{1}{2\left(\frac{7}{2}\right)-3} \stackrel{?}{=} \frac{2}{4\left(\frac{7}{2}\right)^2-9}$$

$$\frac{3}{7+3} - \frac{1}{7-3} \stackrel{?}{=} \frac{2}{49-9}$$

$$\frac{3}{10} - \frac{1}{4} \stackrel{?}{=} \frac{2}{40}$$

$$\frac{6}{20} - \frac{5}{20} = \frac{1}{20}$$

14.

$$\frac{4}{a} = \frac{3}{b} + \frac{2}{c}$$

$$abc\left(\frac{4}{a}\right) = abc\left(\frac{3}{b}\right) + abc\left(\frac{2}{c}\right)$$

$$4bc = 3ac + 2ab$$

$$4bc - 2ab = 3ac$$

$$b(4c - 2a) = 3ac$$

$$b = \frac{3ac}{4c - 2a}$$

16.

$$\frac{\text{mph}}{\text{fps}}: \quad \frac{60}{88} = \frac{x}{110}$$

$$88x = 60(110)$$

$$88x = 6600$$

$$x = 75$$

75 mph

Cumulative Test for Chapters 1–6

2.

$$\frac{2}{3}(3x-1) = \frac{2}{5}x + 3$$

$$15\left[\frac{2}{3}(3x-1)\right] = 15\left(\frac{2}{5}x+3\right)$$

$$10(3x-1) = 6x + 45$$

$$30x - 10 = 6x + 45$$

$$24x - 10 = 45$$

$$24x = 55$$

$$x = \frac{55}{24}$$

4.

$$5x - 6y = 8$$

$$-6y = -5x + 8$$

$$y = \frac{5}{6}x - \frac{4}{3}$$

$$m = \frac{5}{6}$$

$$y - y_1 = m(x - x_1)$$

$$y - (-3) = \frac{5}{6}[x - (-1)]$$

$$y + 3 = \frac{5}{6}(x + 1)$$

$$6y + 18 = 5x + 5$$

$$5x - 6y = 13$$

6. $3(2 - 6x) > 4(x + 1) + 24$

$6 - 18x > 4x + 4 + 24$

$6 - 18x > 4x + 28$

$6 > 22x + 28$

$-22 > 22x$

$-1 > x$

8. $|3x - 4| \le 10$

$-10 \le 3x - 4 \le 10$

$-6 \le 3x \le 14$

$-2 \le x \le \dfrac{14}{3}$

10. $81x^3 - 90x^2y + 25xy^2$

$= x(81x^2 - 90xy + 25y^2)$

$= x[(9x)^2 - 2(9x)(5y) + (5y)^2]$

$= x(9x - 5y)^2$

12. $3x^2 - 11x - 4 = 0$

$(3x + 1)(x - 4) = 0$

$3x + 1 = 0 \qquad$ or $\qquad x - 4 = 0$

$3x = -1 \qquad$ or $\qquad x = 4$

$x = -\dfrac{1}{3} \qquad$ or $\qquad x = 4$

14. $\dfrac{2x^2 + x - 1}{2x^2 - 9x + 4} \cdot \dfrac{3x^2 - 12x}{6x + 15}$

$= \dfrac{(2x - 1)(x + 1)}{(2x - 1)(x - 4)} \cdot \dfrac{3x(x - 4)}{3(2x + 5)}$

$= \dfrac{x(x + 1)}{2x + 5}$

16. $\dfrac{5}{2x - 8} - \dfrac{3x}{x^2 - 9x + 20}$

$= \dfrac{5}{2(x - 4)} - \dfrac{3x}{(x - 5)(x - 4)}$

$= \dfrac{5}{2(x - 4)} \cdot \dfrac{x - 5}{x - 5} - \dfrac{3x}{(x - 5)(x - 4)} \cdot \dfrac{2}{2}$

$= \dfrac{5(x - 5) - 6x}{2(x - 4)(x - 5)}$

$= \dfrac{5x - 25 - 6x}{2(x - 4)(x - 5)}$

$= \dfrac{-x - 25}{2(x - 4)(x - 5)} = -\dfrac{x + 25}{2(x - 4)(x - 5)}$

18. $\dfrac{3}{x - 6} + \dfrac{4}{x + 4}$

$= \dfrac{3}{x - 6} \cdot \dfrac{x + 4}{x + 4} + \dfrac{4}{x + 4} \cdot \dfrac{x - 6}{x - 6}$

$= \dfrac{3(x + 4) + 4(x - 6)}{(x - 6)(x + 4)}$

$= \dfrac{3x + 12 + 4x - 24}{(x - 6)(x + 4)}$

$= \dfrac{7x - 12}{(x - 6)(x + 4)}$

20. $\dfrac{1}{4x} - \dfrac{3}{2x} = \dfrac{5}{8}$

$8x\left(\dfrac{1}{4x}\right) - 8x\left(\dfrac{3}{2x}\right) = 8x\left(\dfrac{5}{8}\right)$

$2 - 12 = 5x$

$-10 = 5x$

$-2 = x$

22. $\dfrac{\text{cars}}{\text{min}} : \dfrac{1650}{12} = \dfrac{x}{60}$

$12x = 60(1650)$

$12x = 99{,}000$

$x = 8250$

8250 cars

Chapter 7

2. $\left(\dfrac{27x^2y^{-5}}{x^{-4}y^4}\right)^{2/3}$

$=\dfrac{27^{2/3}x^{4/3}y^{-10/3}}{x^{-8/3}y^{8/3}}$

$=9x^{4/3-(-8/3)}y^{-10/3-8/3}$

$=9x^4y^{-6}$

$=\dfrac{9x^4}{y^6}$

4. $(-4x^{-1/4}y^{1/3})^3$

$=(-4)^3x^{-3/4}y$

$=-\dfrac{64y}{x^{3/4}}$

6. $\sqrt{169}+\sqrt[3]{-64}=13+(-4)=9$

8. $\sqrt[4]{32x^8y^{15}}$

$=\sqrt[4]{16x^8y^{12}2y^3}$

$=2x^2y^3\sqrt[4]{2y^3}$

10. $\left(3\sqrt{3}-5\sqrt{6}\right)\left(\sqrt{12}-3\sqrt{6}\right)$

$=\left(3\sqrt{3}-5\sqrt{6}\right)\left(2\sqrt{3}-3\sqrt{6}\right)$

$=6(3)-9\sqrt{18}-10\sqrt{18}+15(6)$

$=18-19\sqrt{18}+90$

$=108-57\sqrt{2}$

12. $\dfrac{\sqrt{2}+\sqrt{3}}{\sqrt{2}-\sqrt{3}}$

$=\dfrac{\sqrt{2}+\sqrt{3}}{\sqrt{2}-\sqrt{3}}\cdot\dfrac{\sqrt{2}+\sqrt{3}}{\sqrt{2}+\sqrt{3}}$

$=\dfrac{2+2\sqrt{6}+3}{2-3}$

$=\dfrac{5+2\sqrt{6}}{-1}$

$=-5-2\sqrt{6}$

14. $\sqrt{2x+3}-\sqrt{x-2}=2$

$\sqrt{2x+3}=2+\sqrt{x-2}$

$\left(\sqrt{2x+3}\right)^2=\left(2+\sqrt{x-2}\right)^2$

$2x+3=4+4\sqrt{x-2}+x-2$

$2x+3=2+x+4\sqrt{x-2}$

$x+1=4\sqrt{x-2}$

$(x+1)^2=\left(4\sqrt{x-2}\right)^2$

$x^2+2x+1=16(x-2)$

$x^2+2x+1=16x-32$

$x^2-14x+33=0$

$(x-11)(x-3)=0$

$x-11=0$ or $x-3=0$

$x=11$ $x=3$

Check: $x=11$

$\sqrt{2(11)+3}-\sqrt{11-2}\overset{?}{=}2$

$\sqrt{25}-\sqrt{9}\overset{?}{=}2$

$5-3\overset{?}{=}2$

$2=2$

Check: $x=3$

$\sqrt{2(3)+3}-\sqrt{3-2}\overset{?}{=}2$

$\sqrt{9}-\sqrt{1}\overset{?}{=}2$

$3-1\overset{?}{=}2$

$2=2$

$x=11,\ x=3$

16. $i^{15}+\sqrt{-25}=(i^4)^3i^3+5i$

$=1^3i^3+5i$

$=-i+5i=4i$

18. $\dfrac{3+2i}{2+3i}=\dfrac{3+2i}{2+3i}\cdot\dfrac{2-3i}{2-3i}$

$=\dfrac{6-9i+4i-6i^2}{4-9i^2}$

$=\dfrac{6-5i-6(-1)}{4-9(-1)}$

$=\dfrac{6-5i+6}{4+9}$

$=\dfrac{12-5i}{13}$ or $\dfrac{12}{13}-\dfrac{5}{13}i$

20.　$y = \dfrac{k}{x}$

$12 = \dfrac{k}{6}$

$72 = k$

$y = \dfrac{72}{x}$

$y = \dfrac{72}{10} = 7.2$

7.1 Exercises

2.　$\left(\dfrac{3xy^{-2}}{x^3}\right)^2 = \dfrac{3^2 x^2 y^{-4}}{x^6} = \dfrac{9x^2}{x^6 y^4} = \dfrac{9}{x^4 y^4}$

4.　$\left(\dfrac{a^{-3}b^2}{3b}\right)^3 = \dfrac{a^{-9}b^6}{3^3 b^3}$

$= \dfrac{b^6}{27a^9 b^3}$

$= \dfrac{b^3}{27a^9}$

6.　$(x^{4/3})^6 = x^{24/3} = x^8$

8.　$(y^8)^{1/2} = y^{8/2} = y^4$

10.　$\dfrac{x^{7/8}}{x^{3/8}} = x^{7/8 - 3/8} = x^{4/8} = x^{1/2}$

12.　$\dfrac{x^2}{x^{1/3}} = x^{2 - 1/3} = x^{6/3 - 1/3} = x^{5/3}$

14.　$x^{3/5} \cdot x^{1/5} = x^{3/5 + 1/5} = x^{4/5}$

16.　$y^{7/10} \cdot y^{-1/5} = y^{7/10 + (-1/5)} = y^{7/10 - 2/10}$

$= y^{5/10} = y^{1/2}$

18.　$4^{3/4} \cdot 4^{1/4} = 4^{3/4 + 1/4} = 4$

20.　$6^{-3/8} \cdot 6^{1/2} = 6^{-3/8 + 4/8} = 6^{1/8}$

22.　$x^{-5/6} = \dfrac{1}{x^{5/6}}$

24.　$a^{-5/8}b^{1/4} = \dfrac{b^{1/4}}{a^{5/8}}$

26.　$4^{-1/3} = \dfrac{1}{4^{1/3}}$

28.　$3^{-2/5} \cdot 2^{1/3} = \dfrac{2^{1/3}}{3^{2/5}}$

30.　$\left(x^{-1/3}y^{2/3}\right)\left(x^{1/3}y^{1/4}\right)$

$= x^{-1/3 + 1/3}y^{2/3 + 1/4}$

$= x^0 y^{11/12}$

$= y^{11/12}$

32.　$\left(8x^{-1/5}y^{1/3}\right)\left(-3x^{-1/4}y^{1/6}\right)$

$= -24x^{-1/5 - 1/4}y^{1/3 + 1/6}$

$= -24x^{-9/20}y^{1/2}$

$= -\dfrac{24y^{1/2}}{x^{9/20}}$

34.　$7^{3/4} \cdot 7^{-1/4} = 7^{3/4 - 1/4} = 7^{1/2}$

36.　$\dfrac{3y^{2/3}}{y^{-1/4}} = 3y^{2/3 - (-1/4)} = 3y^{11/12}$

38.　$\dfrac{12x^{-2/3}y}{-6xy^{-3/4}} = -2x^{-2/3 - 1}y^{1 - (-3/4)}$

$= -2x^{-5/3}y^{7/4}$

$= -\dfrac{2y^{7/4}}{x^{5/3}}$

40.　$\left(\dfrac{16a^5 b^{-2}}{a^{-1}b^{-6}}\right)^{1/2} = (16a^6 b^4)^{1/2}$

$= (4^2)^{1/2}(a^6)^{1/2}(b^4)^{1/2}$

$= 4a^3 b^2$

42.　$\left(\dfrac{a^7 b^3}{32a^2 b^{-7}}\right)^{2/5}$

$= \left(\dfrac{a^5 b^{10}}{32}\right)^{2/5}$

$= \dfrac{(a^5)^{2/5}(b^{10})^{2/5}}{(2^5)^{2/5}}$

$= \dfrac{a^2 b^4}{4}$

44. $(5x^{-1/2}y^{1/3}z^{4/5})^3 = 5^3(x^{-1/2})^3(y^{1/3})^3(z^{4/5})^3$

$\quad = 125x^{-3/2}yz^{12/5}$

$\quad = \dfrac{125yz^{12/5}}{x^{3/2}}$

46. $(3^3x^6y^3z^{12})^{1/3}$

$\quad = (3^3)^{1/3}(x^6)^{1/3}(y^3)^{1/3}(z^{12})^{1/3}$

$\quad = 3x^2yz^4$

48. $x^{-1/4}(x^{2/3} + x^{3/4})$

$\quad = x^{-1/4} \cdot x^{2/3} + x^{-1/4} \cdot x^{3/4}$

$\quad = x^{-1/4+2/3} + x^{-1/4+3/4}$

$\quad = x^{5/12} + x^{1/2}$

50. $a^{2/3}(a^{1/2} + 4a^{-1/4})$

$\quad = a^{2/3} \cdot a^{1/2} + a^{2/3} \cdot 4a^{-1/4}$

$\quad = a^{2/3+1/2} + 4a^{2/3-1/4}$

$\quad = a^{7/6} + 4a^{5/12}$

52. $\left(5a^{2/5}b^{1/8}\right)^{4/5} = 5^{4/5}a^{8/25}b^{4/40}$

$\quad = 5^{4/5}a^{8/25}b^{1/10}$

54. $\dfrac{\left(x^{1/3}x^3\right)^{3/2}}{x^{-1/4}} = \dfrac{(x^{1/3})^{3/2}(x^3)^{3/2}}{x^{-1/4}}$

$\quad = \dfrac{x^{1/2} \cdot x^{9/2}}{x^{-1/4}}$

$\quad = \dfrac{x^5}{x^{-1/4}}$

$\quad = x^{21/4}$

56. $(27)^{2/3} = (3^3)^{2/3} = 3^2 = 9$

58. $(4)^{3/2} = (2^2)^{3/2} = 2^3 = 8$

60. $(81)^{3/4} + (25)^{1/2} = (3^4)^{3/4} + (5^2)^{1/2}$

$\quad = 3^3 + 5$

$\quad = 27 + 5$

$\quad = 32$

62. $\dfrac{-82.32206x^8y^{1/2}}{-17.89610x^{-6}y^{1/4}} = 4.6x^{8-(-6)}y^{1/2-1/4}$

$\quad = 4.6x^{14}y^{1/4}$

64. $2y^{1/3} + y^{-2/3} = 2y^{1/3} + \dfrac{1}{y^{2/3}}$

$\quad = \dfrac{2y^{1/3}}{1} \cdot \dfrac{y^{2/3}}{y^{2/3}} + \dfrac{1}{y^{2/3}}$

$\quad = \dfrac{2y}{y^{2/3}} + \dfrac{1}{y^{2/3}}$

$\quad = \dfrac{2y+1}{y^{2/3}}$

66. $3^{-1/2} + y^{-1/2} = \dfrac{1}{3^{1/2}} + \dfrac{1}{y^{1/2}}$

$\quad = \dfrac{1}{3^{1/2}} \cdot \dfrac{y^{1/2}}{y^{1/2}} + \dfrac{1}{y^{1/2}} \cdot \dfrac{3^{1/2}}{3^{1/2}}$

$\quad = \dfrac{y^{1/2}}{3^{1/2}y^{1/2}} + \dfrac{3^{1/2}}{y^{1/2}3^{1/2}}$

$\quad = \dfrac{y^{1/2} + 3^{1/2}}{3^{1/2}y^{1/2}}$

68. $27x^{5/2} - 3x^{3/2} = 3x^{1/2}(9x^2) - 3x^{1/2}(x)$

$\quad = 3x^{1/2}(9x^2 - x)$

70. $6a^{4/3} - 8a^{3/2} = 2a(3a^{1/3}) - 2a(4a^{1/2})$

$\quad = 2a\left(3a^{1/3} - 4a^{1/2}\right)$

72. $x^b \div x^{1/3} = x^{-1/12}$

$\quad x^{b-1/3} = x^{-1/12}$

$\quad b - \dfrac{1}{3} = -\dfrac{1}{12}$

$\quad b = -\dfrac{1}{12} + \dfrac{1}{3} = \dfrac{1}{4}$

74. $r = 0.62(V)^{1/3} = 0.62(64)^{1/3}$

$\quad = 0.62(4^3)^{1/3}$

$\quad = 0.62(4)$

$\quad = 2.48$

2.48 m

Cumulative Review Problems

76. $A = \dfrac{h}{2}(a+b)$

$\quad 2A = ah + hb$

$\quad hb = 2A - ah$

$\quad b = \dfrac{2A - ah}{h}$

78. $y = \dfrac{ax}{a+12}$

$75 = \dfrac{a(250)}{a+12}$

$75a + 900 = 250a$

$900 = 175a$

$5 \approx a$

5 years old

7.2 Exercises

2. A cube root of a number is one of that number's three equal factors.

4. $\sqrt{-4} \ne -2$ since $(-2)(-2) = 4 \ne -4$

6. $\sqrt{100} = \sqrt{10^2} = 10$

8. $\sqrt{16} + \sqrt{81} = \sqrt{4^2} + \sqrt{9^2}$
$= 4 + 9 = 13$

10. $-\sqrt{\dfrac{4}{25}} = -\sqrt{\left(\dfrac{2}{5}\right)^2} = -\dfrac{2}{5}$

12. $\sqrt[3]{64} = \sqrt[3]{4^3} = 4$

14. $\sqrt[3]{-8} = \sqrt[3]{(-2)^3} = -2$

16. $\sqrt[4]{81} = \sqrt[4]{3^4} = 3$

18. $\sqrt[5]{-32} = \sqrt[5]{(-2)^5} = -2$

20. $-\sqrt[8]{1} = -\sqrt[8]{1^8} = -1$

22. Not a real number

24. $\sqrt[6]{(9)^6} = 9$

26. $\sqrt[7]{(11)^7} = 11$

28. $\sqrt[3]{-\dfrac{8}{27}} = \sqrt[3]{\left(-\dfrac{2}{3}\right)^3} = -\dfrac{2}{3}$

30. $\sqrt{5} = 5^{1/2}$

32. $\sqrt[4]{3y} = (3y)^{1/4}$

34. $\sqrt[9]{(a-b)^5} = (a-b)^{5/9}$

36. $\sqrt[5]{\sqrt{y}} = (y^{1/2})^{1/5} = y^{1/10}$

38. $\left(\sqrt[5]{2x}\right)^3 = \left((2x)^{1/5}\right)^3 = (2x)^{3/5}$

40. $\sqrt[4]{x^{12}} = \sqrt[4]{(x^3)^4} = x^3$

42. $\sqrt[5]{(13)^5} = 13$

44. $\sqrt[4]{a^8 b^4} = \left(a^8 b^4\right)^{1/4}$
$= a^{8/4} b^{4/4}$
$= a^2 b$

46. $\sqrt[9]{y^{36}} = y^{36/9} = y^4$

48. $\sqrt{49x^2 y^8} = \sqrt{7^2 x^2 (y^4)^2} = 7xy^4$

50. $\sqrt[3]{64a^9 b^6} = \sqrt[3]{4^3 (a^3)^3 (b^2)^3} = 4a^3 b^2$

52. $\sqrt[3]{-27x^{45}} = \sqrt[3]{(-3)^3 (x^{15})^3} = -3x^{15}$

54. $y^{2/3} = \left(\sqrt[3]{y}\right)^2$

56. $5^{-3/5} = \dfrac{1}{5^{3/5}} = \dfrac{1}{\left(\sqrt[5]{5}\right)^3}$

58. $(x+3y)^{4/7} = \left(\sqrt[7]{x+3y}\right)^4$

60. $(-y)^{5/7} = \left(\sqrt[7]{-y}\right)^5$

62. $(3ab)^{2/7} = \sqrt[7]{(3ab)^2} = \sqrt[7]{9a^2 b^2}$

64. $27^{2/3} = \left(\sqrt[3]{27}\right)^2 = 3^2 = 9$

66. $\left(\dfrac{1}{49}\right)^{1/2} = \sqrt{\dfrac{1}{49}} = \dfrac{1}{7}$

68. $(-125)^{2/3} = \left(\sqrt[3]{-125}\right)^2 = (-5)^2 = 25$

70. $\left(36y^8\right)^{-1/2} = \dfrac{1}{\left(36y^8\right)^{1/2}} = \dfrac{1}{6y^4}$

72. $\sqrt[4]{16a^{20}b^{16}} = 16^{1/4}a^{20/4}b^{16/4} = 2a^5b^4$

74. $\sqrt{49x^8} = \sqrt{7^2(x^4)^2} = 7x^4$

76. $\sqrt{64a^{20}b^8} = \sqrt{8^2(a^{10})^2(b^4)^2}$
$\qquad = 8a^{10}b^4$

78. $\sqrt{100x^{10}y^{12}z^2} = \sqrt{10^2(x^5)^2(y^6)^2z^2}$
$\qquad = 10x^5y^6z$

80. $\sqrt[3]{-125a^6b^{15}c^{21}}$
$\qquad = \sqrt[3]{(-5)^3(a^2)^3(b^5)^3(c^7)^3}$
$\qquad = -5a^2b^5c^7$

82. $\sqrt[5]{32a^5b^{15}} + \sqrt[5]{a^5b^{15}}$
$\qquad = 2ab^3 + ab^3$
$\qquad = 3ab^3$

84. $\sqrt[4]{456,976} = 26$

86. $(117,649)^{5/6} = 16,807$

88. $\sqrt{100x^2} = \sqrt{10^2x^2} = 10|x|$

90. $\sqrt[3]{-27x^9} = \sqrt[3]{(-3)^3\left(x^3\right)^3} = -3x^3$

92. $\sqrt[4]{x^{16}y^{40}} = \sqrt[4]{\left(x^4\right)^4\left(y^{10}\right)^4} = x^4y^{10}$

94. $\sqrt[4]{a^4b^{20}} = \sqrt[4]{a^4\left(b^5\right)^4} = \left|ab^5\right|$

96. $\sqrt{49a^{12}b^4} = \sqrt{7^2\left(a^6\right)^2\left(b^2\right)^2} = 7a^6b^2$

98. $C = 120\sqrt[3]{n} + 375$
$\qquad = 120\sqrt[3]{216} + 375$
$\qquad = 120(6) + 375$
$\qquad = 1095$
The cost is \$1095 per day.

Cumulative Review Problems

100. New level for North America $= .26(1 + .05)$
$\qquad = .273$
New level for World $= 1 + .2 = 1.2$
New percent of World energy produced for
North America $= \dfrac{.273}{1.2} = .2275 = 22.75\%$

7.3 Exercises

2. $\sqrt{20} = \sqrt{4 \cdot 5} = 2\sqrt{5}$

4. $\sqrt{75} = \sqrt{25 \cdot 3} = 5\sqrt{3}$

6. $\sqrt{80} = \sqrt{16 \cdot 5} = 4\sqrt{5}$

8. $\sqrt{108} = \sqrt{36 \cdot 3} = 6\sqrt{3}$

10. $\sqrt{16x^5} = \sqrt{16x^4 \cdot x} = 4x^2\sqrt{x}$

12. $\sqrt{45a^3b^8} = \sqrt{9a^2b^8 \cdot 5a} = 3ab^4\sqrt{5a}$

14. $\sqrt{24xy^8z^3} = \sqrt{4y^8z^2}\sqrt{6xz} = 2y^4z\sqrt{6xz}$

16. $\sqrt[3]{27} = 3$

18. $\sqrt[3]{128} = \sqrt[3]{64 \cdot 2} = 4\sqrt[3]{2}$

20. $\sqrt[3]{54x} = \sqrt[3]{27 \cdot 2x} = 3\sqrt[3]{2x}$

22. $\sqrt[3]{125a^6b^2} = 5a^2\sqrt[3]{b^2}$

24. $\sqrt[3]{72x^5y^{20}} = \sqrt[3]{8x^3y^{18} \cdot 9x^2y^2} = 2xy^6\sqrt[3]{9x^2y^2}$

26. $\sqrt[3]{-40a^3b^7c^{14}} = \sqrt[3]{-8a^3b^6c^{12} \cdot 5bc^2}$
$\qquad = -2ab^2c^4\sqrt[3]{5bc^2}$

28. $\sqrt[4]{32x^5y^{10}} = \sqrt[4]{16x^4y^8 \cdot 2xy^2} = 2xy^2\sqrt[4]{2xy^2}$

30. $\sqrt[4]{16k^{12}p^{18}} = \sqrt[4]{16k^{12}p^{16} \cdot p^2} = 2k^3p^4\sqrt[4]{p^2}$
$\qquad$ or $2k^3p^4p^{2/4} = 2k^3p^4p^{1/2} = 2k^3p^4\sqrt{p}$

32. $\sqrt[5]{-243x^4y^{10}} = \sqrt[5]{-243y^{10} \cdot x^4} = -3y^2\sqrt[5]{x^4}$

34. $\sqrt[6]{64x^6y^8} = \sqrt[6]{64x^6y^6 \cdot y^2} = 2xy\sqrt[6]{y^2}$

    or $2xy \cdot y^{2/6} = 2xy \cdot y^{1/3} = 2xy\sqrt[3]{y}$

36. $\sqrt[3]{3072} = b\sqrt[3]{6}$

    $\sqrt[3]{512 \cdot 6} = b\sqrt[3]{6}$

    $8\sqrt[3]{6} = b\sqrt[3]{6}$

    $8 = b$

38. $\sqrt{25} + \sqrt{81} = 5 + 9 = 14$

40. $\sqrt{11} - 5\sqrt{11} + 3\sqrt{11} = (1 - 5 + 3)\sqrt{11} = -\sqrt{11}$

42. $3\sqrt{50} - \sqrt{2} = 3 \cdot 5\sqrt{2} - \sqrt{2}$

    $= 15\sqrt{2} - \sqrt{2}$

    $= 14\sqrt{2}$

44. $-\sqrt{12} + 2\sqrt{48} - \sqrt{75}$

    $= -2\sqrt{3} + 8\sqrt{3} - 5\sqrt{3}$

    $= \sqrt{3}$

46. $-7\sqrt{10} + 4\sqrt{40} - 8\sqrt{90}$

    $= -7\sqrt{10} + 8\sqrt{10} - 24\sqrt{10}$

    $= -23\sqrt{10}$

48. $\sqrt{75x} + 2\sqrt{108x} - 6\sqrt{3x}$

    $= 5\sqrt{3x} + 12\sqrt{3x} - 6\sqrt{3x}$

    $= 11\sqrt{3x}$

50. $-3\sqrt{45a^6} + a\sqrt{80a^4}$

    $= -9a^3\sqrt{5} + 4a^3\sqrt{5}$

    $= -5a^3\sqrt{5}$

52. $\sqrt[3]{128} - 4\sqrt[3]{16} = 4\sqrt[3]{2} - 8\sqrt[3]{2}$

    $= -4\sqrt[3]{2}$

54. $2x\sqrt[3]{40xy} - 3\sqrt[3]{5x^4y} = 4x\sqrt[3]{5xy} - 3x\sqrt[3]{5xy}$

    $= x\sqrt[3]{5xy}$

56. $-2\sqrt{72x^3y} + \sqrt[3]{3x^4y} - 3x\sqrt{50xy} + 4x\sqrt[3]{81xy}$

    $= -2\sqrt{36x^2}\sqrt{2xy} + \sqrt[3]{x^3} \cdot \sqrt[3]{3xy} - 3x\sqrt{25}\sqrt{2xy}$

        $+ 4x\sqrt[3]{27} \cdot \sqrt[3]{3xy}$

    $= -12x\sqrt{2xy} + x\sqrt[3]{3xy} - 15x\sqrt{2xy} + 12x\sqrt[3]{3xy}$

    $= -27x\sqrt{2xy} + 13x\sqrt[3]{3xy}$

58. $\sqrt{6} \approx 2.449$

60. $\sqrt{142} \approx 11.916$

62. $\sqrt{600} \approx 24.495$

64. $\sqrt{468} \approx 21.633$

66. $\sqrt{98} + \sqrt{50} + \sqrt{128} \overset{?}{=} 20\sqrt{2}$

    $9.899494937 + 7.071067812 + 11.3137085$

        $\overset{?}{=} 28.2842715$

    $28.28427125 = 28.28427125$

68. $I = \sqrt{\dfrac{P}{R}} = \sqrt{\dfrac{480}{8}} = \sqrt{60} = 7.746$

    7.746 amps

Cumulative Review Problems

70. $16x^3 - 56x^2y + 49xy^2$

    $= x\left(16x^2 - 56xy + 49y^2\right)$

    $= x\left[(4x)^2 - 2(4x)(7y) + (7y)^2\right]$

    $= x(4x - 7y)^2$

72. Let x = servings of scallops

    y = servings of milk

    $x + y = 4.5$

    $0.2x + 0.25y = 1$

    $0.2x + 0.25(4.5 - x) = 1$

    $0.2x + 1.125 - 0.25x = 1$

    $0.125 = 0.05x$

    $2.5 = x$

    $y = 4.5 - 2.5 = 2$

    2.5 servings of scallops (15 scallops) and

    2 servings of skim milk (2 cups)

7.4 Exercises

2. $\left(\sqrt{6}\right)\left(\sqrt{11}\right) = \sqrt{6 \cdot 11} = \sqrt{66}$

4. $\left(-4\sqrt{5}\right)\left(2\sqrt{10}\right) = -8\sqrt{5 \cdot 10}$

    $= -8\sqrt{5 \cdot 5 \cdot 2}$

    $= -40\sqrt{2}$

6. $\left(y\sqrt{3}\right)\left(5\sqrt{7}\right) = 5y\sqrt{3\cdot 7} = 5y\sqrt{21}$

8. $\left(3\sqrt{5x}\right)\left(\sqrt{xy}\right) = 3\sqrt{5x^2 y} = 3x\sqrt{5y}$

10. $\left(8\sqrt{5x^4 y}\right)\left(2\sqrt{3xy^3}\right) = 16\sqrt{15x^5 y^4}$
$= 16x^2 y^2 \sqrt{15x}$

12. $\sqrt{6}\left(2\sqrt{6} - 5\sqrt{2}\right) = 2\sqrt{6\cdot 6} - 5\sqrt{6\cdot 2}$
$= 12 - 5\sqrt{3\cdot 2\cdot 2}$
$= 12 - 10\sqrt{3}$

14. $5\sqrt{y}\left(\sqrt{2y} + 3\sqrt{5}\right) = 5\sqrt{2y^2} + 15\sqrt{5y}$
$= 5y\sqrt{2} + 15\sqrt{5y}$

16. $\left(5\sqrt{2} + \sqrt{10}\right)\left(\sqrt{2} - \sqrt{10}\right)$
$= 5(2) - 5\sqrt{20} + \sqrt{20} - 10$
$= 10 - 4\sqrt{20} - 10$
$= -8\sqrt{5}$

18. $\left(3\sqrt{3} + \sqrt{5}\right)\left(\sqrt{3} - 2\sqrt{5}\right)$
$= 3(3) - 6\sqrt{15} + \sqrt{15} - 2(5)$
$= 9 - 5\sqrt{15} - 10$
$= -1 - 5\sqrt{15}$

20. $\left(\sqrt{6} + 3\sqrt{3y}\right)\left(5\sqrt{6} + 2\sqrt{3y}\right)$
$= 5(6) + 2\sqrt{18y} + 15\sqrt{18y} + 6(3y)$
$= 30 + 17\sqrt{18y} + 18y$

22. $\left(3 - \sqrt{x}\right)\left(2 - \sqrt{x}\right) = 6 - 3\sqrt{x} - 2\sqrt{x} + x$
$= 6 - 5\sqrt{x} + x$

24. $\left(3\sqrt{5} + \sqrt{3}\right)\left(\sqrt{2} + 2\sqrt{5}\right)$
$= 3\sqrt{10} + 6(5) + \sqrt{6} + 2\sqrt{15}$
$= 3\sqrt{10} + 30 + \sqrt{6} + 2\sqrt{15}$

26. $\left(2\sqrt{x} + \sqrt{5x}\right)\left(2\sqrt{x} - \sqrt{5x}\right)$
$= 4(x) - 2\sqrt{5x^2} + 2\sqrt{5x^2} - 5x$
$= -x$

28. $\left(\sqrt{3} + 4\sqrt{7}\right)^2$
$= \left(\sqrt{3}\right)^2 + 2\sqrt{3}\left(4\sqrt{7}\right) + \left(4\sqrt{7}\right)^2$
$= 3 + 8\sqrt{21} + 16(7)$
$= 3 + 8\sqrt{21} + 112$
$= 115 + 8\sqrt{21}$

30. $\left(\sqrt{2x+1} - 2\right)^2$
$= \left(\sqrt{2x+1}\right)^2 - 2\left(\sqrt{2x+1}\right)(2) + 2^2$
$= 2x + 1 - 4\sqrt{2x+1} + 4$
$= 2x + 5 - 4\sqrt{2x+1}$

32. $\left(5\sqrt{a} + 4\sqrt{b}\right)^2$
$= \left(5\sqrt{a}\right)^2 + 2\left(5\sqrt{a}\right)\left(4\sqrt{b}\right) + \left(4\sqrt{b}\right)^2$
$= 25a + 40\sqrt{ab} + 16b$

34. $\left(\sqrt[4]{9y^3}\right)\left(2\sqrt[4]{27y^3}\right)$
$= 2\sqrt[4]{3^2 \cdot 3^3 y^6}$
$= 2\sqrt[4]{3^4 y^4 \cdot 3y^2}$
$= 2\cdot 3y\sqrt[4]{3y^2}$
$= 6y\sqrt[4]{3y^2}$

36. $\left(2\sqrt[3]{x}\right)\left(\sqrt[3]{4x^2} - \sqrt[3]{14x}\right)$
$= 2\sqrt[3]{4x^3} - 2\sqrt[3]{14x^2}$
$= 2x\sqrt[3]{4} - 2\sqrt[3]{14x^2}$

38. $\left(4\sqrt[3]{4x} - \sqrt[3]{2x^2}\right)\left(\sqrt[3]{x} + 2\sqrt[3]{2x}\right)$
$= 4\sqrt[3]{4x^2} + 8\sqrt[3]{8x^2} - \sqrt[3]{2x^3} - 2\sqrt[3]{4x^3}$
$= 4\sqrt[3]{4x^2} + 16\sqrt[3]{x^2} - x\sqrt[3]{2} - 2x\sqrt[3]{4}$

40. $\left(\sqrt[3]{9} - \sqrt[3]{4}\right)\left(3\sqrt[3]{3} + \sqrt[3]{36} + 2\sqrt[3]{2}\right)$
$= \left(\sqrt[3]{3^2} - \sqrt[3]{2^2}\right)\left[\left(\sqrt[3]{3^2}\right)^2 + \sqrt[3]{3^2}\sqrt[3]{2^2} + \left(\sqrt[3]{2^2}\right)^2\right]$
$= \left(\sqrt[3]{3^2}\right)^3 - \left(\sqrt[3]{2^2}\right)^3$
$= 3^2 - 2^2$
$= 5$
It is in the factored form of a difference of two cubes.

42. $\sqrt{\dfrac{16}{36}} = \dfrac{\sqrt{16}}{\sqrt{36}} = \dfrac{4}{6} = \dfrac{2}{3}$

44. $\sqrt[3]{\dfrac{216}{27}} = \dfrac{\sqrt[3]{216}}{\sqrt[3]{27}} = \dfrac{6}{3} = 2$

46. $\sqrt{\dfrac{9a^5}{64}} = \dfrac{\sqrt{9a^5}}{\sqrt{64}} = \dfrac{3a^2\sqrt{a}}{8}$

48. $\sqrt[3]{\dfrac{125a^3b^4}{64}} = \dfrac{\sqrt[3]{125a^3b^4}}{\sqrt[3]{64}} = \dfrac{5ab\sqrt[3]{b}}{4}$

50. $\dfrac{\sqrt{72a^5}}{\sqrt{2a}} = \sqrt{\dfrac{72a^5}{2a}} = \sqrt{36a^4} = 6a^2$

52. $\dfrac{\sqrt[3]{250a^4b^6}}{\sqrt[3]{2a}} = \sqrt[3]{\dfrac{250a^4b^6}{2a}} = \sqrt[3]{125a^3b^6} = 5ab^2$

54. $\dfrac{5}{\sqrt{7}} = \dfrac{5}{\sqrt{7}} \cdot \dfrac{\sqrt{7}}{\sqrt{7}} = \dfrac{5\sqrt{7}}{7}$

56. $\sqrt{\dfrac{y}{12}}$

$= \dfrac{\sqrt{y}}{\sqrt{12}}$

$= \dfrac{\sqrt{y}}{2\sqrt{3}}$

$= \dfrac{\sqrt{y}}{2\sqrt{3}} \cdot \dfrac{\sqrt{3}}{\sqrt{3}}$

$= \dfrac{\sqrt{3y}}{2(3)}$

$= \dfrac{\sqrt{3y}}{6}$

58. $\sqrt{\dfrac{9}{7}} = \dfrac{\sqrt{9}}{\sqrt{7}} \cdot \dfrac{\sqrt{7}}{\sqrt{7}} = \dfrac{3\sqrt{7}}{7}$

60. $\dfrac{\sqrt{3a}}{\sqrt{b}} = \dfrac{\sqrt{3a}}{\sqrt{b}} \cdot \dfrac{\sqrt{b}}{\sqrt{b}} = \dfrac{\sqrt{3ab}}{b}$

62. $\dfrac{1}{\sqrt{3x}} = \dfrac{1}{\sqrt{3x}} \cdot \dfrac{\sqrt{3x}}{\sqrt{3x}} = \dfrac{\sqrt{3x}}{3x}$

64. $\dfrac{5\sqrt{2}}{\sqrt{12y}} = \dfrac{5\sqrt{2}}{2\sqrt{3y}} = \dfrac{5\sqrt{2}}{2\sqrt{3y}} \cdot \dfrac{\sqrt{3y}}{\sqrt{3y}} = \dfrac{5\sqrt{6y}}{6y}$

66. $\sqrt{\dfrac{8x}{3y^2}} = \dfrac{\sqrt{8x}}{\sqrt{3y^2}}$

$= \dfrac{2\sqrt{2x}}{y\sqrt{3}}$

$= \dfrac{2\sqrt{2x}}{y\sqrt{3}} \cdot \dfrac{\sqrt{3}}{\sqrt{3}}$

$= \dfrac{2\sqrt{6x}}{3y}$

68. $\dfrac{5}{\sqrt{2}+\sqrt{7}}$

$= \dfrac{5}{\sqrt{2}+\sqrt{7}} \cdot \dfrac{\sqrt{2}-\sqrt{7}}{\sqrt{2}-\sqrt{7}}$

$= \dfrac{5\left(\sqrt{2}-\sqrt{7}\right)}{2-7}$

$= \dfrac{5\left(\sqrt{2}-\sqrt{7}\right)}{-5}$

$= -\left(\sqrt{2}-\sqrt{7}\right)$

$= -\sqrt{2}+\sqrt{7}$

70. $\dfrac{\sqrt{7}}{\sqrt{7}-1} = \dfrac{\sqrt{7}}{\sqrt{7}-1} \cdot \dfrac{\sqrt{7}+1}{\sqrt{7}+1} = \dfrac{7+\sqrt{7}}{7-1} = \dfrac{7+\sqrt{7}}{6}$

72. $\dfrac{\sqrt{x}}{\sqrt{5}+\sqrt{2x}} = \dfrac{\sqrt{x}}{\sqrt{5}+\sqrt{2x}} \cdot \dfrac{\sqrt{5}-\sqrt{2x}}{\sqrt{5}-\sqrt{2x}}$

$= \dfrac{\sqrt{5x}-\sqrt{2x^2}}{5-2x}$

$= \dfrac{\sqrt{5x}-x\sqrt{2}}{5-2x}$

74. $\dfrac{\sqrt{11}-\sqrt{5}}{\sqrt{11}+\sqrt{5}} = \dfrac{\sqrt{11}-\sqrt{5}}{\sqrt{11}+\sqrt{5}} \cdot \dfrac{\sqrt{11}-\sqrt{5}}{\sqrt{11}-\sqrt{5}}$

$= \dfrac{11-\sqrt{55}-\sqrt{55}+5}{11-5}$

$= \dfrac{16-2\sqrt{55}}{6}$

$= \dfrac{2\left(8-\sqrt{55}\right)}{6}$

$= \dfrac{8-\sqrt{55}}{3}$

76. $\dfrac{\sqrt{x}+\sqrt{y}}{\sqrt{x}-2\sqrt{y}}$

$= \dfrac{\sqrt{x}+\sqrt{y}}{\sqrt{x}-2\sqrt{y}} \cdot \dfrac{\sqrt{x}+2\sqrt{y}}{\sqrt{x}+2\sqrt{y}}$

$= \dfrac{x+2\sqrt{xy}+\sqrt{xy}+2y}{x-4y}$

$= \dfrac{x+3\sqrt{xy}+2y}{x-4y}$

78. $\dfrac{2\sqrt{6}+\sqrt{5}}{3\sqrt{6}-\sqrt{5}}$

$= \dfrac{2\sqrt{6}+\sqrt{5}}{3\sqrt{6}-\sqrt{5}} \cdot \dfrac{3\sqrt{6}+\sqrt{5}}{3\sqrt{6}+\sqrt{5}}$

$= \dfrac{6(6)+2\sqrt{30}+3\sqrt{30}+5}{9(6)-5}$

$= \dfrac{36+5\sqrt{30}+5}{54-5}$

$= \dfrac{41+5\sqrt{30}}{49}$

80. $\dfrac{y\sqrt{2}-1}{2\sqrt{2}+1} = \dfrac{y\sqrt{2}-1}{2\sqrt{2}+1} \cdot \dfrac{2\sqrt{2}-1}{2\sqrt{2}-1}$

$= \dfrac{2y(2)-y\sqrt{2}-2\sqrt{2}+1}{4(2)-1}$

$= \dfrac{4y-y\sqrt{2}-2\sqrt{2}+1}{8-1}$

$= \dfrac{4y-y\sqrt{2}-2\sqrt{2}+1}{7}$

82. $\dfrac{3}{7-\sqrt{2}} = \dfrac{3}{7-\sqrt{2}} \cdot \dfrac{7+\sqrt{2}}{7+\sqrt{2}}$

$= \dfrac{3(7+\sqrt{2})}{49-2}$

$= \dfrac{21+3\sqrt{2}}{47}$

84. $\dfrac{6}{\sqrt[4]{8x}} = \dfrac{6}{\sqrt[4]{2^3 x}} \cdot \dfrac{\sqrt[4]{2x^3}}{\sqrt[4]{2x^3}}$

$= \dfrac{6\sqrt[4]{2x^3}}{2x}$

$= \dfrac{3\sqrt[4]{2x^3}}{x}$

86. $\dfrac{\sqrt[3]{6y^4}}{\sqrt[3]{4x^5}} = \dfrac{y\sqrt[3]{6y}}{\sqrt[3]{2^2 x^5}} \cdot \dfrac{\sqrt[3]{2x}}{\sqrt[3]{2x}}$

$= \dfrac{y\sqrt[3]{12xy}}{\sqrt[3]{2^3 x^6}}$

$= \dfrac{y\sqrt[3]{12xy}}{2x^2}$

88. $\dfrac{3xy^2}{\sqrt[5]{8xy^3}} = \dfrac{3xy^2}{\sqrt[5]{2^3 xy^3}} \cdot \dfrac{\sqrt[5]{2^2 x^4 y^2}}{\sqrt[5]{2^2 x^4 y^2}}$

$= \dfrac{3xy^2 \sqrt[5]{4x^4 y^2}}{2xy}$

$= \dfrac{3y\sqrt[5]{4x^4 y^2}}{2}$

90. $\dfrac{\sqrt{5}}{\sqrt{5}+\sqrt{3}} \approx 0.5635083269$

$\dfrac{5-\sqrt{15}}{2} \approx 0.563508327$

Yes

92. $\dfrac{\sqrt{6}}{10} = \dfrac{\sqrt{6}}{10} \cdot \dfrac{\sqrt{6}}{\sqrt{6}}$

$= \dfrac{6}{10\sqrt{6}}$

$= \dfrac{3}{5\sqrt{6}}$

94. $\dfrac{\sqrt{5}-4\sqrt{3}}{6} = \dfrac{\sqrt{5}-4\sqrt{3}}{6} \cdot \dfrac{\sqrt{5}+4\sqrt{3}}{\sqrt{5}+4\sqrt{3}}$

$= \dfrac{5-16(3)}{6(\sqrt{5}+4\sqrt{3})}$

$= \dfrac{-43}{6(\sqrt{5}+4\sqrt{3})}$

96. $A = \dfrac{1}{2}bh$

$= \dfrac{1}{2}\sqrt{17}\sqrt{40}$

$= \dfrac{1}{2}\sqrt{17}(2\sqrt{10})$

$= \sqrt{170}$

Cost $= (\sqrt{170})(0.18) \approx 2.35$

$2.35

Cumulative Review Problems

98. $3x - y - z = 5$ (1)
  $2x + 3y - z = -16$ (2)
  $x + 2y + 2z = -3$ (3)
  Add 2 times (1) and (3)
  $6x - 2y - 2z = 10$
  $\underline{x + 2y + 2z = -3}$
  $7x = 7$
  $x = 1$
  Add 2 times (2) and (3)
  $4x + 6y - 2z = -32$
  $\underline{x + 2y + 2z = -3}$
  $5x + 8y = -35$ (4)
  Substitute 1 for x in (4).
  $5(1) + 8y = -35$
  $8y = -40$
  $y = -5$
  Substitute 1 for x and -5 for y in (3)
  $1 + 2(-5) + 2z = -3$
  $2z = 6$
  $z = 3$
  $x = 1, y = -5, z = 3$

100. Let x = cups of coffee
  y = cups of tea
  $x + y = 11$
  $200x + 80y = 1480$
  $x = 5, y = 6$
  5 cups of coffee and 6 cups of tea
  2nd: $1480 \div 2 = 740$
  6th: $740 \div 2 = 370$
  10th: $370 \div 2 = 185$
  14th: $185 \div 2 = 92.5$
  18th: $92.5 \div 2 = 46.25$
  22nd: $46.25 \div 2 = 23.125$
  On January 22nd he will reach his goal.

7.5 Exercises

2. There is a possibility of extraneous roots; that is, a solution to the equation that, when substituted into the original problem, does not make the original statement true.

4. $\sqrt{x - 4} = 6$
  $\left(\sqrt{x-4}\right)^2 = 6^2$
  $x - 4 = 36$
  $x = 40$
  Check:
  $\sqrt{40 - 4} \stackrel{?}{=} 6$
  $\sqrt{36} \stackrel{?}{=} 6$
  $6 = 6$
  Solution: $x = 40$

6. $\sqrt{2x + 5} = 5$
  $\left(\sqrt{2x+5}\right)^2 = 5^2$
  $2x + 5 = 25$
  $2x = 20$
  $x = 10$
  Check:
  $\sqrt{2(10) + 5} \stackrel{?}{=} 5$
  $\sqrt{25} \stackrel{?}{=} 5$
  $5 = 5$
  Solution: $x = 10$

8. $\sqrt{7x + 8} = x$
  $\left(\sqrt{7x+8}\right)^2 = x^2$
  $7x + 8 = x^2$
  $0 = x^2 - 7x - 8$
  $0 = (x - 8)(x + 1)$
  $x - 8 = 0$ or $x + 1 = 0$
  $x = 8$ $x = -1$
  Check:
  $x = 8$
  $\sqrt{7(8) + 8} \stackrel{?}{=} 8$
  $\sqrt{64} \stackrel{?}{=} 8$
  $8 = 8$
  $x = -1$
  Check:
  $x = -1$
  $\sqrt{7(-1) + 8} \stackrel{?}{=} -1$
  $\sqrt{1} \stackrel{?}{=} -1$
  $1 \neq -1$ Extraneous
  Solution: $x = 8$

10. $\sqrt{2x + 1} = x - 7$
  $\left(\sqrt{2x+1}\right)^2 = (x - 7)^2$
  $2x + 1 = x^2 - 14x + 49$
  $0 = x^2 - 16x + 48$

$0 = (x-4)(x-12)$

$x-4 = 0$ or $x-12 = 0$

$x = 4$ $x = 12$

Check:

$x = 4$

$\sqrt{2(4)+1} \stackrel{?}{=} 4-7$

$\sqrt{9} \stackrel{?}{=} -3$

$3 \neq -3$ Extraneous

Check:

$x = 12$

$\sqrt{2(12)+1} \stackrel{?}{=} 12-7$

$\sqrt{25} \stackrel{?}{=} 5$

$5 = 5$

Solution: $x = 12$

12. $\sqrt{2y-4}+2 = y$

$\sqrt{2y-4} = y-2$

$\left(\sqrt{2y-4}\right)^2 = (y-2)^2$

$2y-4 = y^2 - 4y + 4$

$0 = y^2 - 6y + 8$

$0 = (y-4)(y-2)$

$y-4 = 0$ or $y-2 = 0$

$y = 4$ $y = 2$

Check:

$y = 4$

$\sqrt{2(4)-4}+2 \stackrel{?}{=} 4$

$\sqrt{4}+2 \stackrel{?}{=} 4$

$2+2 \stackrel{?}{=} 4$

$4 = 4$

Check: $y = 2$

$\sqrt{2(2)-4}+2 \stackrel{?}{=} 2$

$\sqrt{0}+2 \stackrel{?}{=} 2$

$2 = 2$

Solutions: $y = 2,\, y = 4$

14. $5+\sqrt{2y+5} = y$

$\sqrt{2y+5} = y-5$

$\left(\sqrt{2y+5}\right)^2 = (y-5)^2$

$2y+5 = y^2 - 10y + 25$

$0 = y^2 - 12y + 20$

$0 = (y-10)(y-2)$

$y-10 = 0$ or $y-2 = 0$

$y = 10$ $y = 2$

Check:

$y = 10$

$5+\sqrt{2(10)+5} \stackrel{?}{=} 10$

$5+\sqrt{25} \stackrel{?}{=} 10$

$5+5 \stackrel{?}{=} 10$

$10 = 10$

Check: $y = 2$

$5+\sqrt{2(2)+5} \stackrel{?}{=} 2$

$5+\sqrt{9} \stackrel{?}{=} 2$

$5+3 \stackrel{?}{=} 2$

$8 \neq 2$ Extraneous

Solution: $y = 10$

16. $2\sqrt{4x+1}+5 = x+9$

$2\sqrt{4x+1} = x+4$

$\left(2\sqrt{4x+1}\right)^2 = (x+4)^2$

$4(4x+1) = x^2 + 8x + 16$

$0 = x^2 - 8x + 12$

$0 = (x-6)(x-2)$

$x-6 = 0$ or $x-2 = 0$

$x = 6$ $x = 2$

Check:

$x = 6$

$2\sqrt{4 \cdot 6 + 1}+5 \stackrel{?}{=} 6+9$

$2\sqrt{25}+5 \stackrel{?}{=} 15$

$10+5 \stackrel{?}{=} 15$

$15 = 15$

Check:

$x = 2$

$2\sqrt{4 \cdot 2 + 1}+5 \stackrel{?}{=} 2+9$

$2 \cdot 3 + 5 \stackrel{?}{=} 11$

$11 = 11$

Solutions: $x = 6,\, x = 2$

18. $\sqrt{x^2+36} = 10$

$\left(\sqrt{x^2+36}\right)^2 = 10^2$

$x^2 + 36 = 100$

$x^2 = 64$

$x = \pm 8$

Check:

$x = 8$

$\sqrt{8^2+36} \stackrel{?}{=} 10$

$\sqrt{100} \stackrel{?}{=} 10$

$10 = 10$

Check:

$x = -8$

$\sqrt{(-8)^2 + 36} \stackrel{?}{=} 10$

$\sqrt{100} \stackrel{?}{=} 10$

$10 = 10$

Solutions: $x = \pm 8$

20. $\sqrt[3]{3x - 6} = 3$

$\left(\sqrt[3]{3x - 6}\right)^3 = 3^3$

$3x - 6 = 27$

$3x = 33$

$x = 11$

Check:

$\sqrt[3]{3(11) - 6} \stackrel{?}{=} 3$

$\sqrt[3]{27} \stackrel{?}{=} 3$

$3 = 3$

Solution: $x = 11$

22. $\sqrt[3]{x^2 + 17x} = 3\sqrt[3]{x}$

$\left(\sqrt[3]{x^2 + 17x}\right)^3 = \left(3\sqrt[3]{x}\right)^3$

$x^2 + 17x = 27x$

$x^2 - 10x = 0$

$x(x - 10) = 0$

$x = 0$ or $x = 10$

Check:

$x = 0$

$\sqrt[3]{0^2 + 17(0)} \stackrel{?}{=} 3\sqrt[3]{0}$

$0 = 0$

Check:

$x = 10$

$\sqrt[3]{10^2 + 17 \cdot 10} \stackrel{?}{=} 3\sqrt[3]{10}$

$\sqrt[3]{270} \stackrel{?}{=} 3\sqrt[3]{10}$

$3\sqrt[3]{10} = 3\sqrt[3]{10}$

Solutions: $x = 0$, $x = 10$

24. $\sqrt[3]{4x - 3} - 5 = 0$

$\sqrt[3]{4x - 3} = 5$

$\left(\sqrt[3]{4x - 3}\right)^3 = 5^3$

$4x - 3 = 125$

$4x = 128$

$x = 32$

Check:

$\sqrt[3]{4(32) - 3} - 5 \stackrel{?}{=} 0$

$\sqrt[3]{125} - 5 \stackrel{?}{=} 0$

$5 - 5 \stackrel{?}{=} 0$

$0 = 0$

Solution: $x = 32$

26. $\sqrt{5x + 1} = 1 + \sqrt{3x}$

$\left(\sqrt{5x + 1}\right)^2 = \left(1 + \sqrt{3x}\right)^2$

$5x + 1 = 1 + 2\sqrt{3x} + 3x$

$2x = 2\sqrt{3x}$

$x = \sqrt{3x}$

$x^2 = \left(\sqrt{3x}\right)^2$

$x^2 = 3x$

$x^2 - 3x = 0$

$x(x - 3) = 0$

$x = 0$ or $x - 3 = 0$

                            $x = 3$

Check:

$x = 0$

$\sqrt{5(0) + 1} \stackrel{?}{=} 1 + \sqrt{3(0)}$

$\sqrt{1} \stackrel{?}{=} 1 + \sqrt{0}$

$1 = 1$

Check:

$x = 3$

$\sqrt{5(3) + 1} \stackrel{?}{=} 1 + \sqrt{3(3)}$

$\sqrt{16} \stackrel{?}{=} 1 + \sqrt{9}$

$4 \stackrel{?}{=} 1 + 3$

$4 = 4$

Solutions: $x = 0$, $x = 3$

28. $\sqrt{x - 1} = 4\sqrt{x + 1}$

$\left(\sqrt{x - 1}\right)^2 = \left(4\sqrt{x + 1}\right)^2$

$x - 1 = 16(x + 1)$

$x - 1 = 16x + 16$

$-17 = 15x$

$x = -\dfrac{17}{15}$

Check:

$\sqrt{-\dfrac{17}{15} - 1} \stackrel{?}{=} 4\sqrt{-\dfrac{17}{15} + 1}$

Not a real number.

No solution

30. $\sqrt{3x+1} - \sqrt{x-4} = 3$

$\sqrt{3x+1} = 3 + \sqrt{x-4}$

$\left(\sqrt{3x+1}\right)^2 = \left(3 + \sqrt{x-4}\right)^2$

$3x+1 = 9 + 6\sqrt{x-4} + x - 4$

$3x+1 = x + 5 + 6\sqrt{x-4}$

$2x-4 = 6\sqrt{x-4}$

$x-2 = 3\sqrt{x-4}$

$(x-2)^2 = \left(3\sqrt{x-4}\right)^2$

$x^2 - 4x + 4 = 9(x-4)$

$x^2 - 4x + 4 = 9x - 36$

$x^2 - 13x + 40 = 0$

$(x-8)(x-5) = 0$

$x-8 = 0 \quad$ or $\quad x-5 = 0$

$x = 8 \qquad\qquad x = 5$

Check:

$x = 8$

$\sqrt{3(8)+1} - \sqrt{8-4} \stackrel{?}{=} 3$

$\sqrt{25} - \sqrt{4} \stackrel{?}{=} 3$

$5 - 2 \stackrel{?}{=} 3$

$3 = 3$

Check:

$x = 5$

$\sqrt{3(5)+1} - \sqrt{5-4} \stackrel{?}{=} 3$

$\sqrt{16} - \sqrt{1} \stackrel{?}{=} 3$

$4 - 1 \stackrel{?}{=} 3$

$3 = 3$

Solutions: $x = 8, x = 5$

32. $\sqrt{3x+3} + \sqrt{x-1} = 4$

$\sqrt{3x+3} = 4 - \sqrt{x-1}$

$\left(\sqrt{3x+3}\right)^2 = \left(4 - \sqrt{x-1}\right)^2$

$3x+3 = 16 - 8\sqrt{x-1} + x - 1$

$3x+3 = 15 - 8\sqrt{x-1} + x$

$2x-12 = -8\sqrt{x-1}$

$x-6 = -4\sqrt{x-1}$

$(x-6)^2 = \left(-4\sqrt{x-1}\right)^2$

$x^2 - 12x + 36 = 16(x-1)$

$x^2 - 12x + 36 = 16x - 16$

$x^2 - 28x + 52 = 0$

$(x-26)(x-2) = 0$

$x-26 = 0 \quad$ or $\quad x-2 = 0$

$x = 26 \qquad\qquad x = 2$

Check:

$x = 26$

$\sqrt{3(26)+3} + \sqrt{26-1} \stackrel{?}{=} 4$

$\sqrt{81} + \sqrt{25} \stackrel{?}{=} 4$

$9 + 5 \stackrel{?}{=} 4$

$14 \neq 4$ Extraneous

Check:

$x = 2$

$\sqrt{3(2)+3} + \sqrt{2-1} \stackrel{?}{=} 4$

$\sqrt{9} + \sqrt{1} \stackrel{?}{=} 4$

$3 + 1 \stackrel{?}{=} 4$

$4 = 4$

Solution: $x = 2$

34. $\sqrt{4x+6} = \sqrt{x+1} - \sqrt{x+5}$

$\left(\sqrt{4x+6}\right)^2 = \left(\sqrt{x+1} - \sqrt{x+5}\right)^2$

$4x+6 = x+1 - 2\sqrt{x+1}\sqrt{x+5} + x + 5$

$2x = -2\sqrt{(x+1)(x+5)}$

$(2x)^2 = \left(-2\sqrt{(x+1)(x+5)}\right)^2$

$4x^2 = 4(x+1)(x+5)$

$4x^2 = 4x^2 + 24x + 20$

$x^2 = x^2 + 6x + 5$

$6x + 5 = 0$

$x = -\dfrac{5}{6}$

Check:

$\sqrt{4\left(-\dfrac{5}{6}\right)+6} \stackrel{?}{=} \sqrt{-\dfrac{5}{6}+1} - \sqrt{-\dfrac{5}{6}+5}$

$\sqrt{-\dfrac{20}{6}+\dfrac{36}{6}} \stackrel{?}{=} \sqrt{\dfrac{1}{6}} - \sqrt{\dfrac{25}{6}}$

$\dfrac{4}{\sqrt{6}} \neq -\dfrac{4}{\sqrt{6}}$ Extraneous

No solution

36. $\sqrt{2x+6} = \sqrt{7-2x} + 1$

$\left(\sqrt{2x+6}\right)^2 = \left(\sqrt{7-2x} + 1\right)^2$

$2x+6 = 7 - 2x + 2\sqrt{7-2x} + 1$

$2x+6 = 8 - 2x + 2\sqrt{7-2x}$

$4x-2 = 2\sqrt{7-2x}$

$2x-1 = \sqrt{7-2x}$

$(2x-1)^2 = \left(\sqrt{7-2x}\right)^2$

$4x^2 - 4x + 1 = 7 - 2x$

$4x^2 - 2x - 6 = 0$

$2x^2 - x - 3 = 0$

$(2x - 3)(x + 1) = 0$

$2x - 3 = 0$ or $x + 1 = 0$

$2x = 3$ $x = -1$

$x = \dfrac{3}{2}$

Check:

$x = \dfrac{3}{2}$

$\sqrt{2\left(\dfrac{3}{2}\right) + 6} \overset{?}{=} \sqrt{7 - 2\left(\dfrac{3}{2}\right)} + 1$

$\sqrt{9} \overset{?}{=} \sqrt{4} + 1$

$3 \overset{?}{=} 2 + 1$

$3 = 3$

Check:

$x = -1$

$\sqrt{2(-1) + 6} \overset{?}{=} \sqrt{7 - 2(-1)} + 1$

$\sqrt{4} \overset{?}{=} \sqrt{9} + 1$

$2 \overset{?}{=} 3 + 1$

$2 \neq 4$ Extraneous

Solution: $x = \dfrac{3}{2}$

38. $\sqrt{x + \sqrt{x + 2}} = 2$

$\left(\sqrt{x + \sqrt{x + 2}}\right)^2 = 2^2$

$x + \sqrt{x + 2} = 4$

$\sqrt{x + 2} = 4 - x$

$\left(\sqrt{x + 2}\right)^2 = (4 - x)^2$

$x + 2 = 16 - 8x + x^2$

$0 = x^2 - 9x + 14$

$0 = (x - 7)(x - 2)$

$x - 7 = 0$ or $x - 2 = 0$

$x = 7$ $x = 2$

Check:

$x = 7$

$\sqrt{7 + \sqrt{7 + 2}} \overset{?}{=} 2$

$\sqrt{7 + \sqrt{9}} \overset{?}{=} 2$

$\sqrt{10} \neq 2$ Extraneous

Check:

$x = 2$

$\sqrt{2 + \sqrt{2 + 2}} \overset{?}{=} 2$

$\sqrt{2 + \sqrt{4}} \overset{?}{=} 2$

$\sqrt{4} \overset{?}{=} 2$

$2 = 2$

Solution: $x = 2$

40. $\sqrt{3 + \sqrt{y}} = 1 + \sqrt{y}$

$\left(\sqrt{3 + \sqrt{y}}\right)^2 = \left(1 + \sqrt{y}\right)^2$

$3 + \sqrt{y} = 1 + 2\sqrt{y} + y$

$2 - y = \sqrt{y}$

$(2 - y)^2 = \left(\sqrt{y}\right)^2$

$4 - 4y + y^2 = y$

$y^2 - 5y + 4 = 0$

$(y - 4)(y - 1) = 0$

$y = 4$ or $y = 1$

Check:

$y = 4$

$\sqrt{3 + \sqrt{4}} \overset{?}{=} 1 + \sqrt{4}$

$\sqrt{5} \neq 3$ Extraneous

Check:

$y = 1$

$\sqrt{3 + \sqrt{1}} \overset{?}{=} 1 + \sqrt{1}$

$2 = 2$

Solution: $y = 1$

42. $\sqrt[4]{2x^2 + 3x - 8} = -1$

$\left(\sqrt[4]{2x^2 + 3x - 8}\right)^4 = (-1)^4$

$2x^2 + 3x - 8 = 1$

$2x^2 + 3x - 9 = 0$

$(2x - 3)(x + 3) = 0$

$2x - 3 = 0$ or $x + 3 = 0$

$2x = 3$ $x = -3$

$x = \dfrac{3}{2}$

Check:

$$x = \frac{3}{2}$$

$$\sqrt[4]{2\left(\frac{3}{2}\right)^2 + 3\left(\frac{3}{2}\right) - 8} \overset{?}{=} -1$$

$$\sqrt[4]{1} \overset{?}{=} -1$$

$1 \neq -1$ Extraneous

Check:

$$x = -3$$

$$\sqrt[4]{2(-3)^2 + 3(-3) - 8} \overset{?}{=} -1$$

$$\sqrt[4]{1} \overset{?}{=} -1$$

$1 \neq -1$ Extraneous

No solution

Or, note that a 4th root can never be negative, thus there is no solution.

44. $\sqrt[3]{5.62x + 9.93} = 1.47$

$$\left(\sqrt[3]{5.62x + 9.93}\right)^3 = (1.47)^3$$

$$5.62x + 9.93 = 3.176523$$

$$5.62x = -6.753477$$

$$x = -1.2017$$

46. $D = \sqrt{\dfrac{3H}{2}}$

(a) $D^2 = \left(\sqrt{\dfrac{3H}{2}}\right)^2$

$$D^2 = \frac{3H}{2}$$

$$2D^2 = 3H$$

$$\frac{2D^2}{3} = H$$

(b) $H = \dfrac{2(5)^2}{3} = \dfrac{50}{3}$

$$= 16\frac{2}{3} \text{ feet}$$

48. $\sqrt{x+b} - \sqrt{x} = -2$

$$\sqrt{16+b} - \sqrt{16} = -2$$

$$\sqrt{16+b} - 4 = -2$$

$$\sqrt{16+b} = 2$$

$$\left(\sqrt{16+b}\right)^2 = 2^2$$

$$16 + b = 4$$

$$b = -12$$

Cumulative Review Problems

50. $(2^{-3}x^{-6})^{1/3} = (2^{-3})^{1/3}(x^{-6})^{1/3}$

$$= 2^{-1}x^{-2}$$

$$= \frac{1}{2x^2}$$

52. $\sqrt[4]{64x^{12}y^{16}} = \sqrt[4]{16x^{12}y^{16} \cdot 4} = 2x^3y^4\sqrt[4]{4}$

54. $d = rt$

Let r be the rate of the lift.

$$\frac{1.75}{r} + \frac{2.5}{5r} = 0.75$$

$$5r\left(\frac{1.75}{r} + \frac{2.5}{5r}\right) = 5r(0.75)$$

$$8.75 + 2.5 = 3.75r$$

$$\frac{11.25}{3.75} = r$$

$$3 = r$$

$$15 = 5r$$

The ski lift travels at 3 miles per hour, and she skis at 15 miles per hour.

7.6 Exercises

2. A complex number is a number that can be written in the form $a + bi$, where a and b are real numbers. Example: $2 + 3i$

4. Add or subtract the real number parts. Add or subtract the imaginary number parts.

6. $\sqrt{-100} = \sqrt{100}\sqrt{-1} = 10i$

8. $\sqrt{-30} = \sqrt{-1}\sqrt{30} = i\sqrt{30}$

10. $\sqrt{-48} = \sqrt{16}\sqrt{-1}\sqrt{3} = 4i\sqrt{3}$

12. $\sqrt{-52} = \sqrt{4}\sqrt{-1}\sqrt{13} = 2i\sqrt{13}$

14. $-\sqrt{-36} = -\sqrt{36}\sqrt{-1} = -6i$

16. $5 + \sqrt{-7} = 5 + \sqrt{-1}\sqrt{7}$

$$= 5 + i\sqrt{7}$$

18. $-6 - \sqrt{-32} = -6 - \sqrt{16}\sqrt{-1}\sqrt{2}$

$$= -6 - 4i\sqrt{2}$$

20. $\sqrt{-25} + \sqrt{-4} = \sqrt{25}\sqrt{-1} + \sqrt{4}\sqrt{-1}$
$= 5i + 2i = 7i$

22. $x - 6i = 7 + yi$
$x = 7$
$y = -6$

24. $x - 5i\sqrt{2} = 3 + yi$
$x = 3$
$y = -5\sqrt{2}$

26. $2 + x - 11i = 19 + yi$
$2 + x = 19$
$x = 17$
$y = -11$

28. $7 - 4i + x + 4yi = -3 + 7i$
$(7 + x) + (-4 + 4y)i = -3 + 7i$
$7 + x = -3$
$x = -10$
$-4 + 4y = 7$
$4y = 11$
$y = \dfrac{11}{4}$

30. $(-3 + 5i) + (23 - 7i) = (-3 + 23) + (5 - 7)i$
$= 20 - 2i$

32. $\left(\dfrac{3}{4} - \dfrac{3}{4}i\right) + \left(\dfrac{9}{4} + \dfrac{5}{4}i\right) = \left(\dfrac{3}{4} + \dfrac{9}{4}\right) + \left(-\dfrac{3}{4} + \dfrac{5}{4}\right)i$
$= \dfrac{12}{4} + \dfrac{2}{4}i$
$= 3 + \dfrac{1}{2}i$

34. $(20 + 5i) - (6 - 3i) = 20 + 5i - 6 + 3i$
$= (20 - 6) + (5 + 3)i$
$= 14 + 8i$

36. $(-2.1 + 1.3i) - (-1.8 + 3.5i)$
$= -2.1 + 1.3i + 1.8 - 3.5i$
$= (-2.1 + 1.8) + (1.3 - 3.5)i$
$= -0.3 - 2.2i$

38. $(4 - 6i)(2 + i) = 8 + 4i - 12i - 6i^2$
$= 8 - 8i - 6(-1)$
$= 14 - 8i$

40. $\left(3 + \dfrac{3}{2}i\right)\left(\dfrac{8}{3} - 4i\right) = 8 - 12i + 4i - 6i^2$
$= 8 - 8i - 6(-1)$
$= 14 - 8i$

42. $6 - 5(7 - 6i) = 6 - 35 + 30i$
$= -29 + 30i$

44. $4i(7 - 2i) = 28i - 8i^2$
$= 28i - 8(-1)$
$= 8 + 28i$

46. $(5 - 4i)^2 = 5^2 - 2(5)(4i) + (4i)^2$
$= 25 - 40i + 16i^2$
$= 25 - 40i + 16(-1)$
$= 9 - 40i$

48. $(8 + 2i)^2 = 8^2 + 2(8)(2i) + (2i)^2$
$= 64 + 32i + 4i^2$
$= 64 + 32i + 4(-1)$
$= 60 + 32i$

50. $\left(i\sqrt{2}\right)\left(i\sqrt{6}\right) = i^2\sqrt{12} = -2\sqrt{3}$

52. $\left(\sqrt{-5}\right)\left(\sqrt{-3}\right) = \left(i\sqrt{5}\right)\left(i\sqrt{3}\right)$
$= i^2\sqrt{15}$
$= -\sqrt{15}$

54. $\left(\sqrt{-25}\right)\left(\sqrt{-9}\right) = (5i)(3i)$
$= 15i^2$
$= 15(-1) = -15$

56. $4i\left(5 + \sqrt{-2}\right) = 4i\left(5 + i\sqrt{2}\right)$
$= 20i + 4i^2\sqrt{2}$
$= 20i + 4(-1)\left(\sqrt{2}\right)$
$= -4\sqrt{2} + 20i$

58. $\left(3 + \sqrt{-2}\right)\left(4 + \sqrt{-5}\right)$
$= \left(3 + i\sqrt{2}\right)\left(4 + i\sqrt{5}\right)$
$= 12 + 3i\sqrt{5} + 4i\sqrt{2} + i^2\sqrt{10}$
$= 12 + 3i\sqrt{5} + 4i\sqrt{2} - \sqrt{10}$
$= 12 - \sqrt{10} + 3i\sqrt{5} + 4i\sqrt{2}$

60. $\left(7-\sqrt{-3}\right)\left(2+\sqrt{-1}\right) = \left(7-i\sqrt{3}\right)(2+i)$

$= 14 + 7i - 2i\sqrt{3} - i^2\sqrt{3}$

$= 14 + 7i - 2i\sqrt{3} - \left(-\sqrt{3}\right)$

$= 14 + \sqrt{3} + 7i - 2i\sqrt{3}$

62. $i^{21} = (i^4)^5 \cdot i = 1^5 \cdot i = i$

64. $i^{16} = (i^4)^4 = 1^4 = 1$

66. $i^{83} = (i^4)^{20} \cdot i^3 = 1^{20} \cdot (-i) = -i$

68. $i^{26} + i^{24} = (i^4)^6 \cdot i^2 + (i^4)^6$

$= 1^6(-1) + 1^6$

$= -1 + 1 = 0$

70. $\dfrac{4+2i}{2-i} = \dfrac{4+2i}{2-i} \cdot \dfrac{2+i}{2+i}$

$= \dfrac{8 + 4i + 4i + 2i^2}{4 - i^2}$

$= \dfrac{8 + 8i + 2(-1)}{4 - (-1)}$

$= \dfrac{6 + 8i}{5}$

72. $\dfrac{-2i}{3+5i} = \dfrac{-2i}{3+5i} \cdot \dfrac{3-5i}{3-5i}$

$= \dfrac{-6i + 10i^2}{9 + 25}$

$= \dfrac{-10 - 6i}{34} = \dfrac{-5 - 3i}{17}$

74. $\dfrac{5+2i}{4i} = \dfrac{5+2i}{4i} \cdot \dfrac{i}{i} = \dfrac{5i + 2i^2}{4i^2}$

$= \dfrac{5i + 2(-1)}{4(-1)}$

$= \dfrac{-2 + 5i}{-4}$

76. $\dfrac{3}{4+2i} = \dfrac{3}{4+2i} \cdot \dfrac{4-2i}{4-2i}$

$= \dfrac{12 - 6i}{16 - 4i^2}$

$= \dfrac{12 - 6i}{16 - 4(-1)}$

$= \dfrac{12 - 6i}{20}$

$= \dfrac{6 - 3i}{10}$

78. $(0.34 - 0.72i)(1.93 - 2.52i)$

$= 0.6562 - 0.8568i - 1.3896i + 1.8144i^2$

$= -1.1582 - 2.2464i$

80. $\dfrac{361 + \sqrt{-256}}{422 - \sqrt{-315}} = \dfrac{361 + 16i}{422 - i\sqrt{315}}$

$= 0.852347985 + 0.0737622655i$

82. $Z = \dfrac{V}{I}$

$= \dfrac{4 + 2i}{-3i}$

$= \dfrac{4 + 2i}{-3i} \cdot \dfrac{i}{i}$

$= \dfrac{4i + 2i^2}{-3i^2}$

$= \dfrac{4i + 2(-1)}{-3(-1)}$

$= \dfrac{4i - 2}{3}$

7.7 Exercises

2. directly; constant

4. $s = kwd^2$

6. $y = kx$

$30 = k(2)$

$15 = k$

$y = 15x = 15(5) = 75$

8. $y = kx^3$

$32 = k(4)^3$

$\dfrac{1}{2} = k$

$y = \dfrac{1}{2}x^3 = \dfrac{1}{2}(7)^3 = \dfrac{343}{2} = 171.5$

10. $d = ks^2$

$40 = k(30)^2$

$\dfrac{2}{45} = k$

$d = \dfrac{2}{45}s^2 = \dfrac{2}{45}(60)^2 = 160$

It will take 160 feet to stop.

12. $T = ks^3$

$7 = k(2)^3$

$\dfrac{7}{8} = k$

$T = \left(\dfrac{7}{8}\right)(3.5)^3$

$= \left(\dfrac{7}{8}\right)(42.875)$

$= 37.515625$

The tank will be filled in approximately 37.5 minutes.

14. $y = \dfrac{k}{x}$

$20 = \dfrac{k}{25}$

$500 = k$

$y = \dfrac{500}{x} = \dfrac{500}{16} \approx 31.3$

16. $y = \dfrac{k}{x^3}, \quad y = 20, \quad x = 4$

$20 = \dfrac{k}{(4)^3} = \dfrac{k}{64}$

$k = 1280$

$y = \dfrac{1280}{x^3} = \dfrac{1280}{3^3} = \dfrac{1280}{27}$

≈ 47.4

18. $w = \dfrac{k}{d^2}$

$1000 = \dfrac{k}{4000^2}$

$16,000,000,000 = k$

$w = \dfrac{16,000,000,000}{d^2}$

$= \dfrac{16,000,000,000}{4500^2} \approx 790.1$

It will weigh 790.1 pounds.

20. $c = \dfrac{k}{R}$

$40 = \dfrac{k}{270}$

$10,800 = k$

$c = \dfrac{10,800}{R} = \dfrac{10,800}{100} = 108$

The current is 108 amperes.

22. $y = kwz, \; y = 100, \; w = \dfrac{1}{2}, z = 38$

$100 = k\left(\dfrac{1}{2}\right)(38)$

$k = \dfrac{2(100)}{38} \approx 5.3$

$y = 5.3wz = 5.3(4)(6) = 127.2$

24. $y = \dfrac{kxz}{\sqrt{w}}$

$10 = \dfrac{k(6)(3)}{\sqrt{4}}$

$20 = 18k$

$\dfrac{10}{9} = k$

$y = \dfrac{\frac{10}{9}xz}{\sqrt{w}} = \dfrac{\frac{10}{9}(8)(10)}{\sqrt{9}} \approx 29.6$

26. $F = \dfrac{km_1m_2}{d^2}$

$10 = \dfrac{k(80)(100)}{100^2}$

$12.5 = k$

$F = \dfrac{12.5m_1m_2}{d^2}$

$= \dfrac{12.5(8)(15)}{20^2}$

$= 3.75$

The force is 3.75 pounds.

28. $f = kAv^2$

$20 = k(3)(30)^2$

$0.007 \approx k$

$f = 0.007Av^2$

$= 0.007(5)(25)^2 \approx 21.9$

The force is approximately 21.9 pounds.

Cumulative Review Problems

30. $2x^2 + 5x - 3 = 0$
$(2x - 1)(x + 3) = 0$
$2x - 1 = 0$ or $x + 3 = 0$
$2x = 1$ $x = -3$
$x = \dfrac{1}{2}$

32. $4x^2 = -28x + 32$
$4x^2 + 28x - 32 = 0$
$x^2 + 7x - 8 = 0$
$(x + 8)(x - 1) = 0$
$x + 8 = 0$ or $x - 1 = 0$
$x = -8$ $x = 1$

34. $\dfrac{7.5}{3} = \dfrac{x}{22}$
$3x = 165$
$x = 55$
It takes 55 gallons of paint.

Putting Your Skills to Work

2. $R = 1 - \left(\dfrac{F}{P}\right)^{1/n}$

$R = 1 - \left(\dfrac{5500}{12{,}000}\right)^{1/7} \approx 0.105$

Approximately 10.5%

4.

Age	Value
0	18,000
1	16,020
2	14,257.8
3	12,689.44
4	11,293.60
5	10,051.31

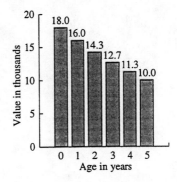

Chapter 7 Review Problems

2. $(-7x^{1/3}y^{1/3})(4xy^{2/3}) = -28x^{1/3+1}y^{1/3+2/3}$
       $= -28x^{4/3}y$

4. $\dfrac{27x^{5/3}}{3x^{-1/3}} = 9x^{5/3-(-1/3)} = 9x^2$

6. $(25a^3b^4)^{1/2} = 25^{1/2}(a^3)^{1/2}(b^4)^{1/2} = 5a^{3/2}b^2$

8. $(2a^{1/3}b^{1/4})(-3a^{1/2}b^{1/2})$
     $= -6a^{1/3+1/2}b^{1/4+1/2}$
     $= -6a^{5/6}b^{3/4}$

10. $(2x^{-1/5}y^{1/10}z^{4/5})^{-5}$
     $= 2^{-5}(x^{-1/5})^{-5}(y^{1/10})^{-5}(z^{4/5})^{-5}$
     $= \dfrac{1}{2^5}xy^{-1/2}z^{-4}$
     $= \dfrac{x}{32y^{1/2}z^4}$

12. $a^{1/5}(2a^{3/4} - 3a^{1/10}) = 2a^{1/5+3/4} - 3a^{1/5+1/10}$
     $= 2a^{19/20} - 3a^{3/10}$

14. $\left(\dfrac{27x^{5n}}{x^{2n-3}}\right)^{1/3} = \left(27x^{5n-(2n-3)}\right)^{1/3}$
     $= (27x^{3n+3})^{1/3}$
     $= 27^{1/3}\left(x^{3n+3}\right)^{1/3}$
     $= 3x^{n+1}$

16. $2x^{1/3} + x^{-2/3} = 2x^{1/3} + \dfrac{1}{x^{2/3}}$

     $= 2x^{1/3} \cdot \dfrac{x^{2/3}}{x^{2/3}} + \dfrac{1}{x^{2/3}}$

     $= \dfrac{2x + 1}{x^{2/3}}$

18. $\sqrt{\sqrt[5]{2x}} = \left((2x)^{1/5}\right)^{1/2} = (2x)^{1/10}$

20. $\sqrt[3]{125} + \sqrt[4]{81} = \sqrt[3]{5^3} + \sqrt[4]{3^4}$
$= 5 + 3 = 8$

22. $27^{-4/3} = \dfrac{1}{27^{4/3}}$
$= \dfrac{1}{\left(\sqrt[3]{3^3}\right)^4}$
$= \dfrac{1}{3^4} = \dfrac{1}{81}$

24. $\sqrt{99x^3y^6z^{10}} = \sqrt{9x^2y^6z^{10} \cdot 11x}$
$= 3xy^3z^5\sqrt{11x}$

26. $\sqrt[4]{16x^8y^3z^{11}} = \sqrt[4]{2^4x^8z^8 \cdot y^3z^3}$
$= 2x^2z^2\sqrt[4]{y^3z^3}$

28. $\sqrt{144x^{10}y^{12}z^0} = \sqrt{12^2x^{10}y^{12} \cdot 1}$
$= 12x^5y^6$

30. $\sqrt[3]{y^3} = y$

32. $\sqrt[4]{x^4y^4} = |xy|$

34. $\sqrt[3]{x^{21}} = x^7$

36. $\sqrt{50} + 2\sqrt{32} - \sqrt{8}$
$= 5\sqrt{2} + 8\sqrt{2} - 2\sqrt{2}$
$= 11\sqrt{2}$

38. $\sqrt[3]{8} + 3\sqrt[3]{16} - 4\sqrt[3]{54}$
$= 2 + 6\sqrt[3]{2} - 12\sqrt[3]{2}$
$= 2 - 6\sqrt[3]{2}$

40. $2\sqrt{32x} - 5x\sqrt{2} + \sqrt{18x} + 2\sqrt{8x^2}$
$= 8\sqrt{2x} - 5x\sqrt{2} + 3\sqrt{2x} + 4x\sqrt{2}$
$= 11\sqrt{2x} - x\sqrt{2}$

42. $\left(5\sqrt{12}\right)\left(3\sqrt{6}\right) = \left(10\sqrt{3}\right)\left(3\sqrt{6}\right)$
$= 30\sqrt{18} = 90\sqrt{2}$

44. $\left(5\sqrt{2} + \sqrt{3}\right)\left(\sqrt{2} - 2\sqrt{3}\right)$
$= 5(2) - 10\sqrt{6} + \sqrt{6} - 2(3)$
$= 10 - 9\sqrt{6} - 6$
$= 4 - 9\sqrt{6}$

46. $\left(2\sqrt{5} - 3\sqrt{6}\right)^2$
$= \left(2\sqrt{5}\right)^2 - 2\left(2\sqrt{5}\right)\left(3\sqrt{6}\right) + \left(3\sqrt{6}\right)^2$
$= 4(5) - 12\sqrt{30} + 9(6)$
$= 20 - 12\sqrt{30} + 54$
$= 74 - 12\sqrt{30}$

48. $\sqrt{140} = 11.832$

50. $4 + \sqrt{31} = 4 + 5.568 = 9.568$

52. $\dfrac{2}{\sqrt{3y}} = \dfrac{2}{\sqrt{3y}} \cdot \dfrac{\sqrt{3y}}{\sqrt{3y}} = \dfrac{2\sqrt{3y}}{3y}$

54. $\dfrac{2}{\sqrt{6} - \sqrt{5}} = \dfrac{2}{\sqrt{6} - \sqrt{5}} \cdot \dfrac{\sqrt{6} + \sqrt{5}}{\sqrt{6} + \sqrt{5}}$
$= \dfrac{2\left(\sqrt{6} + \sqrt{5}\right)}{6 - 5}$
$= 2\sqrt{6} + 2\sqrt{5}$

56. $\dfrac{\sqrt{5}}{\sqrt{7} - 3} = \dfrac{\sqrt{5}}{\sqrt{7} - 3} \cdot \dfrac{\sqrt{7} + 3}{\sqrt{7} + 3}$
$= \dfrac{\sqrt{35} + 3\sqrt{5}}{7 - 9}$
$= \dfrac{\sqrt{35} + 3\sqrt{5}}{-2}$
$= -\dfrac{\sqrt{35} + 3\sqrt{5}}{2}$

58. $\dfrac{5\sqrt{2} - \sqrt{3}}{\sqrt{6} - \sqrt{3}}$
$= \dfrac{5\sqrt{2} - \sqrt{3}}{\sqrt{6} - \sqrt{3}} \cdot \dfrac{\sqrt{6} + \sqrt{3}}{\sqrt{6} + \sqrt{3}}$
$= \dfrac{5\sqrt{12} + 5\sqrt{6} - \sqrt{18} - 3}{6 - 3}$
$= \dfrac{10\sqrt{3} + 5\sqrt{6} - 3\sqrt{2} - 3}{3}$

60. $\dfrac{2xy}{\sqrt[3]{16xy^5}} = \dfrac{2xy}{2y\sqrt[3]{2xy^2}}$

$= \dfrac{x}{\sqrt[3]{2xy^2}}$

$= \dfrac{x}{\sqrt[3]{2xy^2}} \cdot \dfrac{\sqrt[3]{2^2 x^2 y}}{\sqrt[3]{2^2 x^2 y}}$

$= \dfrac{x\sqrt[3]{4x^2 y}}{2xy}$

$= \dfrac{\sqrt[3]{4x^2 y}}{2y}$

62. $\sqrt{\dfrac{7}{5}} = \dfrac{\sqrt{7}}{\sqrt{5}} = \dfrac{\sqrt{7}}{\sqrt{5}} \cdot \dfrac{\sqrt{5}}{\sqrt{5}} = \dfrac{\sqrt{35}}{5}$

64. $2x - 3i + 5 = yi - 2 + \sqrt{6}$

$(2x + 5) - 3i = \left(-2 + \sqrt{6}\right) + yi$

$2x + 5 = -2 + \sqrt{6}$

$2x = -7 + \sqrt{6}$

$x = \dfrac{-7 + \sqrt{6}}{2}$

$-3 = y$

66. $(2 - i) - (12 - 3i) = 2 - i - 12 + 3i = -10 + 2i$

68. $(8 - 4i)^2 = 8^2 - 2(8)(4i) + (4i)^2$

$= 64 - 64i + 16i^2$

$= 64 - 64i + 16(-1)$

$= 48 - 64i$

70. $3 - 4(2 + i) = 3 - 8 - 4i$

$= -5 - 4i$

72. $i^{57} = (i^4)^{14} i = 1^{14} i = i$

74. $\dfrac{5 - 2i}{1 - 3i} = \dfrac{5 - 2i}{1 - 3i} \cdot \dfrac{1 + 3i}{1 + 3i}$

$= \dfrac{5 + 15i - 2i - 6i^2}{1 - 9i^2}$

$= \dfrac{5 + 13i - 6(-1)}{1 - 9(-1)}$

$= \dfrac{11 + 13i}{10}$

76. $\dfrac{12}{3 - 5i} = \dfrac{12}{3 - 5i} \cdot \dfrac{3 + 5i}{3 + 5i}$

$= \dfrac{12(3 + 5i)}{9 - 25i^2}$

$= \dfrac{12(3 + 5i)}{9 - 25(-1)}$

$= \dfrac{12(3 + 5i)}{34}$

$= \dfrac{6(3 + 5i)}{17}$

$= \dfrac{18 + 30i}{17}$

78. $\sqrt{3x + 4} = 5$

$\left(\sqrt{3x + 4}\right)^2 = 5^2$

$3x + 4 = 25$

$3x = 21$

$x = 7$

Check:

$\sqrt{3(7) + 4} \overset{?}{=} 5$

$\sqrt{25} \overset{?}{=} 5$

$5 = 5$

Solution: $x = 7$

80. $2\sqrt{6x + 1} = 10$

$\sqrt{6x + 1} = 5$

$\left(\sqrt{6x + 1}\right)^2 = 5^2$

$6x + 1 = 25$

$6x = 24$

$x = 4$

Check:

$2\sqrt{6(4) + 1} \overset{?}{=} 10$

$2\sqrt{25} \overset{?}{=} 10$

$10 = 10$

Solution: $x = 4$

82. $\sqrt{2x+1} = 2x-5$

$\left(\sqrt{2x+1}\right)^2 = (2x-5)^2$

$2x+1 = 4x^2 - 20x + 25$

$0 = 4x^2 - 22x + 24$

$0 = 2x^2 - 11x + 12$

$0 = (2x-3)(x-4)$

$2x-3 = 0 \quad$ or $\quad x-4 = 0$

$2x = 3 \qquad\qquad x = 4$

$x = \dfrac{3}{2}$

Check:

$x = \dfrac{3}{2}$

$\sqrt{2\left(\dfrac{3}{2}\right)+1} \stackrel{?}{=} 2\left(\dfrac{3}{2}\right)-5$

$\sqrt{4} \stackrel{?}{=} 3-5$

$2 \neq -2$ Extraneous

Check:

$x = 4$

$\sqrt{2(4)+1} \stackrel{?}{=} 2(4)-5$

$\sqrt{9} \stackrel{?}{=} 3$

$3 = 3$

Solution: $x = 4$

84. $\sqrt{3x+1} - \sqrt{2x-1} = 1$

$\sqrt{3x+1} = 1 + \sqrt{2x-1}$

$\left(\sqrt{3x+1}\right)^2 = \left(1+\sqrt{2x-1}\right)^2$

$3x+1 = 1 + 2\sqrt{2x-1} + 2x - 1$

$3x+1 = 2x + 2\sqrt{2x-1}$

$x+1 = 2\sqrt{2x-1}$

$(x+1)^2 = \left(2\sqrt{2x-1}\right)^2$

$x^2 + 2x + 1 = 4(2x-1)$

$x^2 + 2x + 1 = 8x - 4$

$x^2 - 6x + 5 = 0$

$(x-5)(x-1) = 0$

$x-5 = 0 \quad$ or $\quad x-1 = 0$

$x = 5 \qquad\qquad x = 1$

Check:

$x = 5$

$\sqrt{3(5)+1} - \sqrt{2(5)-1} \stackrel{?}{=} 1$

$\sqrt{16} - \sqrt{9} \stackrel{?}{=} 1$

$4-3 \stackrel{?}{=} 1$

$1 = 1$

Check:

$x = 1$

$\sqrt{3(1)+1} - \sqrt{2(1)-1} \stackrel{?}{=} 1$

$\sqrt{4} - \sqrt{1} \stackrel{?}{=} 1$

$2-1 \stackrel{?}{=} 1$

$1 = 1$

Solutions: $x = 5,\ x = 1$

86. $y = kx$

$16 = k(5)$

$\dfrac{16}{5} = k$

$y = \dfrac{16}{5}x = \dfrac{16}{5}(3) = \dfrac{48}{5} = 9.6$

88. $d = ks^2$

$50 = k(30)^2$

$\dfrac{1}{18} = k$

$d = \dfrac{1}{18}s^2 = \dfrac{1}{18}(55)^2 \approx 168$

168 feet

90. $y = \dfrac{k}{x}$

$8 = \dfrac{k}{3}$

$24 = k$

$y = \dfrac{24}{x} = \dfrac{24}{48} = 0.5$

92. $y = \dfrac{kx}{z^2}$

$1 = \dfrac{k(8)}{4^2}$

$2 = k$

$y = \dfrac{2x}{z^2} = \dfrac{2(6)}{3^2} = \dfrac{4}{3}$

Chapter 7 Test

2. $\dfrac{7x^3}{4x^{3/4}} = \dfrac{7x^{3-3/4}}{4} = \dfrac{7x^{9/4}}{4}$

4. $6^{1/5} \cdot 6^{3/5} = 6^{1/5+3/5} = 6^{4/5}$

6. $64^{3/2} = \left(\sqrt{64}\right)^3 = 8^3 = 512$

8. $\sqrt{64x^6 y^5} = \sqrt{64x^6 y^4 \cdot y}$
$= 8x^3 y^2 \sqrt{y}$

10. $3\sqrt{48} - \sqrt[3]{54x^5} + 2\sqrt{27} + 2x\sqrt[3]{16x^2}$
$= 12\sqrt{3} - 3x\sqrt[3]{2x^2} + 6\sqrt{3} + 4x\sqrt[3]{2x^2}$
$= 18\sqrt{3} + x\sqrt[3]{2x^2}$

12. $2\sqrt{3}\left(3\sqrt{6} - 5\sqrt{2}\right) = 6\sqrt{18} - 10\sqrt{6}$
$= 18\sqrt{2} - 10\sqrt{6}$

14. $\dfrac{8}{\sqrt{20x}} = \dfrac{8}{2\sqrt{5x}}$
$= \dfrac{8}{2\sqrt{5x}} \cdot \dfrac{\sqrt{5x}}{\sqrt{5x}}$
$= \dfrac{8\sqrt{5x}}{10x}$
$= \dfrac{4\sqrt{5x}}{5x}$

16. $\dfrac{5 + 2\sqrt{3}}{4 - \sqrt{3}} = \dfrac{5 + 2\sqrt{3}}{4 - \sqrt{3}} \cdot \dfrac{4 + \sqrt{3}}{4 + \sqrt{3}}$
$= \dfrac{20 + 5\sqrt{3} + 8\sqrt{3} + 2(3)}{16 - 3}$
$= \dfrac{20 + 13\sqrt{3} + 6}{13}$
$= \dfrac{26 + 13\sqrt{3}}{13}$
$= \dfrac{13\left(2 + \sqrt{3}\right)}{13} = 2 + \sqrt{3}$

18. $5 + \sqrt{x + 15} = x$
$\sqrt{x + 15} = x - 5$
$\left(\sqrt{x + 15}\right)^2 = (x - 5)^2$
$x + 15 = x^2 - 10x + 25$
$0 = x^2 - 11x + 10$
$0 = (x - 10)(x - 1)$
$x - 10 = 0 \quad$ or $\quad x - 1 = 0$
$x = 10 \qquad\qquad\quad x = 1$

Check:
$x = 10$
$5 + \sqrt{10 + 15} \overset{?}{=} 10$
$5 + \sqrt{25} \overset{?}{=} 10$
$5 + 5 \overset{?}{=} 10$
$10 = 10$
Check: $x = 1$
$5 + \sqrt{1 + 15} \overset{?}{=} 1$
$5 + \sqrt{16} \overset{?}{=} 1$
$5 + 4 \overset{?}{=} 1$
$9 \neq 1$ Extraneous
Solution: $x = 10$

20. $(8 + 2i) - 3(2 - 4i)$
$= 8 + 2i - 6 + 12i$
$= 2 + 14i$

22. $(3 - 2i)(4 + 3i) = 12 + 9i - 8i - 6i^2$
$= 12 + i - 6(-1)$
$= 18 + i$

24. $(6 + 3i)^2 = 6^2 + 2(6)(3i) + (3i)^2$
$= 36 + 36i + 9i^2$
$= 36 + 36i + 9(-1)$
$= 27 + 36i$

26. $y = \dfrac{k}{x}$
$9 = \dfrac{k}{2}$
$18 = k$

$y = \dfrac{18}{x} = \dfrac{18}{6} = 3$

28. $d = ks^2$
$30 = k(30)^2$
$\dfrac{1}{30} = k$

$d = \dfrac{1}{30}s^2 = \dfrac{1}{30}(50)^2 \approx 83.3$
83.3 feet

Cumulative Test for Chapters 1–7

2. $2a(3a^3 - 4) - 3a^2(a - 5)$
$= 6a^4 - 8a - 3a^3 + 15a^2$
$= 6a^4 - 3a^3 + 15a^2 - 8a$

4. $y = \dfrac{2}{3}x - 8$

$3y = 2x - 24$

$3y + 24 = 2x$

$\dfrac{3y + 24}{2} = x$

6. $16x^2 + 24x - 16 = 8(2x^2 + 3x - 2)$

$\qquad = 8(2x - 1)(x + 2)$

8. $\dfrac{7x}{x^2 - 2x - 15} - \dfrac{2}{x - 5}$

$= \dfrac{7x}{(x - 5)(x + 3)} - \dfrac{2}{x - 5}$

$= \dfrac{7x}{(x - 5)(x + 3)} - \dfrac{2}{x - 5} \cdot \dfrac{x + 3}{x + 3}$

$= \dfrac{7x - 2(x + 3)}{(x - 5)(x + 3)}$

$= \dfrac{7x - 2x - 6}{(x - 5)(x + 3)}$

$= \dfrac{5x - 6}{(x - 5)(x + 3)}$

10. $56x + 2 = 8b + 4x$

$52x + 2 = 8b$

$\dfrac{52x + 2}{8} = b$

$\dfrac{2(26x + 1)}{8} = b$

$\dfrac{26x + 1}{4} = b$

12. $\left(3x^{-1/2}y^2\right)^{-1/3}$

$= 3^{-1/3}\left(x^{-1/2}\right)^{-1/3}\left(y^2\right)^{-1/3}$

$= \dfrac{1}{3^{1/3}}x^{1/6}y^{-2/3}$

$= \dfrac{x^{1/6}}{3^{1/3}y^{2/3}}$

14. $\sqrt[3]{40x^5y^9}$

$= \sqrt[3]{8x^3y^9 \cdot 5x^2}$

$= 2xy^3\sqrt[3]{5x^2}$

16. $\left(2\sqrt{3} - 5\sqrt{2}\right)\left(\sqrt{3} + 4\sqrt{2}\right)$

$= 2(3) + 8\sqrt{6} - 5\sqrt{6} - 20(2)$

$= 6 + 3\sqrt{6} - 40$

$= -34 + 3\sqrt{6}$

18. $i^{21} + \sqrt{-16} + \sqrt{-49}$

$= \left(i^4\right)^5 \cdot i + 4i + 7i$

$= 1^5 \cdot i + 11i$

$= i + 11i = 12i$

20. $\dfrac{1 + 4i}{1 + 3i} = \dfrac{1 + 4i}{1 + 3i} \cdot \dfrac{1 - 3i}{1 - 3i}$

$= \dfrac{1 - 3i + 4i - 12i^2}{1 - 9i^2}$

$= \dfrac{1 + i - 12(-1)}{1 - 9(-1)}$

$= \dfrac{13 + i}{10}$

22. $1 + \sqrt{x + 1} = \sqrt{x + 2}$

$\left(1 + \sqrt{x + 1}\right)^2 = \left(\sqrt{x + 2}\right)^2$

$1 + 2\sqrt{x + 1} + x + 1 = x + 2$

$2 + x + 2\sqrt{x + 1} = x + 2$

$2\sqrt{x + 1} = 0$

$\left(2\sqrt{x + 1}\right)^2 = 0^2$

$4(x + 1) = 0$

$4x + 4 = 0$

$4x = -4$

$x = -1$

Check:

$1 + \sqrt{-1 + 1} \overset{?}{=} \sqrt{-1 + 2}$

$1 + \sqrt{0} \overset{?}{=} \sqrt{1}$

$1 = 1$

Solution: $x = -1$

24. $a = \dfrac{k}{d^2}$

$120 = \dfrac{k}{10^2}$

$12{,}000 = k$

$a = \dfrac{12{,}000}{d^2} = \dfrac{12{,}000}{15^2} \approx 53.3$

53.3 lumens

Chapter 8

Pretest Chapter 8

2. $2x^2 - 4x - 3 = 0$

$2x^2 - 4x = 3$

$x^2 - 2x = \dfrac{3}{2}$

$x^2 - 2x + 1 = \dfrac{3}{2} + 1$

$(x-1)^2 = \dfrac{5}{2}$

$x - 1 = \pm\sqrt{\dfrac{5}{2}}$

$x - 1 = \pm\dfrac{\sqrt{10}}{2}$

$x = 1 \pm \dfrac{\sqrt{10}}{2}$

$x = \dfrac{2 \pm \sqrt{10}}{2}$

4. $5x(x+1) = 1 + 6x$

$5x^2 + 5x = 1 + 6x$

$5x^2 - x - 1 = 0$

$a = 5,\ b = -1,\ c = -1$

$x = \dfrac{-b \pm \sqrt{b^2 - 4ac}}{2a}$

$= \dfrac{-(-1) \pm \sqrt{(-1)^2 - 4(5)(-1)}}{2(5)}$

$= \dfrac{1 \pm \sqrt{1 + 20}}{10}$

$= \dfrac{1 \pm \sqrt{21}}{10}$

6. $12x^2 + x - 6 = 0$

$(3x - 2)(4x + 3) = 0$

$3x - 2 = 0$ or $4x + 3 = 0$

$x = \dfrac{2}{3}$ $\qquad x = -\dfrac{3}{4}$

8. $\dfrac{18}{x} + \dfrac{12}{x+1} = 9$

$18(x+1) + 12x = 9x(x+1)$

$18x + 18 + 12x = 9x^2 + 9x$

$0 = 9x^2 - 21x - 18$

$0 = 3x^2 - 7x - 6$

$0 = (3x + 2)(x - 3)$

$3x + 2 = 0$ or $x - 3 = 0$

$x = -\dfrac{2}{3}$ $\qquad x = 3$

10. $w^{4/3} - 6w^{2/3} + 8 = 0$

Let $y = w^{2/3}$.

$y^2 - 6y + 8 = 0$

$(y - 4)(y - 2) = 0$

$y - 4 = 0$ or $y - 2 = 0$

$y = 4$ $\qquad\quad y = 2$

$w^{2/3} = 4$ $\qquad w^{2/3} = 2$

$w = 4^{3/2}$ $\qquad w = 2^{3/2}$

$w = \pm 8$ $\qquad w = \pm\sqrt{8} = \pm 2\sqrt{2}$

12. width: x

length: $3x + 1$

$x(3x + 1) = 52$

$3x^2 + x - 52 = 0$

$(3x + 13)(x - 4) = 0$

$3x + 13 = 0$ or $x - 4 = 0$

$x = -\dfrac{13}{3}$ $\qquad x = 4$

$3x + 1 = 3(4) + 1 = 13$

width = 4 meters; length = 13 meters

14. $g(x) = -x^2 + 6x - 5$

$-\dfrac{b}{2a} = -\dfrac{6}{2(-1)} = 3$

$g(3) = -3^2 + 6(3) - 5 = 4$

Vertex: $(3, 4)$

$g(0) = -0^2 + 6(0) - 5 = -5$

y-intercept: $(0, -5)$

$-x^2 + 6x - 5 = 0$

$x^2 - 6x + 5 = 0$

$(x - 5)(x - 1) = 0$

$x - 5 = 0$ or $x - 1 = 0$

$x = 5$ $\qquad\quad x = 1$

x-intercepts: $(5, 0)$, $(1, 0)$

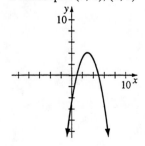

16. $2x^2 + 9x \le -9$

$2x^2 + 9x + 9 \le 0$

$2x^2 + 9x + 9 = 0$

$(2x + 3)(x + 3) = 0$

$2x + 3 = 0$ or $x + 3 = 0$

$2x = -3$ $x = -3$

$x = -\dfrac{3}{2}$

Region I: $x = -4$

$2(-4)^2 + 9(-4) + 9 = 5 > 0$

Region II: $x = -2$

$2(-2)^2 + 9(-2) + 9 = -1 < 0$

Region III: $x = 0$

$2(0)^2 + 9(0) + 9 = 9 > 0$

$-3 \le x \le -\dfrac{3}{2}$

8.1 Exercises

2. $x^2 = 81$

$x = \pm\sqrt{81}$

$x = \pm 9$

4. $x^2 - 50 = 0$

$x^2 = 50$

$x = \pm\sqrt{50}$

$x = \pm 5\sqrt{2}$

6. $3x^2 + 1 = 28$

$3x^2 = 27$

$x^2 = 9$

$x = \pm\sqrt{9}$

$x = \pm 3$

8. $4x^2 + 3 = 43$

$4x^2 = 40$

$x^2 = 10$

$x = \pm\sqrt{10}$

10. $\dfrac{x^2}{3} + 1 = 4$

$x^2 + 3 = 12$

$x^2 = 9$

$x = \pm\sqrt{9}$

$x = \pm 3$

12. $x^2 = -36$

$x = \pm\sqrt{-36}$

$x = \pm 6i$

14. $2x^2 + 24 = 0$

$2x^2 = -24$

$x^2 = -12$

$x = \pm\sqrt{-12}$

$x = \pm 2i\sqrt{3}$

16. $(x + 2)^2 = 18$

$x + 2 = \pm\sqrt{18}$

$x + 2 = \pm 3\sqrt{2}$

$x = -2 \pm 3\sqrt{2}$

18. $(3x + 2)^2 = 5$

$3x + 2 = \pm\sqrt{5}$

$3x = -2 \pm\sqrt{5}$

$x = \dfrac{-2 \pm\sqrt{5}}{3}$

20. $(5x - 2)^2 = 25$

$5x - 2 = \pm\sqrt{25}$

$5x - 2 = \pm 5$

$5x = 2 \pm 5$

$x = \dfrac{2 \pm 5}{5}$

$x = \dfrac{2 + 5}{5} = \dfrac{7}{5}, \quad x = \dfrac{2 - 5}{5} = -\dfrac{3}{5}$

22. $(2x + 7)^2 = 27$

$2x + 7 = \pm\sqrt{27}$

$2x + 7 = \pm 3\sqrt{3}$

$2x = -7 \pm 3\sqrt{3}$

$x = \dfrac{-7 \pm 3\sqrt{3}}{2}$

24. $\left(x - \dfrac{1}{3}\right)^2 = \dfrac{5}{9}$

$x - \dfrac{1}{3} = \pm\sqrt{\dfrac{5}{9}}$

$x - \dfrac{1}{3} = \pm\dfrac{\sqrt{5}}{3}$

$x = \dfrac{1}{3} \pm \dfrac{\sqrt{5}}{3}$

$x = \dfrac{1 \pm\sqrt{5}}{3}$

26. $x^2 - 2x = 5$

$x^2 - 2x + (-1)^2 = 5 + 1$

$(x-1)^2 = 6$

$x - 1 = \pm\sqrt{6}$

$x = 1 \pm \sqrt{6}$

28. $x^2 + 6x + 2 = 0$

$x^2 + 6x = -2$

$x^2 + 6x + 9 = -2 + 9$

$(x+3)^2 = 7$

$x + 3 = \pm\sqrt{7}$

$x = -3 \pm \sqrt{7}$

30. $x^2 - 12x = 4$

$x^2 - 12x + 36 = 4 + 36$

$(x-6)^2 = 40$

$x - 6 = \pm\sqrt{40}$

$x - 6 = \pm 2\sqrt{10}$

$x = 6 \pm 2\sqrt{10}$

32. $x^2 + 20x + 10 = 0$

$x^2 + 20x = -10$

$x^2 + 20x + 100 = -10 + 100$

$(x+10)^2 = 90$

$x + 10 = \pm\sqrt{90}$

$x + 10 = \pm 3\sqrt{10}$

$x = -10 \pm 3\sqrt{10}$

34. $\dfrac{x^2}{3} - \dfrac{x}{3} = 3$

$x^2 - x = 9$

$x^2 - x + \dfrac{1}{4} = \dfrac{9}{1} + \dfrac{1}{4}$

$\left(x - \dfrac{1}{2}\right)^2 = \dfrac{37}{4}$

$x - \dfrac{1}{2} = \pm\sqrt{\dfrac{37}{4}}$

$x = \dfrac{1}{2} \pm \dfrac{\sqrt{37}}{2}$

$x = \dfrac{1 \pm \sqrt{37}}{2}$

36. $6y^2 - 6y = 3$

$y^2 - y = \dfrac{1}{2}$

$y^2 - y + \dfrac{1}{4} = \dfrac{1}{2} + \dfrac{1}{4}$

$\left(y - \dfrac{1}{2}\right)^2 = \dfrac{3}{4}$

$y - \dfrac{1}{2} = \pm\sqrt{\dfrac{3}{4}}$

$y - \dfrac{1}{2} = \pm\dfrac{\sqrt{3}}{2}$

$y = \dfrac{1}{2} \pm \dfrac{\sqrt{3}}{2}$

$y = \dfrac{1 \pm \sqrt{3}}{2}$

38. $2x^2 - 7x + 4 = 0$

$2x^2 - 7x = -4$

$x^2 - \dfrac{7}{2}x = -2$

$x^2 - \dfrac{7}{2}x + \dfrac{49}{16} = -2 + \dfrac{49}{16}$

$\left(x - \dfrac{7}{4}\right)^2 = \dfrac{17}{16}$

$x - \dfrac{7}{4} = \pm\sqrt{\dfrac{17}{16}}$

$x - \dfrac{7}{4} = \pm\dfrac{\sqrt{17}}{4}$

$x = \dfrac{7}{4} \pm \dfrac{\sqrt{17}}{4}$

$x = \dfrac{7 \pm \sqrt{17}}{4}$

40. $2y^2 - y = 15$

$\dfrac{2y^2}{2} - \dfrac{y}{2} = \dfrac{15}{2}$

$y^2 - \dfrac{1}{2}y = \dfrac{15}{2}$

$y^2 - \dfrac{1}{2}y + \dfrac{1}{16} = \dfrac{15}{2} + \dfrac{1}{16}$

$\left(y - \dfrac{1}{4}\right)^2 = \dfrac{121}{16}$

$y - \dfrac{1}{4} = \pm\sqrt{\dfrac{121}{16}}$

$y = \dfrac{1}{4} \pm \dfrac{11}{4}$

$y = \dfrac{12}{4}$ or $y = -\dfrac{10}{4}$

$y = 3$ $y = -\dfrac{5}{2}$

42. $2x^2 + 2 = 3x$

$2x^2 - 3x = -2$

$x^2 - \dfrac{3}{2}x = -1$

$x^2 - \dfrac{3}{2}x + \dfrac{9}{16} = -1 + \dfrac{9}{16}$

$\left(x - \dfrac{3}{4}\right)^2 = -\dfrac{7}{16}$

$x - \dfrac{3}{4} = \pm\sqrt{-\dfrac{7}{16}}$

$x = \dfrac{3}{4} \pm \dfrac{\left(i\sqrt{7}\right)}{4}$

$x = \dfrac{3 \pm i\sqrt{7}}{4}$

44. $4x^2 + 7x + 2 = 3$

$\dfrac{4x^2}{4} + \dfrac{7x}{4} = \dfrac{1}{4}$

$x^2 + \dfrac{7}{4}x = \dfrac{1}{4}$

$x^2 + \dfrac{7}{4}x + \dfrac{49}{64} = \dfrac{1}{4} + \dfrac{49}{64}$

$\left(x + \dfrac{7}{8}\right)^2 = \dfrac{65}{64}$

$x + \dfrac{7}{8} = \pm\sqrt{\dfrac{65}{64}}$

$x = -\dfrac{7}{8} \pm \sqrt{\dfrac{65}{64}}$

$x = -\dfrac{7}{8} \pm \dfrac{\sqrt{65}}{8}$

$x = \dfrac{-7 \pm \sqrt{65}}{8}$

46. $7x^2 - 5x + 2 = 0$

$7x^2 - 5x = -2$

$x^2 - \dfrac{5}{7}x = -\dfrac{2}{7}$

$x^2 - \dfrac{5}{7}x + \dfrac{25}{196} = -\dfrac{2}{7} + \dfrac{25}{196}$

$\left(x - \dfrac{5}{14}\right)^2 = -\dfrac{31}{196}$

$x - \dfrac{5}{14} = \pm\sqrt{-\dfrac{31}{196}}$

$x - \dfrac{5}{14} = \pm\dfrac{i\sqrt{31}}{14}$

$x = \dfrac{5}{14} \pm \dfrac{i\sqrt{31}}{14}$

$x = \dfrac{5 \pm i\sqrt{31}}{14}$

48. $x^2 - 4x + 1 = 0$

$\left(2 + \sqrt{3}\right)^2 - 4\left(2 + \sqrt{3}\right) + 1 \overset{?}{=} 0$

$4 + 4\sqrt{3} + 3 - 8 - 4\sqrt{3} + 1 \overset{?}{=} 0$

$0 = 0$

50. $L = 4t^2$

$3.3 = 4t^2$

$0.825 = t^2$

$\pm\sqrt{0.825} = t$

$\pm 0.91 \approx t$

Time is positive, so approximately 0.91 second.

52. $D = 16t^2$

$1936 = 16t^2$

$121 = t^2$

$\pm\sqrt{121} = t$

$\pm 11 = t$

Time is positive, so 11 seconds.

Cumulative Review Problems

54. $\sqrt{b^2 - 4ac}$

$= \sqrt{(-5)^2 - 4(2)(-3)}$

$= \sqrt{25 + 24}$

$= \sqrt{49} = 7$

56. $2x^2 + 3x - 5$

$= 2(-3)^2 + 3(-3) - 5$

$= 18 - 9 - 5 = 4$

8.2 Exercises

2. $b^2 - 4ac$

4. two different rational

6. $x^2 + 3x - 20 = 0$

$a = 1,\ b = 3,\ c = -20$

$x = \dfrac{-b \pm \sqrt{b^2 - 4ac}}{2a}$

$x = \dfrac{-3 \pm \sqrt{(3)^2 - 4(1)(-20)}}{2(1)}$

$$= \frac{-3 \pm \sqrt{9+80}}{2}$$

$$= \frac{-3 \pm \sqrt{89}}{2}.$$

8. $5x^2 - x - 1 = 0$

$a = 5, \ b = -1, \ c = -1$

$$x = \frac{-b \pm \sqrt{b^2 - 4ac}}{2a}$$

$$x = \frac{-(-1) \pm \sqrt{(-1)^2 - 4(5)(-1)}}{2(5)}$$

$$= \frac{1 \pm \sqrt{1+20}}{10} = \frac{1 \pm \sqrt{21}}{10}$$

10. $\frac{4}{5} x^2 = x$

$\frac{4}{5} x^2 - x = 0$

$4x^2 - 5x = 0$

$a = 4, b = -5, c = 0$

$$x = \frac{-b \pm \sqrt{b^2 - 4ac}}{2a}$$

$$x = \frac{-(-5) \pm \sqrt{(-5)^2 - 4(4)(0)}}{2(4)}$$

$$= \frac{5 \pm \sqrt{25-0}}{8}$$

$$= \frac{5 \pm 5}{8}$$

$$= \frac{0}{8}, \ \frac{10}{8}$$

$x = 0, \ x = \frac{5}{4}$

12. $x^2 - 2x - 17 = 0$

$a = 1, b = -2, c = -17$

$$x = \frac{-b \pm \sqrt{b^2 - 4ac}}{2a}$$

$$x = \frac{-(-2) \pm \sqrt{(-2)^2 - 4(1)(-17)}}{2(1)}$$

$$= \frac{2 \pm \sqrt{4+68}}{2}$$

$$= \frac{2 \pm \sqrt{72}}{2}$$

$$= \frac{2 \pm 6\sqrt{2}}{2}$$

$$= 1 \pm 3\sqrt{2}$$

14. $4x^2 + 11x - 3 = 0$

$a = 4, b = 11, c = -3$

$$x = \frac{-b \pm \sqrt{b^2 - 4ac}}{2a}$$

$$x = \frac{-11 \pm \sqrt{11^2 - 4(4)(-3)}}{2(4)}$$

$$= \frac{-11 \pm \sqrt{121+48}}{8}$$

$$= \frac{-11 \pm \sqrt{169}}{8} = \frac{-11 \pm 13}{8}$$

$$x = \frac{-11+13}{8} = \frac{1}{4}, \ x = \frac{-11-13}{8} = -3$$

16. $6x^2 - 2x - 1 = 0$

$a = 6, \ b = -2, \ c = -1$

$$x = \frac{-b \pm \sqrt{b^2 - 4ac}}{2a}$$

$$x = \frac{-(-2) \pm \sqrt{(-2)^2 - 4(6)(-1)}}{2(6)}$$

$$= \frac{2 \pm \sqrt{4+24}}{12}$$

$$= \frac{2 \pm \sqrt{28}}{12}$$

$$= \frac{2 \pm 2\sqrt{7}}{12}$$

$$= \frac{1 \pm \sqrt{7}}{6}$$

18. $5x^2 - 1 = 5$

$5x^2 - 6 = 0$

$a = 5, b = 0, c = -6$

$$x = \frac{-b \pm \sqrt{b^2 - 4ac}}{2a}$$

$$x = \frac{0 \pm \sqrt{0^2 - 4(5)(-6)}}{2(5)}$$

$$= \pm \frac{\sqrt{120}}{10}$$

$$= \pm \frac{2\sqrt{30}}{10}$$

$$= \pm \frac{\sqrt{30}}{5}$$

20. $2x^2 - 2x + 2 = 7$

$2x^2 - 2x - 5 = 0$

$a = 2, \ b = -2, \ c = -5$

$x = \dfrac{-b \pm \sqrt{b^2 - 4ac}}{2a}$

$x = \dfrac{-(-2) \pm \sqrt{(-2)^2 - 4(2)(-5)}}{2(2)}$

$= \dfrac{2 \pm \sqrt{4 + 40}}{4}$

$= \dfrac{2 \pm \sqrt{44}}{4}$

$= \dfrac{2 \pm 2\sqrt{11}}{4}$

$= \dfrac{1 \pm \sqrt{11}}{2}$

22. $2x^2 - 7x - 3 = 9 - 7x$

$x^2 - 6 = 0$

$a = 1, \ b = 0, \ c = -6$

$x = \dfrac{-b \pm \sqrt{b^2 - 4ac}}{2a}$

$x = \dfrac{0 \pm \sqrt{0^2 - 4(1)(-6)}}{2(1)}$

$= \dfrac{\pm\sqrt{24}}{2}$

$= \dfrac{\pm 2\sqrt{6}}{2} = \pm\sqrt{6}$

24. $(x + 4)(x - 2) = 3x$

$x^2 + 2x - 8 = 3x$

$x^2 - x - 8 = 0$

$a = 1, \ b = -1, \ c = -8$

$x = \dfrac{-b \pm \sqrt{b^2 - 4ac}}{2a}$

$x = \dfrac{-(-1) \pm \sqrt{(-1)^2 - 4(1)(-8)}}{2(1)}$

$= \dfrac{1 \pm \sqrt{1 + 32}}{2}$

$= \dfrac{1 \pm \sqrt{33}}{2}$

26. $2x^2 - 5x + 1 = -3x^2 - 12x$

$5x^2 + 7x + 1 = 0$

$a = 5, \ b = 7, \ c = 1$

$x = \dfrac{-b \pm \sqrt{b^2 - 4ac}}{2a}$

$x = \dfrac{-7 \pm \sqrt{7^2 - 4(5)(1)}}{2(5)}$

$= \dfrac{-7 \pm \sqrt{49 - 20}}{10}$

$= \dfrac{-7 \pm \sqrt{29}}{10}$

28. $\dfrac{1}{x + 2} + \dfrac{1}{x} = \dfrac{1}{3}$

$3x(x + 2)\left(\dfrac{1}{x + 2}\right) + 3x(x + 2)\left(\dfrac{1}{x}\right)$

$\qquad = 3x(x + 2)\left(\dfrac{1}{3}\right)$

$3x + 3x + 6 = x^2 + 2x$

$x^2 - 4x - 6 = 0$

$a = 1, \ b = -4, \ c = -6$

$x = \dfrac{-b \pm \sqrt{b^2 - 4ac}}{2a}$

$x = \dfrac{-(-4) \pm \sqrt{(-4)^2 - 4(1)(-6)}}{2(1)}$

$= \dfrac{4 \pm \sqrt{16 + 24}}{2}$

$= \dfrac{4 \pm \sqrt{40}}{2}$

$= \dfrac{4 \pm 2\sqrt{10}}{2}$

$= 2 \pm \sqrt{10}$

30. $\dfrac{1}{y} + \dfrac{2}{y + 3} = \dfrac{1}{4}$

$(4y)(y + 3)\left(\dfrac{1}{y} + \dfrac{2}{y + 3} - \dfrac{1}{4}\right) = 0(4y)(y + 3)$

$4(y + 3) + 2(4y) - y(y + 3) = 0$

$4y + 12 + 8y - y^2 - 3y = 0$

$y^2 - 9y - 12 = 0$

$a = 1, \ b = -9, \ c = -12$

$y = \dfrac{-b \pm \sqrt{b^2 - 4ac}}{2a}$

$$y = \frac{-(-9) \pm \sqrt{(-9)^2 - 4(1)(-12)}}{2(1)}$$

$$= \frac{9 \pm \sqrt{81 + 48}}{2} = \frac{9 \pm \sqrt{129}}{2}$$

32. $\dfrac{1}{4} + \dfrac{6}{y+2} = \dfrac{6}{y}$

$$4y(y+2)\left(\frac{1}{4}\right) + 4y(y+2)\left(\frac{6}{y+2}\right)$$

$$= 4y(y+2)\left(\frac{6}{y}\right)$$

$$y^2 + 2y + 24y = 24y + 48$$

$$y^2 + 2y - 48 = 0$$

$$a = 1, \, b = 2, \, c = -48$$

$$y = \frac{-b \pm \sqrt{b^2 - 4ac}}{2a}$$

$$y = \frac{-2 \pm \sqrt{2^2 - 4(1)(-48)}}{2(1)}$$

$$= \frac{-2 \pm \sqrt{4 + 192}}{2}$$

$$= \frac{-2 \pm \sqrt{196}}{2}$$

$$= \frac{-2 \pm 14}{2}$$

$$y = \frac{-2 + 14}{2} = 6, \quad y = \frac{-2 - 14}{2} = -8$$

34. $x^2 - 2x + 4 = 0$

$$a = 1, \, b = -2, \, c = 4$$

$$x = \frac{-b \pm \sqrt{b^2 - 4ac}}{2a}$$

$$x = \frac{-(-2) \pm \sqrt{(-2)^2 - 4(1)(4)}}{2(1)}$$

$$= \frac{2 \pm \sqrt{4 - 16}}{2}$$

$$= \frac{2 \pm \sqrt{-12}}{2}$$

$$= \frac{2 \pm 2i\sqrt{3}}{2}$$

$$= 1 \pm i\sqrt{3}$$

36. $5x^2 = -3$

$$5x^2 + 3 = 0$$

$$a = 5, \, b = 0, \, c = 3$$

$$x = \frac{-b \pm \sqrt{b^2 - 4ac}}{2a}$$

$$x = \frac{0 \pm \sqrt{0^2 - 4(5)(3)}}{2(5)}$$

$$= \frac{\pm\sqrt{-60}}{10}$$

$$= \frac{\pm 2i\sqrt{15}}{10}$$

$$= \frac{\pm i\sqrt{15}}{5}$$

38. $3x^2 - 4x + 6 = 0$

$$a = 3, \, b = -4, \, c = 6$$

$$x = \frac{-b \pm \sqrt{b^2 - 4ac}}{2a}$$

$$x = \frac{-(-4) \pm \sqrt{(-4)^2 - 4(3)(6)}}{2(3)}$$

$$= \frac{4 \pm \sqrt{16 - 72}}{6}$$

$$= \frac{4 \pm \sqrt{-56}}{6}$$

$$= \frac{4 \pm 2i\sqrt{14}}{6}$$

$$= \frac{2 \pm i\sqrt{14}}{3}$$

40. $x^2 = \dfrac{1}{3}x - \dfrac{4}{3}$

$$3\left(x^2 - \frac{1}{3}x + \frac{4}{3}\right) = (0)3$$

$$3x^2 - x + 4 = 0$$

$$a = 3, \, b = -1, \, c = 4$$

$$x = \frac{-b \pm \sqrt{b^2 - 4ac}}{2a}$$

$$x = \frac{-(-1) \pm \sqrt{(-1)^2 - 4(3)(4)}}{2(3)}$$

$$= \frac{1 \pm \sqrt{1 - 48}}{6} = \frac{1 \pm \sqrt{-47}}{6}$$

$$= \frac{1 \pm i\sqrt{47}}{6}$$

42.　$2x^2 + 4x + 3 = 0$
$a = 2,\ b = 4,\ c = 3$
$b^2 - 4ac = 4^2 - 4(2)(3)$
$\qquad\qquad = 16 - 24$
$\qquad\qquad = -8 < 0$
two nonreal complex roots

44.　$4x^2 - 20x + 25 = 0$
$a = 4,\ b = -20,\ c = 25$
$b^2 - 4ac = (-20)^2 - 4(4)(25)$
$\qquad\qquad = 400 - 400$
$\qquad\qquad = 0$
one rational root

46.　$2x^2 - 7x - 4 = 0$
$a = 2,\ b = -7,\ c = -4$
$b^2 - 4ac = (-7)^2 - 4(2)(-4)$
$\qquad\qquad = 49 + 32$
$\qquad\qquad = 81 > 0 \quad (\text{perfect square})$
two rational roots

48.　$5x^2 - 8x - 2 = 0$
$a = 5,\ b = -8,\ c = -2$
$b^2 - 4ac = (-8)^2 - 4(5)(-2)$
$\qquad\qquad = 64 + 40$
$\qquad\qquad = 104 > 0 \quad (\text{not a perfect square})$
two irrational roots

50.　$x = 13$　　or　　$x = -2$
$x - 13 = 0$　　　　$x + 2 = 0$
$(x - 13)(x + 2) = 0$
$x^2 - 11x - 26 = 0$

52.　$x = -5$　　or　　$x = -12$
$x + 5 = 0$　　　　$x + 12 = 0$
$(x + 5)(x + 12) = 0$
$x^2 + 17x + 60 = 0$

54.　$x = 4i$　　or　　$x = -4i$
$x - 4i = 0$　　　$x + 4i = 0$
$(x - 4i)(x + 4i) = 0$
$x^2 - 16i^2 = 0$
$x^2 + 16 = 0$

56.　$x = 3i\sqrt{2}$　　or　　$x = -3i\sqrt{2}$
$x - 3i\sqrt{2} = 0$　　　　$x + 3i\sqrt{2} = 0$
$\left(x - 3i\sqrt{2}\right)\left(x + 3i\sqrt{2}\right) = 0$
$x^2 - 18i^2 = 0$
$x^2 + 18 = 0$

58.　$x = -2$　　or　　$x = \dfrac{5}{6}$
$\qquad\qquad\qquad\qquad 6x = 5$
$x + 2 = 0$　　　　$6x - 5 = 0$
$(x + 2)(6x - 5) = 0$
$6x^2 + 7x - 10 = 0$

60.　$1.2x^2 - 12.3x - 4.2 = 0$
$12x^2 - 123x - 42 = 0$
$a = 12,\ b = -123,\ c = -42$
$x = \dfrac{-b \pm \sqrt{b^2 - 4ac}}{2a}$
$ = \dfrac{-(-123) \pm \sqrt{(-123)^2 - 4(12)(-42)}}{2(12)}$
$ = \dfrac{123 \pm \sqrt{15{,}129 + 2016}}{24}$
$ = \dfrac{123 \pm \sqrt{17{,}145}}{24}$
$x = \dfrac{123 + \sqrt{17{,}145}}{24} \approx 10.5808$
or
$x = \dfrac{123 - \sqrt{17{,}145}}{24} \approx -0.3308$

62.　$0.162x^2 + 0.094x - 0.485 = 0$
$a = 0.162,\ b = 0.094,\ c = -0.485$
$x = \dfrac{-b \pm \sqrt{b^2 - 4ac}}{2a}$
$ = \dfrac{-0.094 \pm \sqrt{(0.094)^2 - 4(0.162)(-0.485)}}{2(0.162)}$
$ = \dfrac{-0.094 \pm \sqrt{0.323116}}{0.324}$
$x \approx \dfrac{-0.094 - 0.568433}{0.324} \approx -2.0445$ or
$x \approx \dfrac{-0.094 + 0.568433}{0.324} \approx 1.4643$

64.　$x = \dfrac{-b \pm \sqrt{b^2 - 4ac}}{2a}$
$\dfrac{-7 \pm \sqrt{65}}{4} = \dfrac{-7 \pm \sqrt{7^2 - 4(2)c}}{2(2)}$
$\dfrac{-7 \pm \sqrt{65}}{4} = \dfrac{-7 \pm \sqrt{49 - 8c}}{4}$
$65 = 49 - 8c$
$16 = -8c$
$-2 = c$

66. $4y^2 = 12y - 7$

$$4\left(\frac{3+\sqrt{2}}{2}\right)^2 \overset{?}{=} 12\left(\frac{3+\sqrt{2}}{2}\right) - 7$$

$$\frac{4(9+6\sqrt{2}+2)}{4} \overset{?}{=} 6(3+\sqrt{2}) - 7$$

$$11 + 6\sqrt{2} \overset{?}{=} 18 + 6\sqrt{2} - 7$$

$$11 + 6\sqrt{2} = 11 + 6\sqrt{2}$$

Cumulative Review Problems

68. $3y(2-y) + \dfrac{1}{5}(10y^2 - 15y)$

$= 6y - 3y^2 + 2y^2 - 3y$

$= -y^2 + 3y$

70. Let w = width
l = length
$2w + 2l = 50$
$2(3w) + 2(2l) = 118$
$w + l = 25$
$6w + 4l = 118$
$6w + 4(25 - w) = 118$
$2w = 18$
$w = 9$
$l = 25 - 9 = 16$
The width is 9 feet and the length is 16 feet.

8.3 Exercises

2. $x^4 - 11x^2 + 18 = 0$
Let $y = x^2$, $y^2 = x^4$.
$y^2 - 11y + 18 = 0$
$(y - 9)(y - 2) = 0$

$y - 9 = 0$	or	$y - 2 = 0$
$y = 9$		$y = 2$
$x^2 = 9$		$x^2 = 2$
$x = \pm 3$		$x = \pm\sqrt{2}$

4. $2x^4 - x^2 - 3 = 0$
Let $y = x^2$, $y^2 = x^4$.
$2y^2 - y - 3 = 0$
$(2y - 3)(y + 1) = 0$

$2y - 3 = 0$	or	$y + 1 = 0$
$y = \dfrac{3}{2}$		$y = -1$

$x^2 = \dfrac{3}{2}$ or $x^2 = -1$

$x = \pm\sqrt{\dfrac{3}{2}}$	$x = \pm\sqrt{-1}$
$x = \pm\dfrac{\sqrt{6}}{2}$	$x = \pm i$

6. $5x^4 = 4x^2 + 1$
$5x^4 - 4x^2 - 1 = 0$
Let $y = x^2$, $y^2 = x^4$.
$5y^2 - 4y - 1 = 0$
$(5y + 1)(y - 1) = 0$

$5y + 1 = 0$	or	$y - 1 = 0$
$y = -\dfrac{1}{5}$		$y = 1$
$x^2 = -\dfrac{1}{5}$		$x^2 = 1$
$x = \pm\sqrt{-\dfrac{1}{5}}$		$x = \pm 1$
$x = \pm\dfrac{i\sqrt{5}}{5}$		

8. $x^6 - 3x^3 - 4 = 0$
Let $y = x^3$, $y^2 = x^6$.
$y^2 - 3y - 4 = 0$
$(y - 4)(y + 1) = 0$

$y - 4 = 0$	or	$y + 1 = 0$
$y = 4$		$y = -1$
$x^3 = 4$		$x^3 = -1$
$x = \sqrt[3]{4}$		$x = \sqrt[3]{-1}$
		$x = -1$

10. $12x^6 + 5x^3 - 2 = 0$
Let $y = x^3$, $y^2 = x^6$.
$12y^2 + 5y - 2 = 0$
$(4y - 1)(3y + 2) = 0$

$4y - 1 = 0$	or	$3y + 2 = 0$
$4y = 1$		$3y = -2$
$y = \dfrac{1}{4}$		$y = -\dfrac{2}{3}$
$x^3 = \dfrac{1}{4}$		$x^3 = -\dfrac{2}{3}$
$x = \sqrt[3]{\dfrac{1}{4}}$		$x = \sqrt[3]{-\dfrac{2}{3}}$
$x = \dfrac{\sqrt[3]{2}}{2}$		$x = -\dfrac{\sqrt[3]{18}}{3}$

12. $x^8 = 7x^4 - 12$

$x^8 - 7x^4 + 12 = 0$

Let $y = x^4$, $y^2 = x^8$.

$y^2 - 7y + 12 = 0$

$(y - 4)(y - 3) = 0$

$y - 4 = 0$ or $y - 3 = 0$

$y = 4$ $y = 3$

$x^4 = 4$ $x^4 = 3$

$x = \pm\sqrt[4]{4} = \pm\sqrt{2}$ $x = \pm\sqrt[4]{3}$

14. $3x^8 - 10x^4 = 8$

$3x^8 - 10x^4 - 8 = 0$

Let $y = x^4$, $y^2 = x^8$.

$3y^2 - 10y - 8 = 0$

$(3y + 2)(y - 4) = 0$

$3y + 2 = 0$ or $y - 4 = 0$

$3y = -2$ $y = 4$

$y = -\dfrac{2}{3}$ $x^4 = 4$

$x^4 = -\dfrac{2}{3}$ $x = \pm\sqrt[4]{4}$

No real roots $x = \pm\sqrt{2}$

16. $x^{2/3} + x^{1/3} - 12 = 0$

Let $y = x^{1/3}$, $y^2 = x^{2/3}$.

$y^2 + y - 12 = 0$

$(y + 4)(y - 3) = 0$

$y + 4 = 0$ or $y - 3 = 0$

$y = -4$ $y = 3$

$x^{1/3} = -4$ $x^{1/3} = 3$

$x = (-4)^3$ $x = 3^3$

$x = -64$ $x = 27$

18. $x^{2/3} + 9x^{1/3} = -18$

$x^{2/3} + 9x^{1/3} + 18 = 0$

Let $y = x^{1/3}$, $y^2 = x^{2/3}$.

$y^2 + 9y + 18 = 0$

$(y + 3)(y + 6) = 0$

$y + 3 = 0$ or $y + 6 = 0$

$y = -3$ $y = -6$

$x^{1/3} = -3$ $x^{1/3} = -6$

$x = (-3)^3$ $x = (-6)^3$

$x = -27$ $x = -216$

20. $3x^{1/2} - 14x^{1/4} - 5 = 0$

Let $y = x^{1/4}$, $y^2 = x^{1/2}$.

$3y^2 - 14y - 5 = 0$

$(3y + 1)(y - 5) = 0$

$3y + 1 = 0$ or $y - 5 = 0$

$y = -\dfrac{1}{3}$ $y = 5$

$x^{1/4} = -\dfrac{1}{3}$ $x^{1/4} = 5$

$x = \left(-\dfrac{1}{3}\right)^4$ $x = 5^4$

$x = \dfrac{1}{81}$ $x = 625$

(Extraneous)

22. $2x^{1/2} - x^{1/4} - 1 = 0$

Let $y = x^{1/4}$, $y^2 = x^{1/2}$.

$2y^2 - y - 1 = 0$

$(2y + 1)(y - 1) = 0$

$2y + 1 = 0$ or $y - 1 = 0$

$y = -\dfrac{1}{2}$ $y = 1$

$x^{1/4} = -\dfrac{1}{2}$ $x^{1/4} = 1$

$x = \left(-\dfrac{1}{2}\right)^4$ $x = (1)^4$

$x = \dfrac{1}{16}$ $x = 1$

(Extraneous)

24. $2x^{2/5} + 7x^{1/5} + 3 = 0$

Let $y = x^{1/5}$, $y^2 = x^{2/5}$.

$2y^2 + 7y + 3 = 0$

$(2y + 1)(y + 3) = 0$

$2y + 1 = 0$ or $y + 3 = 0$

$y = -\dfrac{1}{2}$ $y = -3$

$x^{1/5} = -\dfrac{1}{2}$ $x^{1/5} = -3$

$x = \left(-\dfrac{1}{2}\right)^5$ $x = (-3)^5$

$x = -\dfrac{1}{32}$ $x = -243$

26. $(x^2 - 2x)^2 + 2(x^2 - 2x) = 3$

Let $y = x^2 - 2x$, $y^2 = (x^2 - 2x)^2$.

$y^2 + 2y = 3$

$y^2 + 2y - 3 = 0$

$(y + 3)(y - 1) = 0$

$y + 3 = 0$　　or　　$y - 1 = 0$
$y = -3$　　　　　　　$y = 1$
$x^2 - 2x = -3$　　　　$x^2 - 2x = 1$
$x^2 - 2x + 1 = -3 + 1$　$x^2 - 2x + 1 = 1 + 1$
$(x - 1)^2 = -2$　　　$(x - 1)^2 = 2$
$x - 1 = \pm\sqrt{-2}$　　$x - 1 = \pm\sqrt{2}$
$x = 1 \pm i\sqrt{2}.$　　　$x = 1 \pm \sqrt{2}$

28. $x - 6x^{1/2} + 8 = 0$
Let $y = x^{1/2}, \; y^2 = x.$
$y^2 - 6y + 8 = 0$
$(y - 4)(y - 2) = 0$
$y - 4 = 0$　　or　　$y - 2 = 0$
$y = 4$　　　　　　　$y = 2$
$x^{1/2} = 4$　　　　$x^{1/2} = 2$
$x = 4^2$　　　　　$x = 2^2$
$x = 16$　　　　　　$x = 4$

30. $20x^{-2} + 9x^{-1} + 1 = 0$
Let $y = x^{-1}, \; y^2 = x^{-2}.$
$20y^2 + 9y + 1 = 0$
$(4y + 1)(5y + 1) = 0$
$4y + 1 = 0$　　or　　$5y + 1 = 0$
$4y = -1$　　　　　$5y = -1$
$y = -\dfrac{1}{4}$　　　　$y = -\dfrac{1}{5}$
$x^{-1} = -\dfrac{1}{4}$　　　$x^{-1} = -\dfrac{1}{5}$
$x = \left(-\dfrac{1}{4}\right)^{-1}$　　$x = \left(-\dfrac{1}{5}\right)^{-1}$
$x = -4$　　　　　　$x = -5$

32. $\dfrac{3}{(x-2)^2} - \dfrac{4}{x-2} + 1 = 0$
Let $y = \dfrac{1}{x-2}, \; y^2 = \dfrac{1}{(x-2)^2}.$
$3y^2 - 4y + 1 = 0$
$(3y - 1)(y - 1) = 0$
$3y - 1 = 0$　　or　　$y - 1 = 0$
$y = \dfrac{1}{3}$　　　　　$y = 1$
$\dfrac{1}{x-2} = \dfrac{1}{3}$　　　$\dfrac{1}{x-2} = 1$
$3 = x - 2$　　　　$1 = x - 2$
$5 = x$　　　　　　$3 = x$

34. $0.97x^{1/2} - 5.02x^{1/4} + 5.96 = 0$
$97x^{1/2} - 502x^{1/4} + 596 = 0$
Let $y = x^{1/4}, \; y^2 = x^{1/2}.$
$97y^2 - 502y + 596 = 0$
$y = \dfrac{-b \pm \sqrt{b^2 - 4ac}}{2a}$
$= \dfrac{-(-502) \pm \sqrt{(-502)^2 - 4(97)(596)}}{2(97)}$
$y \approx 3.330254782$　　or　　$y \approx 1.84500295$
$x^{1/4} \approx 3.330254782$　　$x^{1/4} \approx 1.84500295$
$x \approx (3.330254782)^4$　　$x \approx (1.84500295)^4$
$x \approx 123.00$　　　　　　$x \approx 11.59$

36. $4 - \dfrac{x^3 + 1}{x^3 + 6} = \dfrac{x^3 - 3}{x^3 + 2}$
$\dfrac{4(x^3 + 6) - (x^3 + 1)}{x^3 + 6} = \dfrac{x^3 - 3}{x^3 + 2}$
$\dfrac{4x^3 + 24 - x^3 - 1}{x^3 + 6} = \dfrac{x^3 - 3}{x^3 + 2}$
$\dfrac{3x^3 + 23}{x^3 + 6} = \dfrac{x^3 - 3}{x^3 + 2}$
$(3x^3 + 23)(x^3 + 2) = (x^3 + 6)(x^3 - 3)$
$3x^6 + 29x^3 + 46 = x^6 + 3x^3 - 18$
$2x^6 + 26x^3 + 64 = 0$
$x^6 + 13x^3 + 32 = 0$
Let $y = x^3, \; y^2 = x^6.$
$y^2 + 13y + 32 = 0$
$y = \dfrac{-b \pm \sqrt{b^2 - 4ac}}{2a}$
$= \dfrac{-13 \pm \sqrt{13^2 - 4(1)(32)}}{2(1)}$
$y = \dfrac{-13 \pm \sqrt{41}}{2}$
$x^3 = \dfrac{-13 \pm \sqrt{41}}{2}$
$x = \sqrt[3]{\dfrac{-13 \pm \sqrt{41}}{2}}$

Cumulative Review Problems

38. $\sqrt{27x} + 5\sqrt{3x} - 2\sqrt{48x}$
　　$= 3\sqrt{3x} + 5\sqrt{3x} - 8\sqrt{3x} = 0$

40. $\left(\sqrt{2}+\sqrt{6}\right)\left(3\sqrt{2}-2\sqrt{5}\right)$

$= 3(2) - 2\sqrt{10} + 3\sqrt{12} - 2\sqrt{30}$

$= 6 - 2\sqrt{10} + 6\sqrt{3} - 2\sqrt{30}$

42. Male: $30(894) = 26{,}820$

Female: $\dfrac{26{,}820}{689} \approx 38.93$

$38.9 - 30 = 8.9$ years

Approximately 8.9 years

8.4 Exercises

2. $E = mc^2$

$c^2 = \dfrac{E}{m}$

$c = \pm\sqrt{\dfrac{E}{m}}$

4. $H = 0.4nd^2$

$d^2 = \dfrac{H}{0.4n}$

$d = \pm\sqrt{\dfrac{H}{0.4n}}$

6. $5B = \dfrac{2}{3}hx^2$

$x^2 = \dfrac{15B}{2h}$

$x = \pm\sqrt{\dfrac{15B}{2h}}$

8. $9x^2 - 2 = 3B$

$9x^2 = 2 + 3B$

$x^2 = \dfrac{2 + 3B}{9}$

$x = \pm\sqrt{\dfrac{2 + 3B}{9}}$

$x = \pm\dfrac{\sqrt{2 + 3B}}{3}$

10. $P = \dfrac{gtw^2}{x}$

$gtw^2 = Px$

$w^2 = \dfrac{Px}{gt}$

$w = \pm\sqrt{\dfrac{Px}{gt}}$

12. $H = b(a^2 + w^2)$

$a^2 + w^2 = \dfrac{H}{b}$

$w^2 = \dfrac{H}{b} - a^2$

$w^2 = \dfrac{H - a^2 b}{b}$

$w = \pm\sqrt{\dfrac{H - a^2 b}{b}}$

14. $B = \dfrac{3gy^4}{a^2}$

$Ba^2 = 3gy^4$

$y^4 = \dfrac{Ba^2}{3g}$

$y = \pm\sqrt[4]{\dfrac{Ba^2}{3g}}$

16. $y^2 - 4yw - 45w^2 = 0$

$(y - 9w)(y + 5w) = 0$

$y - 9w = 0$ or $y + 5w = 0$

$y = 9w$ $y = -5w$

18. $\dfrac{w^2}{5} - 3y^2 = \dfrac{2wy}{5}$

$w^2 - 15y^2 - 2wy = 0$

$(w - 5y)(w + 3y) = 0$

$w - 5y = 0$ or $w + 3y = 0$

$w = 5y$ $w = -3y$

20. $A = P(1 + r)^2$

$(1 + r)^2 = \dfrac{A}{P}$

$1 + r = \pm\sqrt{\dfrac{A}{P}}$

$r = -1 \pm\sqrt{\dfrac{A}{P}}$

$r = -1 \pm \dfrac{\sqrt{AP}}{P}$

$r = \dfrac{-P \pm \sqrt{AP}}{P}$

22. $7w^2 - 5bw + 3 = 0$

$$w = \frac{-b \pm \sqrt{b^2 - 4ac}}{2a}$$

$$= \frac{-(-5b) \pm \sqrt{(-5b)^2 - 4(7)(3)}}{2(7)}$$

$$= \frac{5b \pm \sqrt{25b^2 - 84}}{14}$$

24. $B = 3abx^2 - 5x$

$0 = 3abx^2 - 5x - B$

$$x = \frac{-b \pm \sqrt{b^2 - 4ac}}{2a}$$

$$= \frac{-(-5) \pm \sqrt{(-5)^2 - 4(3ab)(-B)}}{2(3ab)}$$

$$= \frac{5 \pm \sqrt{25 + 12abB}}{6ab}$$

26. $(b-2)x^2 - 3x + 5y = 0$

$$x = \frac{-b \pm \sqrt{b^2 - 4ac}}{2a}$$

$$= \frac{-(-3) \pm \sqrt{(-3)^2 - 4(b-2)(5y)}}{2(b-2)}$$

$$= \frac{3 \pm \sqrt{9 - 20by + 40y}}{2b - 4}$$

28. $c^2 = a^2 + b^2$

$c^2 = \left(2\sqrt{3}\right)^2 + 3^2$

$c^2 = 12 + 9$

$c^2 = 21$

$c = \sqrt{21}$

30. $a^2 + b^2 = c^2$

$15^2 + b^2 = 17^2$

$225 + b^2 = 289$

$b^2 = 64$

$b = 8$

32. $a^2 + b^2 = c^2$

$a^2 + \left(\sqrt{19}\right)^2 = \left(\sqrt{34}\right)^2$

$a^2 + 19 = 34$

$a^2 = 15$

$a = \sqrt{15}$

34. $a^2 + b^2 = c^2$

$(2b)^2 + b^2 = 15^2$

$4b^2 + b^2 = 225$

$5b^2 = 225$

$b^2 = 45$

$b = 3\sqrt{5}$

$a = 2b = 2\left(3\sqrt{5}\right) = 6\sqrt{5}$

36. longer leg: x
shorter leg: $x - 2$

$x^2 + (x-2)^2 = (10)^2$

$x^2 + x^2 - 4x + 4 = 100$

$2x^2 - 4x - 96 = 0$

$x^2 - 2x - 48 = 0$

$(x-8)(x+6) = 0$

$x - 8 = 0$ or $x + 6 = 0$

$x = 8$ $x = -6$

$x - 2 = 6$

The longer leg is 8 miles.
The shorter leg is 6 miles.

38. second distance: x
final distance: $x + 4$

$x^2 + (x+4)^2 = (12)^2$

$x^2 + x^2 + 8x + 16 = 144$

$2x^2 + 8x - 128 = 0$

$x^2 + 4x - 64 = 0$

$a = 1, b = 4, c = -64$

$$x = \frac{-4 \pm \sqrt{4^2 - 4(1)(-64)}}{2(1)}$$

$$= \frac{-4 \pm \sqrt{272}}{2}$$

$x \approx -10.25$ or $x \approx 6.25$
x cannot be negative.
$x + 4 = 10.25$
The second distance is approximately 6.25 miles.
The final distance is approximately 10.25 miles.

40. width: x
length: $2x - 6$
area = width × length

$140 = x(2x - 6)$

$140 = 2x^2 - 6x$

$x^2 - 3x - 70 = 0$

$(x-10)(x+7) = 0$

$x - 10 = 0$ or $x + 7 = 0$

$x = 10$ $x = -7$

x cannot be negative.

$2x - 6 = 2(10) - 6 = 14$
The width is 10 meters and the length is 14 meters.

42. base: x
altitude: $5x + 2$

$$\frac{1}{2}x(5x + 2) = 96$$

$$x(5x + 2) = 192$$

$$5x^2 + 2x = 192$$

$$5x^2 + 2x - 192 = 0$$

$$(5x + 32)(x - 6) = 0$$

$5x + 32 = 0$ or $x - 6 = 0$
$5x = -32$ $\quad\quad$ $x = 6$

$x = -\dfrac{32}{5}$ $\quad\quad$ $5x + 2 = 5(6) + 2 = 32$

base: 6 cm; altitude: 32 cm

44.

	$D/$	$R =$	T
1st part	225	x	$\frac{225}{x}$
2nd part	150	$x + 5$	$\frac{150}{x+5}$

$$\frac{225}{x} + \frac{150}{x+5} = 8$$

$$225(x + 5) + 150x = 8x(x + 5)$$

$$225x + 1125 + 150x = 8x^2 + 40x$$

$$375x + 1125 = 8x^2 + 40x$$

$$0 = 8x^2 - 335x - 1125$$

$$0 = (8x + 25)(x - 45)$$

$8x + 25 = 0$ or $x - 45 = 0$
$8x = -25$ $\quad\quad$ $x = 45$

$x = -\dfrac{25}{8}$ $\quad\quad$ $x + 5 = 45 + 5 = 50$

1st part: 45 mph; 2nd part: 50 mph

46. Time(home to work) = x hours
Time(work to home)

$$= \left(1\frac{16}{60} - x\right) = \left(\frac{19}{15} - x\right) \text{ hrs}$$

$D = RT$

$$50x = 45\left(\frac{19}{15} - x\right)$$

$$50x = 57 - 45x$$

$$95x = 57$$

$$x = \frac{57}{95} = \frac{3}{5} \text{ hours}$$

$$D = 50\left(\frac{3}{5}\right) = 30 \text{ miles}$$

48. $A = P(1 + r)^2$
$1514.24 = 1400(1 + r)^2$

$1.0816 = (1 + r)^2$

$\sqrt{1.0816} = 1 + r$

$1.04 = 1 + r$

$0.04 = r$

4%

Cumulative Review Problems

50. $\dfrac{5\sqrt{6}}{2\sqrt{5}} = \dfrac{5\sqrt{6}}{2\sqrt{5}} \cdot \dfrac{\sqrt{5}}{\sqrt{5}} = \dfrac{5\sqrt{30}}{10} = \dfrac{\sqrt{30}}{2}$

52. $\dfrac{2\sqrt{3}}{\sqrt{3} - \sqrt{6}}$

$= \dfrac{2\sqrt{3}}{\sqrt{3} - \sqrt{6}} \cdot \dfrac{\sqrt{3} + \sqrt{6}}{\sqrt{3} + \sqrt{6}}$

$= \dfrac{2(3) + 2\sqrt{18}}{3 - 6}$

$= \dfrac{6 + 6\sqrt{2}}{-3}$

$= -2 - 2\sqrt{2}$

Putting Your Skills to Work

2.

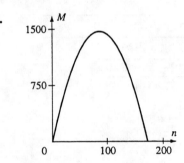

The maximum movement of cars occurs when there are 86 cars per mile.

4. $M = an^2 + bn$
$(n, m) = (180, 468)$
$(n, m) = (100, 1700)$
$468 = a(180)^2 + b(180)$
$1700 = a(100)^2 + b(100)$

$468 = 32,400a + 180b$
$1700 = 10,000a + 100b$

$-4680 = -324,000a - 1800b$
$\underline{30,600 = \quad 180,000a + 1800b}$
$\overline{25,920 = -144,000a}$
$-0.18 = a$
$468 = 32,400(-0.18) + 180b$

$b = \dfrac{468 + 5832}{180} = 35$

$a = -0.18, b = 35$

$M = -0.18n^2 + 35n$

8.5 Exercises

2. $f(x) = x^2 - 4x - 12$

$-\dfrac{b}{2a} = -\dfrac{(-4)}{2(1)} = 2$

$f(2) = 2^2 - 4(2) - 12 = -16$

Vertex: $(2, -16)$

$f(0) = 0^2 - 4(0) - 12 = -12$

y-intercept: $(0, -12)$

$x^2 - 4x - 12 = 0$

$(x - 6)(x + 2) = 0$

$x - 6 = 0 \qquad$ or $\qquad x + 2 = 0$

$x = 6 \qquad\qquad\qquad x = -2$

x-intercepts: $(-2, 0), (6, 0)$

4. $g(x) = x^2 + 10x - 24$

$-\dfrac{b}{2a} = -\dfrac{10}{2(1)} = -5$

$g(-5) = (-5)^2 + 10(-5) - 24 = -49$

Vertex: $(-5, -49)$

$g(0) = 0^2 + 10(0) - 24 = -24$

y-intercept: $(0, -24)$

$x^2 + 10x - 24 = 0$

$(x + 12)(x - 2) = 0$

$x + 12 = 0 \quad$ or $\quad x - 2 = 0$

$x = -12 \qquad\qquad x = 2$

x-intercepts: $(-12, 0), (2, 0)$

6. $p(x) = 2x^2 + 4x + 1$

$-\dfrac{b}{2a} = \dfrac{-4}{2(2)} = -1$

$p(-1) = 2(-1)^2 + 4(-1) + 1 = -1$

Vertex: $(-1, -1)$

$p(0) = 2(0)^2 + 4(0) + 1 = 1$

y-intercept: $(0, 1)$

$2x^2 + 4x + 1 = 0$

$x = \dfrac{-4 \pm \sqrt{4^2 - 4(2)(1)}}{2(2)}$

$x = \dfrac{-4 \pm \sqrt{8}}{4} = \dfrac{-4 \pm 2\sqrt{2}}{4} = \dfrac{-2 \pm \sqrt{2}}{2}$

x-intercepts: Approximately $(-1.7, 0), (-0.3, 0)$

8. $r(x) = -3x^2 - 4x - 3$

$-\dfrac{b}{2a} = -\dfrac{-4}{2(-3)} = -\dfrac{2}{3}$

$r\left(-\dfrac{2}{3}\right) = -3\left(-\dfrac{2}{3}\right)^2 - 4\left(-\dfrac{2}{3}\right) - 3 = -\dfrac{5}{3}$

Vertex: $\left(-\dfrac{2}{3}, -\dfrac{5}{3}\right)$

$r(0) = -3(0)^2 - 4(0) - 3 = -3$

y-intercept: $(0, -3)$

$-3x^2 - 4x - 3 = 0$

$x = \dfrac{-(-4) \pm \sqrt{(-4)^2 - 4(-3)(-3)}}{2(-3)}$

$= \dfrac{4 \pm \sqrt{-20}}{-6} = \dfrac{4 \pm 2i\sqrt{5}}{-6} = -\dfrac{2 \pm i\sqrt{5}}{3}$

No x-intercepts

10. $s(x) = -2x^2 + 6x + 5$

$-\dfrac{b}{2a} = -\dfrac{6}{2(-2)} = \dfrac{3}{2}$

$s\left(\dfrac{3}{2}\right) = -2\left(\dfrac{3}{2}\right)^2 + 6\left(\dfrac{3}{2}\right) + 5 = \dfrac{19}{2}$

Vertex: $\left(\dfrac{3}{2}, \dfrac{19}{2}\right)$

$s(0) = -2(0)^2 + 6(0) + 5 = 5$

y-intercept: $(0, 5)$

$-2x^2 + 6x + 5 = 0$

$x = \dfrac{-6 \pm \sqrt{6^2 - 4(-2)(5)}}{2(-2)}$

$= \dfrac{-6 \pm \sqrt{76}}{-4} = \dfrac{-6 \pm 2\sqrt{19}}{-4} = \dfrac{3 \pm \sqrt{19}}{2}$

$x \approx -0.7$ or $x \approx 3.7$

x-intercepts: Approximately $(-0.7, 0), (3.7, 0)$

12. $f(x) = 2x^2 + 3x - 9$

$-\dfrac{b}{2a} = -\dfrac{3}{2(2)} = -\dfrac{3}{4}$

$f\left(-\dfrac{3}{4}\right) = 2\left(-\dfrac{3}{4}\right)^2 + 3\left(-\dfrac{3}{4}\right) - 9 = -\dfrac{81}{8}$

Vertex: $\left(-\dfrac{3}{4}, -\dfrac{81}{8}\right)$

$f(0) = 2(0)^2 + 3(0) - 9 = -9$

y-intercept: $(0, -9)$

$2x^2 + 3x - 9 = 0$

$(x + 3)(2x - 3) = 0$

$x + 3 = 0$ or $2x - 3 = 0$

$x = -3$ $x = \dfrac{3}{2} = 1.5$

x-intercepts: $(-3, 0)$, $(1.5, 0)$

14. $h(x) = 4x^2 + 8x + 38$

$-\dfrac{b}{2a} = -\dfrac{8}{2(4)} = -1$

$h(-1) = 4(-1)^2 + 8(-1) + 38 = 34$

Vertex: $(-1, 34)$

$h(0) = 4(0)^2 + 8(0) + 38 = 38$

y-intercept: $(0, 38)$

$4x^2 + 8x + 38 = 0$

$x = \dfrac{-8 \pm \sqrt{8^2 - 4(4)(38)}}{2(4)}$

$= \dfrac{-8 \pm \sqrt{-544}}{8} = \dfrac{-8 \pm 4i\sqrt{34}}{8} = \dfrac{-2 \pm i\sqrt{34}}{2}$

No x-intercepts

16. $f(x) = x^2 + 6x + 8$

$-\dfrac{b}{2a} = -\dfrac{6}{2(1)} = -3$

$f(-3) = (-3)^2 + 6(-3) + 8 = -1$

Vertex: $(-3, -1)$

$f(0) = 0^2 + 6(0) + 8 = 8$

y-intercept: $(0, 8)$

$x^2 + 6x + 8 = 0$

$(x + 4)(x + 2) = 0$

$x + 4 = 0$ or $x + 2 = 0$

$x = -4$ $x = -2$

x-intercepts: $(-4, 0)$, $(-2, 0)$

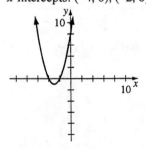

18. $g(x) = x^2 - 2x - 8$

$-\dfrac{b}{2a} = -\dfrac{-2}{2(1)} = 1$

$g(1) = 1^2 - 2(1) - 8 = -9$

Vertex: $(1, -9)$

$g(0) = 0^2 - 2(0) - 8 = -8$

y-intercept: $(0, -8)$

$x^2 - 2x - 8 = 0$

$(x - 4)(x + 2) = 0$

$x - 4 = 0$ or $x + 2 = 0$

$x = 4$ $x = -2$

x-intercepts: $(4, 0)$, $(-2, 0)$

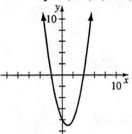

20. $p(x) = -x^2 - 3x - 2$

$-\dfrac{b}{2a} = -\dfrac{-3}{2(-1)} = -\dfrac{3}{2}$

$p\left(-\dfrac{3}{2}\right) = -\left(-\dfrac{3}{2}\right)^2 - 3\left(-\dfrac{3}{2}\right) - 2 = \dfrac{1}{4}$

Vertex: $\left(-\dfrac{3}{2}, \dfrac{1}{4}\right)$

$p(0) = -(0)^2 - 3(0) - 2 = -2$

y-intercept: $(0, -2)$

$-x^2 - 3x - 2 = 0$

$x^2 + 3x + 2 = 0$

$(x + 2)(x + 1) = 0$

$x + 2 = 0$ or $x + 1 = 0$

$x = -2$ $x = -1$

x-intercepts: $(-2, 0)$, $(-1, 0)$

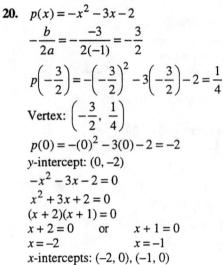

22. $r(x) = -x^2 + 4x - 5$

$-\dfrac{b}{2a} = -\dfrac{4}{2(-1)} = 2$

$r(2) = -2^2 + 4(2) - 5 = -1$

Vertex: $(2, -1)$

$r(0) = -0^2 + 4(0) - 5 = -5$

y-intercept: $(0, -5)$

$-x^2 + 4x - 5 = 0$

$$x = \frac{-4 \pm \sqrt{4^2 - 4(-1)(-5)}}{2(-1)}$$

$$= \frac{-4 \pm \sqrt{-4}}{-2} = \frac{-4 \pm 2i}{-2} = 2 \pm i$$

No x-intercepts

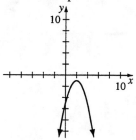

24. $f(x) = x^2 - 4x + 4$

$$-\frac{b}{2a} = -\frac{-4}{2(1)} = 2$$

$$f(2) = 2^2 - 4(2) + 4 = 0$$

Vertex: $(2, 0)$

$$f(0) = 0^2 - 4(0) + 4 = 4$$

y-intercept: $(0, 4)$

$$x^2 - 4x + 4 = 0$$

$$(x - 2)^2 = 0$$

$$x - 2 = 0$$

$$x = 2$$

x-intercept: $(2, 0)$

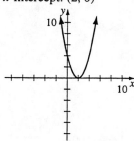

26. $g(x) = 2x^2 - 2x + 1$

$$-\frac{b}{2a} = -\frac{-2}{2(2)} = \frac{1}{2}$$

$$g\left(\frac{1}{2}\right) = 2\left(\frac{1}{2}\right)^2 - 2\left(\frac{1}{2}\right) + 1 = \frac{1}{2}$$

Vertex: $\left(\frac{1}{2}, \frac{1}{2}\right)$

$$g(0) = 2(0)^2 - 2(0) + 1 = 1$$

y-intercept: $(0, 1)$

$$2x^2 - 2x + 1 = 0$$

$$x = \frac{-(-2) \pm \sqrt{(-2)^2 - 4(2)(1)}}{2(2)}$$

$$x = \frac{2 \pm \sqrt{-4}}{4} = \frac{2 \pm 2i}{4} = \frac{1 \pm i}{2}$$

No x-intercepts

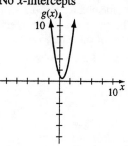

28. $d(t) = -16t^2 + 64t + 160$

Max d is at the vertex

$$-\frac{b}{2a} = -\frac{64}{2(-16)} = 2$$

$$d(2) = -16(2)^2 + 64(2) + 160 = 224$$

Max height = 224 feet

At the ground $d = 0$

$$-16t^2 + 64t + 160 = 0$$

$$-16(t^2 - 4t - 10) = 0$$

$$t = \frac{-(-4) \pm \sqrt{(-4)^2 - 4(1)(-10)}}{2(1)}$$

$$t = \frac{4 \pm \sqrt{56}}{2} = \frac{4 \pm 2\sqrt{14}}{2} = 2 \pm \sqrt{14}$$

$t \approx -1.74$ or $t \approx 5.74$

Time can't be negative.

Time = 5.7 seconds

30. $y = x^2 + 7.8x + 13.8$

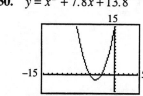

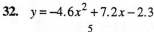

Vertex: $(-3.9, -1.4)$

y-intercept: $(0, 13.8)$

x-intercepts: $(-5.1, 0)$, $(-2.7, 0)$

32. $y = -4.6x^2 + 7.2x - 2.3$

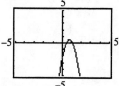

x-intercepts: $(0.4, 0)$, $(1.1, 0)$

8.6 Exercises

2. Solving a problem such as $ax^2 + bx + c \geq 0$ indicates that the endpoints of an interval are included in the solution. The endpoints are not included when $ax^2 + bx + c > 0$.

4. $x^2 + 2x - 15 < 0$
$x^2 + 2x - 15 = 0$
$(x + 5)(x - 3) = 0$
$x + 5 = 0$ or $x - 3 = 0$
$x = -5$ $x = 3$
Region I: $x = -6$
$(-6)^2 + 2(-6) - 15 = 9 > 0$
Region II: $x = 0$
$0^2 + 2(0) - 15 = -15 < 0$
Region III: $x = 4$
$4^2 + 2(4) - 15 = 9 > 0$
$-5 < x < 3$

6. $3x^2 + 11x < 0$
$3x^2 + 11x = 0$
$x(3x + 11) = 0$
$x = 0$ or $3x + 11 = 0$
$x = -\dfrac{11}{3}$
Region I: $x = -4$
$3(-4)^2 + 11(-4) = 4 > 0$
Region II: $x = -1$
$3(-1)^2 + 11(-1) = -8 < 0$
Region III: $x = 1$
$3(1)^2 + 11(1) = 14 > 0$
$-\dfrac{11}{3} < x < 0$

8. $6x^2 - 5x + 1 < 0$
$6x^2 - 5x + 1 = 0$
$(3x - 1)(2x - 1) = 0$
$3x - 1 = 0$ or $2x - 1 = 0$
$3x = 1$ $2x = 1$
$x = \dfrac{1}{3}$ $x = \dfrac{1}{2}$
Region I: $x = 0$
$6(0)^2 - 5(0) + 1 = 1 > 0$
Region II: $x = \dfrac{5}{12}$

$6\left(\dfrac{5}{12}\right)^2 - 5\left(\dfrac{5}{12}\right) + 1 = -\dfrac{1}{24} < 0$
Region III: $x = 1$
$6(1)^2 - 5(1) + 1 = 2 > 0$
$\dfrac{1}{3} < x < \dfrac{1}{2}$

10. $x^2 + 8x + 12 \geq 0$
$x^2 + 8x + 12 = 0$
$(x + 6)(x + 2) = 0$
$x + 6 = 0$ or $x + 2 = 0$
$x = -6$ $x = -2$
Region I: $x = -7$
$(-7)^2 + 8(-7) + 12 = 5 > 0$
Region II: $x = -3$
$(-3)^2 + 8(-3) + 12 = -3 < 0$
Region III: $x = 0$
$0^2 + 8(0) + 12 = 12 > 0$
$x \leq -6$ or $x \geq -2$

12. $2x^2 \leq -13x + 7$
$2x^2 + 13x - 7 \leq 0$
$2x^2 + 13x - 7 = 0$
$(2x - 1)(x + 7) = 0$
$2x - 1 = 0$ or $x + 7 = 0$
$2x = 1$ $x = -7$
$x = \dfrac{1}{2}$
Region I: $x = -8$
$2(-8)^2 + 13(-8) - 7 = 17 > 0$
Region II: $x = 0$
$2(0)^2 + 13(0) - 7 = -7 < 0$
Region III: $x = 1$
$2(1)^2 + 13(1) - 7 = 8 > 0$
$-7 \leq x \leq \dfrac{1}{2}$

14. $28 - 3x - x^2 > 0$
$x^2 + 3x - 28 < 0$
$x^2 + 3x - 28 = 0$
$(x + 7)(x - 4) = 0$
$x + 7 = 0$ or $x - 4 = 0$
$x = -7$ $x = 4$
Region I: $x = -8$
$28 - 3(-8) - (-8)^2 = -12 < 0$
Region II: $x = 0$

$28 - 3(0) - 0^2 = 28 > 0$

Region III: $x = 5$

$28 - 3(5) - 5^2 = -12 < 0$

$-7 < x < 4$

16. $3x^2 + 17x > -10$

$3x^2 + 17x + 10 > 0$

$3x^2 + 17x + 10 = 0$

$(3x + 2)(x + 5) = 0$

$3x + 2 = 0$ or $x + 5 = 0$

$3x = -2$ $x = -5$

$x = -\dfrac{2}{3}$

Region I: $x = -6$

$3(-6)^2 + 17(-6) + 10 = 16 > 0$

Region II: $x = -1$

$3(-1)^2 + 17(-1) + 10 = -4 < 0$

Region III: $x = 0$

$3(0)^2 + 17(0) + 10 = 10 > 0$

$x < -5$ or $x > -\dfrac{2}{3}$

18. $5x^2 + 13x - 6 \le 0$

$5x^2 + 13x - 6 = 0$

$(5x - 2)(x + 3) = 0$

$5x - 2 = 0$ or $x + 3 = 0$

$5x = 2$ $x = -3$

$x = \dfrac{2}{5}$

Region I: $x = -4$

$5(-4)^2 + 13(-4) - 6 = 22 > 0$

Region II: $x = 0$

$5(0)^2 + 13(0) - 6 = -6 < 0$

Region III: $x = 1$

$5(1)^2 + 13(1) - 6 = 12 > 0$

$-3 \le x \le \dfrac{2}{5}$

20. $-x^2 - 7x + 44 \ge 0$

$x^2 + 7x - 44 \le 0$

$x^2 + 7x - 44 = 0$

$(x + 11)(x - 4) = 0$

$x + 11 = 0$ or $x - 4 = 0$

$x = -11$ $x = 4$

Region I: $x = -12$

$-(-12)^2 - 7(-12) + 44 = -16 < 0$

Region II: $x = 0$

$-0^2 - 7(0) + 44 = 44 > 0$

Region III: $x = 5$

$-5^2 - 7(5) + 44 = -16 < 0$

$-11 \le x \le 4$

22. $x^2 - 6x \le -9$

$x^2 - 6x + 9 \le 0$

$x^2 - 6x + 9 = 0$

$(x - 3)^2 = 0$

$x - 3 = 0$

$x = 3$

Region I: $x = 0$

$0^2 - 6(0) + 9 = 9 > 0$

Region II: $x = 4$

$4^2 - 6(4) + 9 = 1 > 0$

Since $x^2 - 6x + 9$ equals 0 when $x = 3$ and $x^2 - 6x + 9$ is never less than 0, the solution set is $x = 3$.

24. $x^2 + 6x > 8$

$x^2 + 6x - 8 > 0$

$x = \dfrac{-6 \pm \sqrt{6^2 - 4(1)(-8)}}{2(1)}$

$= \dfrac{-6 \pm \sqrt{68}}{2} = \dfrac{-6 \pm 2\sqrt{17}}{2} = -3 \pm \sqrt{17}$

$x \approx 1.1$ or $x \approx -7.1$

Region I: $x = -8$

$(-8)^2 + 6(-8) - 8 = 8 > 0$

Region II: $x = 0$

$0^2 + 6(0) - 8 = -8 < 0$

Region III: $x = 2$

$2^2 + 6(2) - 8 = 8 > 0$

$x < -3 - \sqrt{17} \approx -7.1$ or $x > -3 + \sqrt{17} \approx 1.1$

26. $x^2 < 2x + 1$

$x^2 - 2x - 1 < 0$

$x^2 - 2x - 1 = 0$

$x = \dfrac{-(-2) \pm \sqrt{(-2)^2 - 4(1)(-1)}}{2(1)}$

$= \dfrac{2 \pm \sqrt{8}}{2} = \dfrac{2 \pm 2\sqrt{2}}{2} = 1 \pm \sqrt{2}$

$x \approx 2.4$ or $x \approx -0.4$

Region I: $x = -1$

$(-1)^2 - 2(-1) - 1 = 2 > 0$

Region II: $x = 0$

$0^2 - 2(0) - 1 = -1 < 0$

Region III: $x = 3$

$3^2 - 2(3) - 1 = 2 > 0$

$1 - \sqrt{2} < x < 1 + \sqrt{2}$
or approximately $-0.4 < x < 2.4$

28. $4x^2 \geq 6x - 1$

$4x^2 - 6x + 1 \geq 0$

$4x^2 - 6x + 1 = 0$

$x = \dfrac{-(-6) \pm \sqrt{(-6)^2 - 4(4)(1)}}{(2)(4)}$

$x = \dfrac{6 \pm \sqrt{20}}{8}$

$= \dfrac{6 \pm 2\sqrt{5}}{8}$

$= \dfrac{3 \pm \sqrt{5}}{4}$

$x \approx 1.3$ or $x \approx 0.2$
Region I: $x = 0$
$4(0)^2 - 6(0) + 1 = 1 > 0$
Region II: $x = 1$
$4(1)^2 - 6(1) + 1 = -1 < 0$
Region III: $x = 2$
$4(2)^2 - 6(2) + 1 = 5 > 0$

$x \leq \dfrac{3 - \sqrt{5}}{4} \approx 0.2$ or $x \geq \dfrac{3 + \sqrt{5}}{4} \approx 1.3$

30. $x^2 + 2x + 6 \leq 0$

$x^2 + 2x + 6 = 0$

$x = \dfrac{-2 \pm \sqrt{2^2 - 4(1)(6)}}{2(1)}$

$= \dfrac{-2 \pm \sqrt{-20}}{2}$

No real number solution, so no critical values.
Check one value of x.
$x = 0$
$0^2 + 2(0) + 6 = 6 > 0$
No solution

32. $s = -16t^2 + 640t > 6000$

$-16t^2 + 640t - 6000 > 0$

$-16(t^2 - 40t + 375) > 0$

$t^2 - 40t + 375 < 0$

$t^2 - 40t + 375 = 0$

$(t - 25)(t - 15) = 0$

$t - 25 = 0$ or $t - 15 = 0$
$t = 25$ $t = 15$
Region I: $t = 0$
$0^2 - 40(0) + 375 = 375 > 0$
Region II: $t = 20$
$20^2 - 40(20) + 375 = -25 < 0$

Region III: $t = 30$
$30^2 - 40(30) + 375 = 75 > 0$
$15 < t < 25$
The time must be between 15 sec and 25 sec.

34. a. Profit $= -20(x^2 - 220x + 2400)$
$-20(x^2 - 220x + 2400) > 0$
$x^2 - 220x + 2400 < 0$
$x^2 - 220x + 2400 = 0$

$x = \dfrac{220 \pm \sqrt{38,800}}{2} = \dfrac{220 \pm 20\sqrt{97}}{2}$

$= 110 \pm 10\sqrt{97}$
$x \approx 11.5$ or $x \approx 208.5$
Region I: $x = 0$
$0^2 - 220(0) + 2400 = 2400 > 0$
Region II: $x = 100$
$100^2 - 220(100) + 2400 = -9600 < 0$
Region III: $x = 300$
$300^2 - 220(300) + 2400 = 26,400 > 0$
Approximately $11.5 < x < 208.5$

b. $P = -20(50^2 - 220(50) + 2400) = \$122,000$

c. $P = -20(60^2 - 220(60) + 2400) = \$144,000$

36.

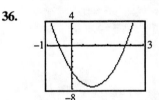

$3.9x^2 - 6.8x - 4.6 \leq 0$

$39x^2 - 68x - 46 \leq 0$

$39x^2 - 68x - 46 = 0$

$x = \dfrac{-(-68) \pm \sqrt{(-68)^2 - 4(39)(-46)}}{2(39)}$

$= \dfrac{68 \pm \sqrt{11,800}}{78}$

$x \approx 2.3$ or $x \approx -0.5$
Region I: $x = -1$
$39(-1)^2 - 68(-1) - 46 = 61 > 0$
Region II: $x = 0$
$39(0)^2 - 68(0) - 46 = -46 < 0$
Region III: $x = 3$
$39(3)^2 - 68(3) - 46 = 101 > 0$
Approximately $-0.5 \leq x \leq 2.3$

Cumulative Review Problems

38. Let x = ounces of potato chips
$x + 70$ = ounces of peanuts
$x + 10$ = ounces of popcorn
$2(x + 10)$ = ounces of pretzels
$x + x + 70 + x + 10 + 2(x + 10) = 360$
$5x + 100 = 360$
$5x = 260$
$x = 52$
$x + 70 = 122$
$x + 10 = 62$
$2(x + 10) = 124$
There are 52 ounces of potato chips, 122 ounces of peanuts, 62 ounces of popcorn, and 124 ounces of pretzels.

Chapter 8 Review Problems

2. $(x + 2)^2 = 25$
$x + 2 = \pm\sqrt{25}$
$x + 2 = \pm 5$
$x = -2 \pm 5$
$x = -2 + 5$ or $x = -2 - 5$
$x = 3$ $x = -7$

4. $4x^2 - 8x + 1 = 0$
$x^2 - 2x + \dfrac{1}{4} = 0$
$x^2 - 2x = -\dfrac{1}{4}$
$x^2 - 2x + 1 = -\dfrac{1}{4} + 1$
$(x - 1)^2 = \dfrac{3}{4}$
$x - 1 = \pm\sqrt{\dfrac{3}{4}}$
$x - 1 = \pm\dfrac{\sqrt{3}}{2}$
$x = 1 \pm \dfrac{\sqrt{3}}{2}$ or $x = \dfrac{2 \pm \sqrt{3}}{2}$

6. $x^2 - 6x - 4 = 0$
$a = 1,\ b = -6,\ c = -4$
$x = \dfrac{-b \pm \sqrt{b^2 - 4ac}}{2a}$
$= \dfrac{-(-6) \pm \sqrt{(-6)^2 - 4(1)(-4)}}{2(1)}$
$= \dfrac{6 \pm \sqrt{36 + 16}}{2}$
$= \dfrac{6 \pm \sqrt{52}}{2}$
$= \dfrac{6 \pm 2\sqrt{13}}{2}$
$= 3 \pm \sqrt{13}$

8. $4x^2 - 12 + 9 = 0$
$(2x - 3)^2 = 0$
$2x - 3 = 0$
$2x = 3$
$x = \dfrac{3}{2}$

10. $8x^2 - 26x + 15 = 0$
$(4x - 3)(2x - 5) = 0$
$4x - 3 = 0$ or $2x - 5 = 0$
$4x = 3$ $2x = 5$
$x = \dfrac{3}{4}$ $x = \dfrac{5}{2}$

12. $9x^2 + 27 = 0$
$9x^2 = -27$
$x^2 = -3$
$x = \pm\sqrt{-3}$
$x = \pm i\sqrt{3}$

14. $25x^2 - 10x + 1 = 1$
$25x^2 - 10x = 0$
$5x(5x - 2) = 0$
$5x = 0$ or $5x - 2 = 0$
$x = 0$ $5x = 2$
                         $x = \dfrac{2}{5}$

16. $6x^2 + 12x - 24 = 0$
$x^2 + 2x - 4 = 0$
$a = 1,\ b = 2,\ c = -4$
$x = \dfrac{-b \pm \sqrt{b^2 - 4ac}}{2a}$
$= \dfrac{-2 \pm \sqrt{2^2 - 4(1)(-4)}}{2(1)}$
$= \dfrac{-2 \pm \sqrt{4 + 16}}{2}$
$= \dfrac{-2 \pm \sqrt{20}}{2}$
$= \dfrac{-2 \pm 2\sqrt{5}}{2}$
$= -1 \pm \sqrt{5}$

18. $3x^2 + 5x + 1 = 0$
$a = 3, \ b = 5, \ c = 1$

$x = \dfrac{-b \pm \sqrt{b^2 - 4ac}}{2a}$

$= \dfrac{-5 \pm \sqrt{5^2 - 4(3)(1)}}{2(3)}$

$= \dfrac{-5 \pm \sqrt{25 - 12}}{6}$

$= \dfrac{-5 \pm \sqrt{13}}{6}$

20. $10x(x - 2) + 10 = 2x$
$10x^2 - 20x + 10 = 2x$
$10x^2 - 22x + 10 = 0$
$5x^2 - 11x + 5 = 0$
$a = 5, \ b = -11, \ c = 5$

$x = \dfrac{-b \pm \sqrt{b^2 - 4ac}}{2a}$

$= \dfrac{-(-11) \pm \sqrt{(-11)^2 - 4(5)(5)}}{2(5)}$

$= \dfrac{11 \pm \sqrt{121 - 100}}{10}$

$= \dfrac{11 \pm \sqrt{21}}{10}$

22. $\dfrac{(x - 2)^2}{20} + x = -3$

$(x - 2)^2 + 20x = -60$

$x^2 - 4x + 4 + 20x = -60$

$x^2 + 16x + 64 = 0$

$(x + 8)^2 = 0$

$x + 8 = 0$

$x = -8$

24. $\dfrac{4}{5}x^2 + x + \dfrac{1}{5} = 0$

$4x^2 + 5x + 1 = 0$

$(4x + 1)(x + 1) = 0$

$4x + 1 = 0$ or $x + 1 = 0$
$4x = -1$ $x = -1$

$x = -\dfrac{1}{4}$

26. $\dfrac{19}{y} - \dfrac{15}{y^2} + 10 = 0$

$19y - 15 + 10y^2 = 0$

$10y^2 + 19y - 15 = 0$

$(5y - 3)(2y + 5) = 0$
$5y - 3 = 0$ or $2y + 5 = 0$
$5y = 3$ $2y = -5$

$y = \dfrac{3}{5}$ $y = -\dfrac{5}{2}$

28. $y - 18 + \dfrac{81}{y} = 0$

$y^2 - 18y + 81 = 0$

$(y - 9)^2 = 0$

$y - 9 = 0$

$y = 9$

30. $y(y + 1) + (y + 2)^2 = 4$

$y^2 + y + y^2 + 4y + 4 = 4$

$2y^2 + 5y = 0$

$y(2y + 5) = 0$

$y = 0$ or $2y + 5 = 0$
                  $2y = -5$

                  $y = -\dfrac{5}{2}$

32. $\dfrac{4x + 1}{2x + 5} + \dfrac{3x}{x + 4} = 2$

$(x + 4)(2x + 5)\left(\dfrac{4x + 1}{2x + 5}\right) + (x + 4)(2x + 5)\left(\dfrac{3x}{x + 4}\right)$

$= (x + 4)(2x + 5)(2)$

$(x + 4)(4x + 1) + (2x + 5)(3x)$

$= 2(x + 4)(2x + 5)$

$4x^2 + 17x + 4 + 6x^2 + 15x = 4x^2 + 26x + 40$

$10x^2 + 32x + 4 = 4x^2 + 26x + 40$

$6x^2 + 6x - 36 = 0$

$x^2 + x - 6 = 0$

$(x + 3)(x - 2) = 0$

$x + 3 = 0$ or $x - 2 = 0$
$x = -3$ $x = 2$

34. $3x^2 - 7x - 12 = 0$
$a = 3, \ b = -7, \ c = -12$
$b^2 - 4ac = (-7)^2 - 4(3)(-12)$
$= 49 + 144 = 193 > 0$ (Not a perfect square)
Two irrational solutions

36. $25x^2 - 20x + 4 = 0$
$a = 25, \ b = -20, \ c = 4$
$b^2 - 4ac = (-20)^2 - 4(25)(4) = 400 - 400 = 0$
One rational solution

38.
$$x = 3i \qquad\qquad x = -3i$$
$$x - 3i = 0 \qquad\qquad x + 3i = 0$$
$$(x - 3i)(x + 3i) = 0$$
$$x^2 - 9i^2 = 0$$
$$x^2 + 9 = 0$$

40.
$$x = -\frac{3}{4} \qquad\qquad x = -\frac{1}{2}$$
$$4x = -3 \qquad\qquad 2x = -1$$
$$4x + 3 = 0 \qquad\qquad 2x + 1 = 0$$
$$(4x + 3)(2x + 1) = 0$$
$$8x^2 + 10x + 3 = 0$$

42.
$$5x^2 - 2x - 9 = 0$$
$$a = 5,\ b = -2,\ c = -9$$
$$x = \frac{-b \pm \sqrt{b^2 - 4ac}}{2a}$$
$$= \frac{-(-2) \pm \sqrt{(-2)^2 - 4(5)(-9)}}{2(5)}$$
$$= \frac{2 \pm \sqrt{4 + 180}}{10}$$
$$= \frac{2 \pm \sqrt{184}}{10} = \frac{2 \pm 2\sqrt{46}}{10} = \frac{1 \pm \sqrt{46}}{5}$$
$$x \approx 1.6 \text{ or } x \approx -1.2$$

44.
$$2x^6 - 5x^3 - 3 = 0$$
Let $y = x^3$, $y^2 = x^6$.
$$2y^2 - 5y - 3 = 0$$
$$(2y + 1)(y - 3) = 0$$
$$2y + 1 = 0 \quad \text{or} \quad y - 3 = 0$$
$$2y = -1 \qquad\qquad y = 3$$
$$y = -\frac{1}{2}$$
$$x^3 = -\frac{1}{2} \qquad\qquad x^3 = 3$$
$$x = \sqrt[3]{-\frac{1}{2}} \qquad\qquad x = \sqrt[3]{3}$$
$$x = \frac{-1}{\sqrt[3]{2}}$$
$$x = -\frac{\sqrt[3]{4}}{2}$$

46.
$$x^{2/3} + 9x^{1/3} = -8$$
$$x^{2/3} + 9x^{1/3} + 8 = 0$$
Let $y = x^{1/3}$, $y^2 = x^{2/3}$.
$$y^2 + 9y + 8 = 0$$
$$(y + 8)(y + 1) = 0$$
$$y + 8 = 0 \quad \text{or} \quad y + 1 = 0$$
$$y = -8 \qquad\qquad y = -1$$

$$x^{1/3} = -8 \qquad\qquad x^{1/3} = -1$$
$$x = (-8)^3 \qquad\qquad x = (-1)^3$$
$$x = -512 \qquad\qquad x = -1$$

48.
$$1 + 4x^{-8} = 5x^{-4}$$
$$4x^{-8} - 5x^{-4} + 1 = 0$$
Let $y = x^{-4}$, $y^2 = x^{-8}$.
$$4y^2 - 5y + 1 = 0$$
$$(4y - 1)(y - 1) = 0$$
$$4y - 1 = 0 \quad \text{or} \quad y - 1 = 0$$
$$4y = 1 \qquad\qquad y = 1$$
$$y = \frac{1}{4}$$
$$x^{-4} = \frac{1}{4} \qquad\qquad x^{-4} = 1$$
$$\frac{1}{x^4} = \frac{1}{4} \qquad\qquad \frac{1}{x^4} = 1$$
$$x^4 = 4 \qquad\qquad x^4 = 1$$
$$x = \pm\sqrt[4]{4} \qquad\qquad x = \pm\sqrt[4]{1}$$
$$x = \pm\sqrt[4]{2^2} \qquad\qquad x = \pm 1$$
$$x = \pm\sqrt{2}$$

50.
$$2H = 3g(a^2 + b^2)$$
$$\frac{2H}{3g} = a^2 + b^2$$
$$\frac{2H}{3g} - a^2 = b^2$$
$$\pm\sqrt{\frac{2H}{3g} - a^2} = b$$

52.
$$yx^2 - 3x - 7 = 0$$
$$a = y,\ b = -3,\ c = -7$$
$$x = \frac{-b \pm \sqrt{b^2 - 4ac}}{2a}$$
$$= \frac{-(-3) \pm \sqrt{(-3)^2 - 4(y)(-7)}}{2(y)}$$
$$= \frac{3 \pm \sqrt{9 + 28y}}{2y}$$

54.
$$PV = 5x^2 + 3y^2 + 2x$$
$$0 = 5x^2 + 2x + 3y^2 - PV$$
$$a = 5,\ b = 2,\ c = 3y^2 - PV$$
$$x = \frac{-b \pm \sqrt{b^2 - 4ac}}{2a}$$

$$= \frac{-2 \pm \sqrt{2^2 - 4(5)(3y^2 - PV)}}{2(5)}$$

$$= \frac{-2 \pm \sqrt{4 - 60y^2 + 20PV}}{10}$$

$$= \frac{-2 \pm \sqrt{4(1 - 15y^2 + 5PV)}}{10}$$

$$= \frac{-2 \pm 2\sqrt{1 - 15y^2 + 5PV}}{10}$$

$$= \frac{-1 \pm \sqrt{1 - 15y^2 + 5PV}}{5}$$

56. $a^2 + b^2 = c^2$

$a^2 + 4^2 = 16^2$

$a^2 + 16 = 256$

$a^2 = 240$

$a = \sqrt{240}$

$a = 4\sqrt{15}$

58. width: x

length: $4x + 1$

$x(4x + 1) = 203$

$4x^2 + x = 203$

$4x^2 + x - 203 = 0$

$(4x + 29)(x - 7) = 0$

$4x + 29 = 0$ or $x - 7 = 0$

$4x = -29$ $x = 7$

$x = -\dfrac{29}{4}$

$4x + 1 = 4(7) + 1 = 29$

width: 7 meters; length: 29 meters

60.

	D	/	R	= T
1st part	200		x	$\frac{200}{x}$
2nd part	90		$x - 5$	$\frac{90}{x-5}$

$$\frac{200}{x} + \frac{90}{x - 5} = 6$$

$200(x - 5) + 90x = 6x(x - 5)$

$200x - 1000 + 90x = 6x^2 - 30x$

$290x - 1000 = 6x^2 - 30x$

$0 = 6x^2 - 320x + 1000$

$0 = 3x^2 - 160x + 500$

$0 = (3x - 10)(x - 50)$

$3x - 10 = 0$ or $x - 50 = 0$

$3x = 10$ $x = 50$

$x = \dfrac{10}{3}$

$x - 5 = 50 - 5 = 45$

$x - 5 = \dfrac{10}{3} - 5 = -\dfrac{5}{3}$ (Extraneous)

1st part: 50 mph; 2nd part: 45 mph

62. Total Area – Garden Area = Walkway Area

$(10 + 2x)(6 + 2x) - 10(6) = 100$

$60 + 32x + 4x^2 - 60 = 100$

$4x^2 + 32x - 100 = 0$

$x^2 + 8x - 25 = 0$

$$x = \frac{-8 \pm \sqrt{8^2 - 4(1)(-25)}}{2(1)}$$

$$= \frac{-8 \pm \sqrt{164}}{2} = \frac{-8 \pm 2\sqrt{41}}{2} = -4 \pm \sqrt{41}$$

$x \approx 2.4$

2.4 ft wide

64. $f(x) = x^2 + 10x + 25$

$-\dfrac{b}{2a} = -\dfrac{10}{2(1)} = -5$

$f(-5) = (-5)^2 + 10(-5) + 25 = 0$

Vertex: $(-5, 0)$

$f(0) = 0^2 + 10(0) + 25 = 25$

y-intercept: $(0, 25)$

$x^2 + 10x + 25 = 0$

$(x + 5)^2 = 0$

$x + 5 = 0$

$x = -5$

x-intercept: $(-5, 0)$

66. $f(x) = x^2 + 4x + 3$

$-\dfrac{b}{2a} = -\dfrac{4}{2(1)} = -2$

$f(-2) = (-2)^2 + 4(-2) + 3 = -1$

Vertex: $(-2, -1)$

$f(0) = 0^2 + 4(0) + 3 = 3$

y-intercept: $(0, 3)$

$x^2 + 4x + 3 = 0$

$(x + 3)(x + 1) = 0$

$x + 3 = 0$ or $x + 1 = 0$

$x = -3$ $x = -1$

x-intercepts: $(-3, 0)$, $(-1, 0)$

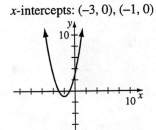

68. $f(x) = -x^2 + 6x - 5$

$-\dfrac{b}{2a} = -\dfrac{6}{2(-1)} = 3$

$f(3) = -3^2 + 6(3) - 5 = 4$

Vertex: $(3, 4)$

$f(0) = -0^2 + 6(0) - 5 = -5$

y-intercept: $(0, -5)$

$-x^2 + 6x - 5 = 0$

$x^2 - 6x + 5 = 0$

$(x - 5)(x - 1) = 0$

$x - 5 = 0$ or $x - 1 = 0$

$x = 5$ $x = 1$

x-intercepts: $(5, 0)$, $(1, 0)$

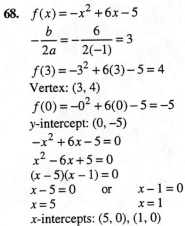

70. $h(t) = -16t^2 + 400t + 40$

$-\dfrac{b}{2a} = -\dfrac{400}{2(-16)} = \dfrac{25}{2}$

$h\left(\dfrac{25}{2}\right) = -16\left(\dfrac{25}{2}\right)^2 + 400\left(\dfrac{25}{2}\right) + 40 = 2540$

Maximum height: 2540 ft

$0 = -16t^2 + 400t + 40$

$0 = 2t^2 - 50t - 5$

$t = \dfrac{-(-50) \pm \sqrt{(-50)^2 - 4(2)(-5)}}{2(2)}$

$= \dfrac{50 \pm \sqrt{2540}}{4}$

$t \approx 25.1$ or $t \approx -0.1$

25.1 sec

72. $x^2 + 4x - 21 < 0$

$x^2 + 4x - 21 = 0$

$(x + 7)(x - 3) = 0$

$x + 7 = 0$ or $x - 3 = 0$

$x = -7$ $x = 3$

Region I: $x = -8$

$(-8)^2 + 4(-8) - 21 = 11 > 0$

Region II: $x = 0$

$0^2 + 4(0) - 21 = -21 < 0$

Region III: $x = 4$

$4^2 + 4(4) - 21 = 11 > 0$

$-7 < x < 3$

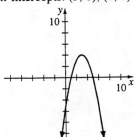

74. $x^2 - 11x + 28 > 0$

$x^2 - 11x + 28 = 0$

$(x - 7)(x - 4) = 0$

$x - 7 = 0$ or $x - 4 = 0$

$x = 7$ $x = 4$

Region I: $x = 0$

$0^2 - 11(0) + 28 = 28 > 0$

Region II: $x = 5$

$5^2 - 11(5) + 28 = -2 < 0$

Region III: $x = 8$

$8^2 - 11(8) + 28 = 4 > 0$

$x < 4$ or $x > 7$

76. $2x^2 - 5x - 3 \le 0$

$2x^2 - 5x - 3 = 0$

$(2x + 1)(x - 3) = 0$

$2x + 1 = 0$ or $x - 3 = 0$

$2x = -1$ $x = 3$

$x = -\dfrac{1}{2}$

Region I: $x = -1$

$2(-1)^2 - 5(-1) - 3 = 4 > 0$

Region II: $x = 0$

$2(0)^2 - 5(0) - 3 = -3 < 0$

Region III: $x = 4$

$2(4)^2 - 5(4) - 3 = 9 > 0$

$-\dfrac{1}{2} \le x \le 3$

78. $16x^2 - 25 > 0$

$16x^2 - 25 = 0$

$16x^2 = 25$

$x^2 = \dfrac{25}{16}$

$$x = \pm\sqrt{\frac{25}{16}}$$

$$x = \pm\frac{5}{4}$$

Region I: $x = -2$

$16(-2)^2 - 25 = 39 > 0$

Region II: $x = 0$

$16(0)^2 - 25 = -25 < 0$

Region III: $x = 2$

$16(2)^2 - 25 = 39 > 0$

$x < -\frac{5}{4}$ or $x > \frac{5}{4}$

80. $4x^2 - 8x \leq 12 + 5x^2$

$0 \leq x^2 + 8x + 12$

$0 = x^2 + 8x + 12$

$0 = (x + 6)(x + 2)$

$x + 6 = 0$ or $x + 2 = 0$

$x = -6$ $x = -2$

Region I: $x = -7$

$(-7)^2 + 8(-7) + 12 = 5 > 0$

Region II: $x = -3$

$(-3)^2 + 8(-3) + 12 = -3 < 0$

Region III: $x = 0$

$0^2 + 8(0) + 12 = 12 > 0$

$x \leq -6$ or $x \geq -2$

82. $3x^2 - 12x > -11$

$3x^2 - 12x + 11 > 0$

$3x^2 - 12x + 11 = 0$

$$x = \frac{-(-12) \pm \sqrt{(-12)^2 - 4(3)(11)}}{2(3)}$$

$$= \frac{12 \pm \sqrt{12}}{6} = \frac{12 \pm 2\sqrt{3}}{6} = \frac{6 \pm \sqrt{3}}{3}$$

$x \approx 2.6$ or $x \approx 1.4$

Region I: $x = 0$

$3(0)^2 - 12(0) + 11 = 11 > 0$

Region II: $x = 2$

$3(2)^2 - 12(2) + 11 = -1 < 0$

Region III: $x = 3$

$3(3)^2 - 12(3) + 11 = 2 > 0$

$x < \frac{6 - \sqrt{3}}{3} \approx 1.4$ or $x > \frac{6 + \sqrt{3}}{3} \approx 2.6$

84. $-2x^2 + 7x + 12 \leq -3x^2 + x$

$x^2 + 6x + 12 \leq 0$

$x^2 + 6x + 12 = 0$

$$x = \frac{-6 \pm \sqrt{6^2 - 4(1)(12)}}{2(1)}$$

$$= \frac{-6 \pm \sqrt{-12}}{2} = \frac{-6 \pm 2i\sqrt{3}}{2} = -3 \pm i\sqrt{3}$$

No real number solution, so no critical values.

Check one value of x.

$x = 0$: $0^2 + 6(0) + 12 = 12 > 0$

No solution

86. $(x + 1)(x + 4)(2 - x) < 0$

$(x + 1)(x + 4)(2 - x) = 0$

$x + 1 = 0$ $x + 4 = 0$ $2 - x = 0$

$x = -1$ $x = -4$ $2 = x$

Region I: $x = -5$

$(-5 + 1)(-5 + 4)(2 + 5) = 28 > 0$

Region II: $x = -2$

$(-2 + 1)(-2 + 4)(2 + 2) = -8 < 0$

Region III: $x = 0$

$(0 + 1)(0 + 4)(2 - 0) = 8 > 0$

Region IV: $x = 3$

$(3 + 1)(3 + 4)(2 - 3) = -28 < 0$

$-4 < x < -1$ or $x > 2$

Chapter 8 Test

2. $3x^2 + 5x = 2$

$3x^2 + 5x - 2 = 0$

$(3x - 1)(x + 2) = 0$

$3x - 1 = 0$ or $x + 2 = 0$

$3x = 1$ $x = -2$

$x = \frac{1}{3}$

4. $x(x - 8) + 16 = 8(x - 6)$

$x^2 - 8x + 16 = 8x - 48$

$x^2 - 16x + 64 = 0$

$(x - 8)^2 = 0$

$x - 8 = 0$

$x = 8$

6. $\dfrac{2x}{2x + 1} - \dfrac{6}{4x^2 - 1} = \dfrac{x + 1}{2x - 1}$

$\dfrac{2x}{2x + 1} - \dfrac{6}{(2x + 1)(2x - 1)} = \dfrac{x + 1}{2x - 1}$

$2x(2x - 1) - 6 = (x + 1)(x + 1)$

$4x^2 - 2x - 6 = 2x^2 + 3x + 1$

$2x^2 - 5x - 7 = 0$

$(2x - 7)(x + 1) = 0$

$2x - 7 = 0$ or $x + 1 = 0$

$2x = 7$ $x = -1$

$x = \frac{7}{2}$

8. $2x^2 - 6x + 5 = 0$

$a = 2,\ b = -6,\ c = 5$

$x = \dfrac{-b \pm \sqrt{b^2 - 4ac}}{2a}$

$= \dfrac{-(-6) \pm \sqrt{(-6)^2 - 4(2)(5)}}{2(2)}$

$= \dfrac{6 \pm \sqrt{36 - 40}}{4}$

$= \dfrac{6 \pm \sqrt{-4}}{4}$

$= \dfrac{6 \pm 2i}{4}$

$= \dfrac{3 \pm i}{2}$

10. $3x^{-2} - 11x^{-1} - 20 = 0$

Let $y = x^{-1},\ y^2 = x^{-2}$.

$3y^2 - 11y - 20 = 0$

$(3y + 4)(y - 5) = 0$

$3y + 4 = 0$ or $y - 5 = 0$

$3y = -4$ $\qquad\quad y = 5$

$y = -\dfrac{4}{3}$

$x^{-1} = -\dfrac{4}{3}$ $\qquad x^{-1} = 5$

$x = \left(-\dfrac{4}{3}\right)^{-1}$ $\qquad x = 5^{-1}$

$x = -\dfrac{3}{4}$ $\qquad\qquad x = \dfrac{1}{5}$

12. $B = \dfrac{xyw}{z^2}$

$Bz^2 = xyw$

$z^2 = \dfrac{xyw}{B}$

$z = \pm\sqrt{\dfrac{xyw}{B}}$

14. $c^2 = a^2 + b^2$

$c^2 = 6^2 + (2\sqrt{3})^2$

$c^2 = 36 + 12$

$c^2 = 48$

$c = \sqrt{48}$

$c = 4\sqrt{3}$

16.

	D	/	R	$= T$
1st part	6		x	$\dfrac{6}{x}$
2nd part	3		$x + 1$	$\dfrac{3}{x+1}$

$\dfrac{6}{x} + \dfrac{3}{x+1} = 4$

$6(x + 1) + 3x = 4x(x + 1)$

$6x + 6 + 3x = 4x^2 + 4x$

$9x + 6 = 4x^2 + 4x$

$0 = 4x^2 - 5x - 6$

$0 = (4x + 3)(x - 2)$

$4x + 3 = 0$ or $x - 2 = 0$

$4x = -3$ $\qquad\qquad x = 2$

$x = -\dfrac{3}{4}$

$x + 1 = 2 + 1 = 3$

1st part: 2 mph; 2nd part: 3 mph

18. $-3x^2 + 10x + 8 \ge 0$

$-3x^2 + 10x + 8 = 0$

$3x^2 - 10x - 8 = 0$

$(3x + 2)(x - 4) = 0$

$3x + 2 = 0$ or $x - 4 = 0$

$3x = -2$ $\qquad\qquad x = 4$

$x = -\dfrac{2}{3}$

Region I: $x = -1$

$-3(-1)^2 + 10(-1) + 8 = -5 < 0$

Region II: $x = 0$

$-3(0)^2 + 10(0) + 8 = 8 > 0$

Region III: $x = 5$

$-3(5)^2 + 10(5) + 8 = -17 < 0$

$-\dfrac{2}{3} \le x \le 4$

20. $x^2 + 3x - 7 > 0$

$x^2 + 3x - 7 = 0$

$x = \dfrac{-3 \pm \sqrt{3^2 - 4(1)(-7)}}{2(1)}$

$= \dfrac{-3 \pm \sqrt{37}}{2}$

$x \approx 1.5$ or $x \approx -4.5$

Region I: $x = -5$

$(-5)^2 + 3(-5) - 7 = 3 > 0$

Region II: $x = 0$

$0^2 + 3(0) - 7 = -7 < 0$

Region III: $x = 2$

$$2^2 + 3(2) - 7 = 3 > 0$$

$$x < \frac{-3 - \sqrt{37}}{2} \approx -4.5 \text{ or } x > \frac{-3 + \sqrt{37}}{2} \approx 1.5$$

Cumulative Test for Chapters 1-8

2. $\dfrac{1}{2}a^3 - 2a^2 + 3a - \dfrac{1}{4}a^3 - 6a + a^2$

$= \left(\dfrac{1}{2} - \dfrac{1}{4}\right)a^3 + (-2 + 1)a^2 + (3 - 6)a$

$= \dfrac{1}{4}a^3 - a^2 - 3a$

4. $6x - 3y = -12$

x	y
0	4
-2	0

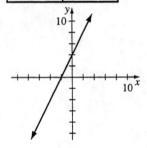

6. $V = \dfrac{4}{3}\pi r^3 = \dfrac{4}{3}\pi(2)^3 = \dfrac{32\pi}{3}$

$\dfrac{32\pi}{3}$ cubic inches

8. $\sqrt{48x^4y^5} = \sqrt{16x^4y^4 \cdot 3y}$

$= 4x^2y^2\sqrt{3y}$

10. $\dfrac{5}{\sqrt{7}} = \dfrac{5}{\sqrt{7}} \cdot \dfrac{\sqrt{7}}{\sqrt{7}} = \dfrac{5\sqrt{7}}{7}$

12. $3x^2 + 14x = 5$

$3x^2 + 14x - 5 = 0$

$(3x - 1)(x + 5) = 0$

$3x - 1 = 0$　or　$x + 5 = 0$

$3x = 1$　　　　　$x = -5$

$x = \dfrac{1}{3}$

14. $3 - \dfrac{4}{x} + \dfrac{5}{x^2} = 0$

$3x^2 - 4x + 5 = 0$

$a = 3,\ b = -4,\ c = 5$

$x = \dfrac{-b \pm \sqrt{b^2 - 4ac}}{2a}$

$= \dfrac{-(-4) \pm \sqrt{(-4)^2 - 4(3)(5)}}{2(3)}$

$= \dfrac{4 \pm \sqrt{16 - 60}}{6}$

$= \dfrac{4 \pm \sqrt{-44}}{6}$

$= \dfrac{4 \pm 2i\sqrt{11}}{6}$

$= \dfrac{2 \pm i\sqrt{11}}{3}$

16. $x^{2/3} + 9x^{1/3} + 18 = 0$

Let $y = x^{1/3}$, $y^2 = x^{2/3}$.

$y^2 + 9y + 18 = 0$

$(y + 6)(y + 3) = 0$

$y + 6 = 0$　　or　　$y + 3 = 0$

$y = -6$　　　　　$y = -3$

$x^{1/3} = -6$　　　$x^{1/3} = -3$

$x = (-6)^3$　　　$x = (-3)^3$

$x = -216$　　　$x = -27$

18. $3y^2 + 16z^2 = 5w$

$3y^2 = 5w - 16z^2$

$y^2 = \dfrac{5w - 16z^2}{3}$

$y = \pm\sqrt{\dfrac{5w - 16z^2}{3}}$

20. base: x

altitude: $3x + 3$

$\dfrac{1}{2}x(3x + 3) = 45$

$x(3x + 3) = 90$

$3x^2 + 3x = 90$

$3x^2 + 3x - 90 = 0$

$x^2 + x - 30 = 0$

$(x + 6)(x - 5) = 0$

$x + 6 = 0$　　or　　$x - 5 = 0$

$x = -6$　　　　　$x = 5$

$3x + 3 = 3(5) + 3 = 18$

base: 5 m; altitude: 18 m

22. $f(x) = -x^2 + 8x - 12$

$$-\frac{b}{2a} = -\frac{8}{2(-1)} = 4$$

$f(4) = -4^2 + 8(4) - 12 = 4$

Vertex: $(4, 4)$

$f(0) = -0^2 + 8(0) - 12 = -12$

y-intercept: $(0, -12)$

$-x^2 + 8x - 12 = 0$

$x^2 - 8x + 12 = 0$

$(x - 6)(x - 2) = 0$

$x - 6 = 0$ or $x - 2 = 0$

$x = 6$ $x = 2$

x-intercepts: $(6, 0), (2, 0)$

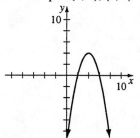

24. $6x^2 - x \le 2$

$6x^2 - x - 2 \le 0$

$6x^2 - x - 2 = 0$

$(3x - 2)(2x + 1) = 0$

$3x - 2 = 0$ or $2x + 1 = 0$

$3x = 2$ $2x = -1$

$x = \dfrac{2}{3}$ $x = -\dfrac{1}{2}$

Region I: $x = -1$

$6(-1)^2 - (-1) - 2 = 5 > 0$

Region II: $x = 0$

$6(0)^2 - 0 - 2 = -2 < 0$

Region III: $x = 1$

$6(1)^2 - 1 - 2 = 3 > 0$

$$-\frac{1}{2} \le x \le \frac{2}{3}$$

Chapter 9

2. $(x-h)^2 + (y-k)^2 = r^2$

$(x-8)^2 + [y-(-2)]^2 = (\sqrt{7})^2$

$(x-8)^2 + (y+2)^2 = 7$

4. $x = (y+1)^2 + 2$

x	y
3	-2
2	-1
3	0

Vertex: $(2, -1)$

x-intercept: $(3, 0)$

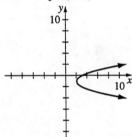

6. $4x^2 + y^2 - 36 = 0$

$4x^2 + y^2 = 36$

$\dfrac{x^2}{9} + \dfrac{y^2}{36} = 1$

$a^2 = 9 \qquad b^2 = 36$

$a = 3 \qquad b = 6$

Intercepts: $(3, 0), (-3, 0), (0, 6), (0, -6)$

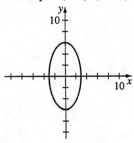

8. $25y^2 - 9x^2 = 225$

$\dfrac{y^2}{9} - \dfrac{x^2}{25} = 1$

$a^2 = 25, \ a = 5$

$b^2 = 9, \ b = 3$

Vertices: $(0, \pm 3)$

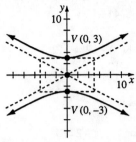

10. $y = x^2 + 1$

$4y^2 = 4 - x^2$

$4(x^2 + 1)^2 = 4 - x^2$

$4(x^4 + 2x^2 + 1) = 4 - x^2$

$4x^4 + 8x^2 + 4 = 4 - x^2$

$4x^4 + 9x^2 = 0$

$x^2(4x^2 + 9) = 0$

$x^2 = 0 \qquad \text{or} \qquad 4x^2 + 9 = 0$

$x = 0 \qquad\qquad\qquad 4x^2 = -9$

$\qquad\qquad\qquad\qquad\qquad x^2 = -\dfrac{9}{4}$

$\qquad\qquad\qquad\qquad\qquad\text{Extraneous}$

$y = 0^2 + 1 = 1$

$(0, 1)$

9.1 Exercises

2. Use the distance formula

$d = \sqrt{(-4-3)^2 + [0-(-1)]^2}$

$= \sqrt{49+1} = \sqrt{50} = 5\sqrt{2}$

4. To change the equation to standard form, complete the square for each variable on the left-hand side of the given equation.

6. $d = \sqrt{(x_2 - x_1)^2 + (y_2 - y_1)^2}$

$= \sqrt{(6-4)^2 + (3-1)^2}$

$= \sqrt{4+4} = \sqrt{8} = 2\sqrt{2}$

8. $(-4, 1)$ and $(2, -3)$

$d = \sqrt{(-3-1)^2 + [2-(-4)]^2}$

$= \sqrt{(-4)^2 + 6^2}$

$= \sqrt{52} = 2\sqrt{13}$

10. $(-7, -1)$ and $(3, -2)$

$d = \sqrt{[3-(-7)]^2 + [-2-(-1)]^2}$

$= \sqrt{10^2 + (-1)^2} = \sqrt{101}$

12. $(-1, -1)$ and $(3, 2)$

$d = \sqrt{(-1-3)^2 + [-1-2]^2}$

$= \sqrt{16+9}$

$= \sqrt{25}$

$= 5$

14. $(8, 4)$ and $(-4, -1)$

$d = \sqrt{[8-(-4)]^2 + [4-(-1)]^2}$

$= \sqrt{144+25}$

$= \sqrt{169}$

$= 13$

16. $(-5, -6)$ and $(2, 0)$

$d = \sqrt{(-5-2)^2 + (-6-0)^2}$

$= \sqrt{49+36}$

$= \sqrt{85}$

18. $\left(-\dfrac{1}{4}, \dfrac{1}{7}\right)$ and $\left(\dfrac{3}{4}, \dfrac{6}{7}\right)$

$d = \sqrt{\left(-\dfrac{1}{4}-\dfrac{3}{4}\right)^2 + \left(\dfrac{1}{7}-\dfrac{6}{7}\right)^2}$

$= \sqrt{1+\dfrac{25}{49}}$

$= \sqrt{\dfrac{74}{49}}$

$= \dfrac{\sqrt{74}}{7}$

20. $(8.2, 3.5)$ and $(6.2, -0.5)$

$d = \sqrt{(8.2-6.2)^2 + [3.5-(-0.5)]^2}$

$= \sqrt{4+16}$

$= \sqrt{20}$

$= 2\sqrt{5}$

22. $\left(4, \sqrt{2}\right)$ and $\left(-1, 3\sqrt{2}\right)$

$d = \sqrt{[4-(-1)]^2 + \left(\sqrt{2}-3\sqrt{2}\right)^2}$

$= \sqrt{25+8}$

$= \sqrt{33}$

24. $(8.67, -5.33)$ and $(-2.58, 5.82)$

$d = \sqrt{[8.67-(-2.58)]^2 + (-5.33-5.82)^2}$

$= 15.83934973$

26. $9 = \sqrt{(3-3)^2 + [y-(-5)]^2}$

$9 = \sqrt{(y+5)^2}$

$81 = y^2 + 10y + 25$

$0 = y^2 + 10y - 56$

$0 = (y+14)(y-4)$

$y+14 = 0 \qquad$ or $\qquad y-4 = 0$

$y = -14 \qquad\qquad\qquad y = 4$

28. $10 = \sqrt{(x-1)^2 + \left(-\dfrac{1}{2}-\dfrac{15}{2}\right)^2}$

$10 = \sqrt{(x-1)^2 + (-8)^2}$

$100 = x^2 - 2x + 1 + 64$

$0 = x^2 - 2x - 35$

$0 = (x-7)(x+5)$

$x-7 = 0 \qquad$ or $\qquad x+5 = 0$

$x = 7 \qquad\qquad\qquad x = -5$

30. $\sqrt{5} = \sqrt{(4-2)^2 + (5-y)^2}$

$\sqrt{5} = \sqrt{4 + (5-y)^2}$

$5 = 4 + 25 - 10y + y^2$

$0 = y^2 - 10y + 24$

$0 = (y-6)(y-4)$

$y-6 = 0 \qquad$ or $\qquad y-4 = 0$

$y = 6 \qquad\qquad\qquad y = 4$

32. Let $(2, y)$ represent the shortest distance north of the airport at which the plane can be detected by radar.

$4 = \sqrt{(2-5)^2 + (y-7)^2}$

$16 = 9 + y^2 - 14y + 49$

$0 = y^2 - 14y + 42$

$y = \dfrac{14 \pm \sqrt{(-14)^2 - 4(1)(42)}}{2(1)}$

$= \dfrac{14 \pm \sqrt{28}}{2}$

$y = 7 \pm \sqrt{7}$

Solution: the shortest distance is

$y = 7 - \sqrt{7} \approx 4.4$ miles

34. $(x-h)^2+(y-k)^2=r^2$
$(x-2)^2+(y-5)^2=7^2$
$(x-2)^2+(y-5)^2=49$

36. $(x-h)^2+(y-k)^2=r^2$
$(x-5)^2+[y-(-14)]^2=6^2$
$(x-5)^2+(y+14)^2=36$

38. $[x-(-3)]^2+[y-(-5)]^2=\left(\sqrt{2}\right)^2$
$(x+3)^2+(y+5)^2=2$

40. $(x-h)^2+(y-k)^2=r^2$
$(x-0)^2+[y-(-5)]^2=11^2$
$x^2+(y+5)^2=121$

42. $(x-0)^2+[y-(-4.5)]^2=4^2$
$x^2+(y+4.5)^2=16$

44. $(x-h)^2+(y-k)^2=r^2$
$[x-(-35.82)]^2+(y-88.37)^2=29.63^2$
$(x+35.82)^2+(y-88.37)^2=877.9369$

46. $x^2+y^2=25$
$(x-0)^2+(y-0)^2=5^2$
Center (0, 0); $r=5$

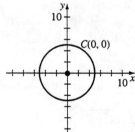

48. $(x-5)^2+(y-3)^2=16$
$(x-5)^2+(y-3)^2=4^2$
Center (5, 3); $r=4$

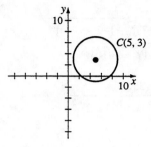

50. $\left(x-\dfrac{3}{2}\right)^2+(y+2)^2=9$
$\left(x-\dfrac{3}{2}\right)^2+[y-(-2)]^2=3^2$
Center $\left(\dfrac{3}{2},\,-2\right)$; $r=3$

52. $x^2+(y+4)^2=7$
Center = (0, –4); $r=\sqrt{7}$

54. $x^2+y^2+8x-6y-24=0$
$x^2+8x+y^2-6y=24$
$x^2+8x+16+y^2-6y+9=24+16+9$
$(x+4)^2+(y-3)^2=49$
Center (–4, 3); $r=7$

56. $x^2+y^2+4x-4y+7=0$
$x^2+4x+y^2-4y=-7$
$x^2+4x+4+y^2-4y+4=-7+4+4$
$(x+2)^2+(y-2)^2=1$
Center (–2, 2); $r=1$

58. $x^2 + y^2 - 6x - 21 = 0$

$x^2 - 6x + y^2 = 21$

$x^2 - 6x + 9 + y^2 = 21 + 9$

$(x-3)^2 + (y-0)^2 = 30$

Center (3, 0); $r = \sqrt{30}$

60. Center = (44.8, 31.8); $r = 25.3$

$(x - 44.8)^2 + (y - 31.8)^2 = (25.3)^2$

$(x - 44.8)^2 + (y - 31.8)^2 = 640.09$

62. $x^2 + 9.56x + y^2 - 7.12y + 8.9995 = 0$

$y^2 - 7.12y + (x^2 + 9.56x + 8.9995) = 0$

Using the quadratic formula:

$a = 1, \ b = -7.12, \ c = x^2 + 9.56x + 8.9995$

$y = \dfrac{-(-7.12) \pm \sqrt{(-7.12)^2 - 4(1)(x^2 + 9.56x + 8.9995)}}{2(1)}$

$= 3.56 \pm \dfrac{\sqrt{50.6944 - 4x^2 - 38.24x - 35.998}}{2}$

$= 3.56 \pm \dfrac{\sqrt{-4x^2 - 38.24x + 14.6964}}{2}$

Graph:

$y_1 = 3.56 + \dfrac{\sqrt{-4x^2 - 38.24x + 14.6964}}{2}$

$y_2 = 3.56 - \dfrac{\sqrt{-4x^2 - 38.24x + 14.6964}}{2}$

Cumulative Review Problems

64. $9 + \dfrac{3}{x} = \dfrac{2}{x^2}$

$9x^2 + 3x = 2$

$9x^2 + 3x - 2 = 0$

$(3x + 2)(3x - 1) = 0$

$3x + 2 = 0$ or $3x - 1 = 0$

$3x = -2$ $3x = 1$

$x = -\dfrac{2}{3}$ $x = \dfrac{1}{3}$

66. $5x^2 - 6x - 7 = 0$

$y = \dfrac{-b \pm \sqrt{b^2 - 4ac}}{2a}$

$x = \dfrac{-(-6) \pm \sqrt{(-6)^2 - 4(5)(-7)}}{2(5)}$

$= \dfrac{6 \pm \sqrt{36 + 140}}{10}$

$= \dfrac{6 \pm \sqrt{176}}{10}$

$$= \frac{6 \pm 4\sqrt{11}}{10}$$

$$= \frac{3 \pm 2\sqrt{11}}{5}$$

9.2 Exercises

2. $y = -5$

4. The negative sign makes the parabola open downward. The 6 stretches the parabola.

6.

x	y
−6	12
−3	3
0	0
3	3
6	12

Vertex: $(0, 0)$
y-intercept: $(0, 0)$

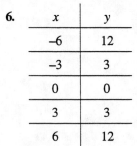

8. $y = -4x^2$

x	y
−2	−16
−1	−4
0	0
1	−4
2	−16

Vertex: $(0, 0)$
y-intercept: $(0, 0)$

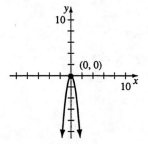

10. $y = x^2 + 2$

x	y
−2	6
−1	3
0	2
1	3
2	6

Vertex: $(0, 2)$
y-intercept: $(0, 2)$

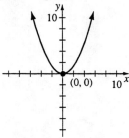

12. $y = -3x^2 + 1$

x	y
−2	−11
−1	−2
0	1
1	−2
2	−11

Vertex: $(0, 1)$
y-intercept: $(0, 1)$

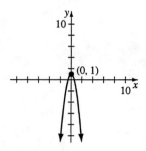

14. $y = (x - 4)^2 + 3$
Vertex: (4, 3)
y-intercept: (0, 19)

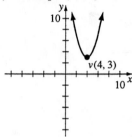

16. $y = -(x + 1)^2 + 4$

x	y
0	3
−1	4
1	0
−2	3

Vertex: (−1, 4)
y-intercept: (0, 3)

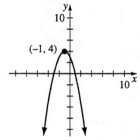

18. $y = 2(x - 3)^2 + 1$

x	y
0	19
2	3
3	1
4	3

Vertex: (3, 1)
y-intercept: (0, 19)

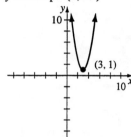

20. $y = \frac{1}{2}(x + 3)^2 - 4$
Vertex: (−3, −4)
y-intercept: $\left(0, \frac{1}{2}\right)$

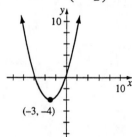

22. $y = -2(x + 3)^2 - 1$

x	y
−4	−3
−3	−1
−2	−3
0	−19

Vertex: (−3, −1)
y-intercept: (0, −19)

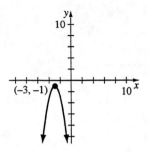

24. $x = \dfrac{1}{4}y^2 - 2$

x	y
2	4
−1	2
−2	0
2	−4

Vertex: (−2, 0)
x-intercept: (−2, 0)

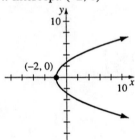

26. $x = -3y^2$

x	y
−3	−1
0	0
−3	1

Vertex: (0, 0)
x-intercept: (0, 0)

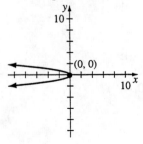

28. $x = (y - 4)^2 + 1$

x	y
17	0
5	2
1	4
2	5

Vertex: (1, 4)
x-intercept: (17, 0)

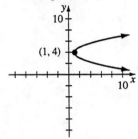

30. $x = -2(y + 3)^2 - 1$
Vertex: (−1, −3)
x-intercept: (−19, 0)

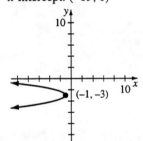

32. $x = \dfrac{1}{2}(y + 2)^2 + 1$
Vertex: (1, −2)
x-intercept: (3, 0)

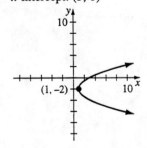

34. $x = -(y - 2)^2 + 1$

x	y
-3	0
0	1
1	2
0	3

Vertex: $(1, 2)$
x-intercept: $(-3, 0)$

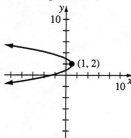

36. $y = x^2 - 4x - 1$
$y = x^2 - 4x + 4 - 4 - 1$
$y = (x - 2)^2 - 5$

  (a) Vertical; x is squared

  (b) Opens up; $a > 0$

  (c) Vertex: $(2, -5)$

38. $y = -2x^2 + 4x + 5$
$y = -2\left(x^2 - 2x\right) + 5$
$y = -2\left(x^2 - 2x + 1\right) + 2 + 5$
$y = -2(x - 1)^2 + 7$

  (a) Vertical; x is squared

  (b) Opens down; $a < 0$

  (c) Vertex: $(1, 7)$

40. $x = y^2 + 8y + 9$
$x = y^2 + 8y + 16 - 16 + 9$
$x = (y + 4)^2 - 7$

  (a) Horizontal; y is squared

  (b) Opens right; $a > 0$

  (c) Vertex: $(-7, -4)$

42. $y = ax^2$
$x = \dfrac{1}{2}$ width $= \dfrac{1}{2}(32) = 16$
$y = $ height $= 8$
$8 = a(16)^2 \Rightarrow a = \dfrac{1}{32}$
$y = \dfrac{1}{32}x^2$

44. $a = \dfrac{1}{4p}$
$\dfrac{1}{32} = \dfrac{1}{4p}$
$p = \dfrac{32}{4} = 8$
The distance p is 8 inches.

46. $y = -3x^2 + 33.66x - 73.5063$
$y = -3(x - 5.61)^2 + 20.91$
Vertex: $(5.61, 20.91)$
y-intercept: $y = -3(0 - 5.61)^2 + 20.91$
$y = -73.5063$
$(0, -73.5063)$

x-intercepts: $0 = -3(x - 5.61)^2 + 20.91$
$-20.91 = -3(x - 5.61)^2$
$6.97 = (x - 5.61)^2$
$\pm\sqrt{6.97} = x - 5.61$
$x = 5.61 \pm \sqrt{6.97}$
$x = 8.250075756$ or $x = 2.969924244$
$(8.250075756, 0); (2.969924244, 0)$

48. $P = -2x^2 + 200x + 47000$
$P = -2\left(x^2 - 100x\right) + 47000$
$P = -2\left(x^2 - 100x + 2500\right) + 47000 + 5000$
$P = -2(x - 50)^2 + 52000$
Maximum profit: \$52,000
Number of items: 50

50. $S = 650d - 2d^2$
$S = -2\left(d^2 - 325d\right)$
$S = -2\left(d^2 - 325d + 26406.25\right) + 52812.5$
$S = -2(d - 162.5)^2 + 52812.5$
Maximum sensitivity: 52812.5
Dosage: 162.5 mg

Cumulative Review Problems

52. $\sqrt[3]{40x^3y^4}$

$= \sqrt[3]{8x^3y^3 \cdot 5y}$

$= 2xy\sqrt[3]{5y}$

54. $\sqrt[3]{16x^4} + 4x\sqrt[3]{2} - 8x\sqrt[3]{54}$

$= 2x\sqrt[3]{2x} + 4x\sqrt[3]{2} - 24x\sqrt[3]{2}$

$= 2x\sqrt[3]{2x} - 20x\sqrt[3]{2}$

56. $d = rt$

$30t = 50(2.25 - t)$

$80t = 112.5$

$t = 1.40625$

$d = 30(1.40625)$

$d \approx 42.2$ miles

9.3 Exercises

2. The center of the ellipse is (–2, 3).

4. $\dfrac{x^2}{4} + \dfrac{y^2}{25} = 1$

$a^2 = 4 \qquad b^2 = 25$

$a = 2 \qquad\quad b = 5$

Intercepts: (2, 0), (–2, 0), (0, 5), (0, –5)

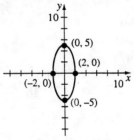

6. $\dfrac{x^2}{36} + \dfrac{y^2}{4} = 1$

$a^2 = 36 \qquad b^2 = 4$

$a = 6 \qquad\quad b = 2$

Intercepts: (6, 0), (–6, 0), (0, 2), (0, –2)

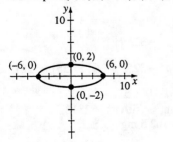

8. $\dfrac{x^2}{81} + \dfrac{y^2}{100} = 1$

$a^2 = 81 \qquad\qquad b^2 = 100$

$a = 9 \qquad\qquad\quad b = 10$

Intercepts: (9, 0), (–9, 0), (0, 10), (0, –10)

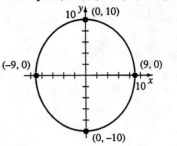

10. $x^2 + 25y^2 - 25 = 0$

$x^2 + 25y^2 = 25$

$\dfrac{x^2}{25} + \dfrac{y^2}{1} = 1$

$a^2 = 25 \qquad\quad b^2 = 1$

$a = 5 \qquad\qquad b = 1$

Intercepts: (5, 0), (–5, 0), (0, 1), (0, –1)

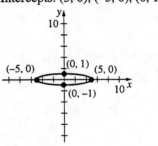

12. $4x^2 + 25y^2 = 100$

$\dfrac{x^2}{25} + \dfrac{y^2}{4} = 1$

$a^2 = 25 \qquad\quad b^2 = 4$

$a = 5 \qquad\qquad b = 2$

Intercepts: (–5, 0), (5, 0), (0, 2), (0, –2)

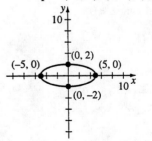

14. $8x^2 + y^2 = 16$

$$\frac{x^2}{2} + \frac{y^2}{16} = 1$$

$a^2 = 2 \qquad b^2 = 16$

$a = \sqrt{2} \qquad b = 4$

Intercepts: $\left(\sqrt{2},\ 0\right), \left(-\sqrt{2},\ 0\right), (0, 4), (0, -4)$

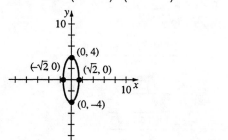

16. $5x^2 + 6y^2 = 30$

$$\frac{x^2}{6} + \frac{y^2}{5} = 1$$

$a^2 = 6 \qquad b^2 = 5$

$a = \sqrt{6} \qquad b = \sqrt{5}$

Intercepts:

$\left(\sqrt{6},\ 0\right), \left(-\sqrt{6},\ 0\right), \left(0,\ \sqrt{5}\right), \left(0,\ -\sqrt{5}\right)$

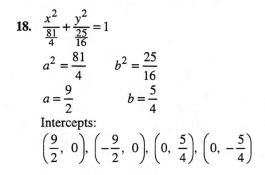

18. $\dfrac{x^2}{\frac{81}{4}} + \dfrac{y^2}{\frac{25}{16}} = 1$

$a^2 = \dfrac{81}{4} \qquad b^2 = \dfrac{25}{16}$

$a = \dfrac{9}{2} \qquad b = \dfrac{5}{4}$

Intercepts:

$\left(\dfrac{9}{2},\ 0\right), \left(-\dfrac{9}{2},\ 0\right), \left(0,\ \dfrac{5}{4}\right), \left(0,\ -\dfrac{5}{4}\right)$

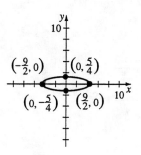

20. $a = 9,\ b = 2$

$$\frac{x^2}{a^2} + \frac{y^2}{b^2} = 1$$

$$\frac{x^2}{9^2} + \frac{y^2}{2^2} = 1$$

$$\frac{x^2}{81} + \frac{y^2}{4} = 1$$

22. Center $(0, 0)$, x-int. $(3, 0)$, y-int. $\left(0,\ \sqrt{7}\right)$

$$\frac{x^2}{a^2} + \frac{y^2}{b^2} = 1$$

$$\frac{3^2}{a^2} + \frac{0^2}{b^2} = 1 \Rightarrow a = 3$$

$$\frac{0^2}{a^2} + \frac{\left(\sqrt{7}\right)^2}{b^2} = 1 \Rightarrow b = \sqrt{7}$$

$$\frac{x^2}{9} + \frac{y^2}{7} = 1$$

24. $a = \dfrac{60}{2} = 30, \qquad b = 18$

$a^2 = 900 \qquad b^2 = 324$

$$\frac{x^2}{a^2} + \frac{y^2}{b^2} = 1$$

$$\frac{x^2}{900} + \frac{y^2}{324} = 1$$

26. $\dfrac{(x-5)^2}{9} + \dfrac{(y-2)^2}{1} = 1$

Center $(5, 2)$

$a^2 = 9 \qquad b^2 = 1$

$a = 3 \qquad b = 1$

$(5 \pm 3,\ 2),\ (5,\ 2 \pm 1)$

Vertices: $(8, 2),\ (2, 2),\ (5, 3),\ (5, 1)$

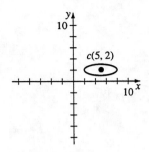

28. $\dfrac{(x+2)^2}{49} + \dfrac{y^2}{25} = 1$

Center $(-2, 0)$

$a^2 = 49$ $b^2 = 25$

$a = 7$ $b = 5$

$(-2 \pm 7,\ 0),\ (-2,\ \pm 5)$

Vertices: $(-9, 0),\ (5, 0),\ (-2, -5),\ (-2, 5)$

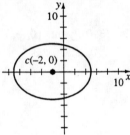

30. $\dfrac{(x+1)^2}{36} + \dfrac{(y+4)^2}{16} = 1$

Center $(-1, -4)$

$a^2 = 36$ $b^2 = 16$

$a = 6$ $b = 4$

$(-1 \pm 6,\ -4),\ (-1,\ -4 \pm 4)$

Vertices: $(5, -4),\ (-7, -4),\ (-1, 0),\ (-1, -8)$

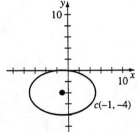

32. Center $= \left(\dfrac{2+6}{2},\ \dfrac{3+3}{2} \right) = (4, 3)$

$a = |6 - 4| = 2$

$b = |7 - 3| = 4$

$\dfrac{(x-4)^2}{a^2} + \dfrac{(y-3)^2}{b^2} = 1$

$\dfrac{(x-4)^2}{4} + \dfrac{(y-3)^2}{16} = 1$

34. $\dfrac{(x+5)^2}{4} + \dfrac{(y+a)^2}{9} = 1,\ (-4,\ 4)$

$\dfrac{(-4+5)^2}{4} + \dfrac{(4+a)^2}{9} = 1$

$\dfrac{1}{4} + \dfrac{16 + 8a + a^2}{9} = 1$

$9 + 64 + 32a + 4a^2 = 36$

$4a^2 + 32a + 37 = 0$

$a = \dfrac{-32 \pm \sqrt{(32)^2 - 4(4)(37)}}{2(4)}$

$a = \dfrac{-32 \pm \sqrt{432}}{8}$

$a = \dfrac{-32 \pm \sqrt{144} \cdot \sqrt{3}}{8}$

$a = \dfrac{-32 \pm 12\sqrt{3}}{8} = \dfrac{-8 \pm 3\sqrt{3}}{2}$

36. $\dfrac{(x-3.6)^2}{14.98} + \dfrac{(y-5.3)^2}{28.98} = 1$

Solve for y:

$\dfrac{(y-5.3)^2}{28.98} = 1 - \dfrac{(x-3.6)^2}{14.98}$

$(y-5.3)^2 = 28.98 \left(1 - \dfrac{(x-3.6)^2}{14.98} \right)$

$y = 5.3 \pm \sqrt{28.98 \left(1 - \dfrac{(x-3.6)^2}{14.98} \right)}$

Use the trace, zoom, and table features of your graphing calculator to determine the intercepts of the ellipse.

x-intercepts: $(4.2783, 0),\ (2.9217, 0)$

y-intercepts: $(0, 7.2768),\ (0, 3.3232)$

38. $a = \dfrac{185}{2} = 92.5$

$b = \dfrac{154}{2} = 77$

$A = \pi ab$

$= (3.1416)(92.5)(77)$

$= 22376.0$ sq meters

Cumulative Review Problems

40. $\sqrt{3xy}\left(\sqrt{2x} + \sqrt{3y} + \sqrt{27} \right)$

$= \sqrt{6x^2 y} + \sqrt{9xy^2} + \sqrt{81xy}$

$= x\sqrt{6y} + 3y\sqrt{x} + 9\sqrt{xy}$

42. $\dfrac{5}{\sqrt{2x} - \sqrt{y}}$

$= \dfrac{5}{\sqrt{2x} - \sqrt{y}} \cdot \dfrac{\sqrt{2x} + \sqrt{y}}{\sqrt{2x} + \sqrt{y}}$

$= \dfrac{5\left(\sqrt{2x} + \sqrt{y}\right)}{2x - y}$

9.4 Exercises

2. The vertices are (0, 3) and (0, –3). This is a vertical hyperbola because the vertices are on the y-axis and the equation is the standard form of the hyperbola.

4. The center of the hyperbola is (2, –3).

6. $\dfrac{x^2}{9} - \dfrac{y^2}{36} = 1$

$a^2 = 9 \qquad\qquad b^2 = 36$
$a = 3 \qquad\qquad b = 6$
Vertices: $(\pm 3,\ 0)$

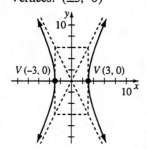

8. $\dfrac{y^2}{49} - \dfrac{x^2}{9} = 1$

$b^2 = 49 \qquad\qquad a^2 = 9$
$b = 7 \qquad\qquad a = 3$
Vertices: $(0,\ \pm 7)$

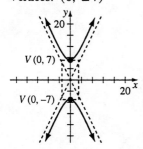

10. $\dfrac{x^2}{9} - \dfrac{y^2}{1} = 1$

Center (0, 0), $a = 3$, $b = 1$
Vertices: (3, 0), (–3, 0)

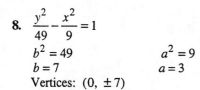

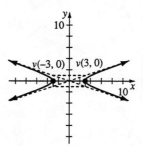

12. $4y^2 - 25x^2 = 100$

$\dfrac{y^2}{25} - \dfrac{x^2}{4} = 1$

$b^2 = 25 \qquad\qquad a^2 = 4$
$b = 5 \qquad\qquad a = 2$
Vertices: $(0,\ \pm 5)$

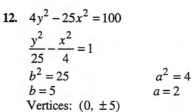

14. $4x^2 - y^2 = 64$

$\dfrac{x^2}{16} - \dfrac{y^2}{64} = 1$

$a^2 = 16 \qquad\qquad b^2 = 64$
$a = 4 \qquad\qquad b = 8$
Vertices: $(\pm 4,\ 0)$

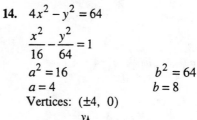

16. $8x^2 - y^2 = 16$

$\dfrac{x^2}{2} - \dfrac{y^2}{16} = 1$

$a^2 = 2 \qquad\qquad b^2 = 16$
$a = \sqrt{2} \qquad\qquad b = 4$
Vertices: $\left(\pm\sqrt{2},\ 0\right)$

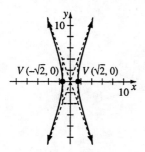

18. $5y^2 - 6x^2 = 30$

$$\frac{y^2}{6} - \frac{x^2}{5} = 1$$

$b^2 = 6$ $\qquad a^2 = 5$

$b = \sqrt{6}$ $\qquad a = \sqrt{5}$

Vertices: $\left(0,\ \pm\sqrt{6}\right)$

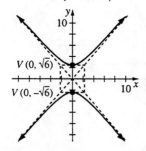

20. $\dfrac{x^2}{16} - \dfrac{y^2}{16} = 1$

Center $= (0, 0)$, $a = 4$, $b = 4$

Vertices: $(4, 0)$, $(-4, 0)$

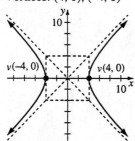

22. $8y^2 - 8x^2 = 24$

$$\frac{y^2}{3} - \frac{x^2}{3} = 1$$

Center $(0, 0)$, $a = \sqrt{3}$, $b = \sqrt{3}$

Vertices: $\left(0,\ \sqrt{3}\right)$, $\left(0,\ -\sqrt{3}\right)$

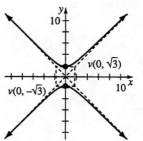

24. $a = 3$

$a^2 = 9$

$\dfrac{4}{3} = \dfrac{b}{a}$

$\dfrac{4}{3} = \dfrac{b}{3}$

$4 = b$

$16 = b^2$

$\dfrac{x^2}{a^2} - \dfrac{y^2}{b^2} = 1$

$\dfrac{x^2}{9} - \dfrac{y^2}{16} = 1$

26. $b = 6$

$b^2 = 36$

$\dfrac{6}{5} = \dfrac{b}{a}$

$\dfrac{6}{5} = \dfrac{6}{a}$

$5 = a$

$25 = a^2$

$\dfrac{y^2}{b^2} - \dfrac{x^2}{a^2} = 1$

$\dfrac{y^2}{36} - \dfrac{x^2}{25} = 1$

28. $a = 120$

$a^2 = 14400$

$3 = \dfrac{b}{a}$

$3 = \dfrac{b}{120}$

$360 = b$

$129600 = b^2$

$\dfrac{x^2}{a^2} - \dfrac{y^2}{b^2} = 1$

$\dfrac{x^2}{14400} - \dfrac{y^2}{129600} = 1$

Where x and y are measured in millions of miles.

30. $\dfrac{(x-6)^2}{25} - \dfrac{(y-4)^2}{49} = 1$

Center $(6, 4)$, $a = 5$, $b = 7$

Vertices: $(11, 4)$, $(1, 4)$

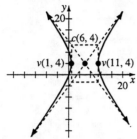

32. $\dfrac{(y+1)^2}{49} - \dfrac{(x+3)^2}{81} = 1$

Center $(-3, -1)$

$b^2 = 49$ $a^2 = 81$

$b = 7$ $a = 9$

Vertices: $(-3, -1 \pm 7) = (-3, 6)$, $(-3, -8)$

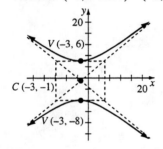

34. $\dfrac{(x+6)^2}{7} - \dfrac{y^2}{3} = 1$

Center $(-6, 0)$

$a^2 = 7$

$a = \sqrt{7}$

Vertices: $\left(-6 \pm \sqrt{7}, \ 0\right)$

36. Center $\left(4, \ \dfrac{-14+0}{2}\right) = (4, -7)$

$b = \dfrac{-14-0}{2} = -7$

$b^2 = 49$

$-\dfrac{b}{a} = -\dfrac{7}{4}$

$\dfrac{-7}{a} = -\dfrac{7}{4}$

$a = 4$

$a^2 = 16$

$\dfrac{(y-k)^2}{b^2} - \dfrac{(x-h)^2}{a^2} = 1$

$\dfrac{[y-(-7)]^2}{49} - \dfrac{(x-4)^2}{16} = 1$

$\dfrac{(y+7)^2}{49} - \dfrac{(x-4)^2}{16} = 1$

38. $x^2 - 12y^2 = 36$

$(8.2)^2 - 12y^2 = 36$

$67.24 - 12y^2 = 36$

$-12y^2 = -31.24$

$y^2 = 2.60\overline{3}$

$y = \pm\sqrt{2.603}$

$y = \pm 1.613484841$

Cumulative Review Problems

40. $12x^2 + x - 6$

$= 12x^2 + 9x - 8x - 6$

$= 3x(4x+3) - 2(4x+3)$

$= (4x+3)(3x-2)$

42. $\dfrac{2x}{5x^2+9x-2} - \dfrac{3}{5x-1}$

$= \dfrac{2x}{(5x-1)(x+2)} - \dfrac{3}{5x-1}$

$= \dfrac{2x}{(5x-1)(x+2)} - \dfrac{3(x+2)}{(5x-1)(x+2)}$

$= \dfrac{2x - 3(x+2)}{(5x-1)(x+2)}$

$= \dfrac{2x - 3x - 6}{(5x-1)(x+2)}$

$= \dfrac{-x-6}{(5x-1)(x+2)}$

44. (a) $\dfrac{104,755}{365} = 287$

287 songs per day

(b) $24(60) - 287(4) = 292$

292 minutes per day

(c) $\dfrac{287(4)}{24(60)} \approx 0.797$

79.7% of the air time is music

9.5 Exercises

2. $y^2 = 4x$ (1)

     $y = x + 1$ (2)

     Substitute (2) into (1)

     $(x+1)^2 = 4x$

     $x^2 + 2x + 1 = 4x$

     $x^2 - 2x + 1 = 0$

     $(x-1)^2 = 0$

     $x = 1$

     Substitute 1 for x in (2)

     $y = 1 + 1 = 2$

     $(1, 2)$

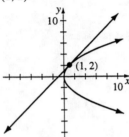

4. $y - 4x = 0$

     $4x^2 + y^2 = 20$

     $y = 4x$

     $4x^2 + (4x)^2 = 20$

     $4x^2 + 16x^2 = 20$

     $20x^2 = 20$

     $x^2 = 1$

     $x = 1$ or $x = -1$

     $y = 4(1)$ $y = 4(-1)$

     $= 4$ $= -4$

     $(1, 4), (-1, -4)$

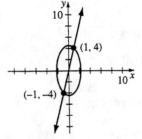

6. $y = (x+3)^2 - 3$

     $2x - y + 2 = 0$

     $2x - \left[(x+3)^2 - 3\right] + 2 = 0$

     $2x - x^2 - 6x - 9 + 3 + 2 = 0$

     $x^2 + 4x + 4 = 0$

     $(x+2)^2 = 0$

     $x + 2 = 0$

     $x = -2$

     $y = (-2+3)^2 - 3 = -2$

     $(-2, -2)$

8. $x^2 + y^2 - 25 = 0$

     $3y = x + 5$

     $x = 3y - 5$

     $(3y-5)^2 + y^2 - 25 = 0$

     $9y^2 - 30y + 25 + y^2 - 25 = 0$

     $10y^2 - 30y = 0$

     $10y(y - 3) = 0$

     $10y = 0$ or $y - 3 = 0$

     $y = 0$ $y = 3$

     $x = 3(0) - 5 = -5$ $x = 3(3) - 5 = 4$

     $(-5, 0), (4, 3)$

10. $y = (x-3)^2$

     $x - 1 - y = 0$

     $x - 1 - (x-3)^2 = 0$

     $x - 1 - \left(x^2 - 6x + 9\right) = 0$

     $x - 1 - x^2 + 6x - 9 = 0$

     $x^2 - 7x + 10 = 0$

     $(x-5)(x-2) = 0$

     $x - 5 = 0$ or $x - 2 = 0$

     $x = 5$ $x = 2$

     $y = (5-3)^2 = 4$ $y = (2-3)^2 = 1$

     $(5, 4), (2, 1)$

12. $\dfrac{x^2}{3} - \dfrac{y^2}{12} = 1$

     $y = -x$

     $y^2 = x^2$

     $\dfrac{x^2}{3} - \dfrac{x^2}{12} = 1$

     $4x^2 - x^2 = 12$

     $3x^2 = 12$

     $x^2 = 4$

     $x = 2$ or $x = -2$

     $y = -2$ $y = -(-2) = 2$

     $(2, -2), (-2, 2)$

14. $9x^2 + 4y^2 = 36$

$x^2 + y^2 = 9$

$9x^2 + 4y^2 = 36$

$\underline{-4x^2 - 4y^2 = -36}$

$5x^2 = 0$

$x^2 = 0$

$x = 0$

$0^2 + y^2 = 9$

$y^2 = 9$

$y = \pm 3$

$(0, 3), (0, -3)$

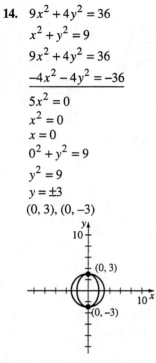

16. $2x^2 - 3y^2 = 5$

$3x^2 + 4y^2 = 16$

$8x^2 - 12y^2 = 20$

$\underline{9x^2 + 12y^2 = 48}$

$17x^2 = 68$

$x^2 = 4$

$x = \pm 2$

$2(\pm 2)^2 - 3y^2 = 5$

$8 - 3y^2 = 5$

$-3y^2 = -3$

$y^2 = 1$

$y = \pm 1$

$(2, 1), (2, -1), (-2, 1), (-2, -1)$

18. $2x^2 + 5y^2 = 42$

$3x^2 + 4y^2 = 35$

$-6x^2 - 15y^2 = -126$

$\underline{6x^2 + 8y^2 = 70}$

$-7y^2 = -56$

$y^2 = 8$

$y = \pm\sqrt{8}$

$y = \pm 2\sqrt{2}$

$2x^2 + 5\left(\pm 2\sqrt{2}\right)^2 = 42$

$2x^2 + 5(8) = 42$

$2x^2 + 40 = 42$

$2x^2 = 2$

$x^2 = 1$

$x = \pm 1$

$\left(1, \ 2\sqrt{2}\right), \left(-1, \ 2\sqrt{2}\right), \left(1, \ -2\sqrt{2}\right),$

$\left(-1, \ -2\sqrt{2}\right)$

20. $x^2 + 4y^2 = 13$

$x^2 - 3y^2 = -8$

$x^2 + 4y^2 = 13$

$\underline{-x^2 + 3y^2 = 8}$

$7y^2 = 21$

$y^2 = 3$

$y = \pm\sqrt{3}$

$x^2 - 3\left(\pm\sqrt{3}\right)^2 = -8$

$x^2 - 3(3) = -8$

$x^2 - 9 = -8$

$x^2 = 1$

$x = \pm 1$

$\left(1, \ \sqrt{3}\right), \left(-1, \ \sqrt{3}\right), \left(1, \ -\sqrt{3}\right), \left(-1, \ -\sqrt{3}\right)$

22. $x^2 + (y - 3)^2 = 9$

$x^2 + y^2 = 4$

$x^2 + (y - 3)^2 = 9$

$\underline{-x^2 - y^2 = -4}$

$(y - 3)^2 - y^2 = 5$

$y^2 - 6y + 9 - y^2 = 5$

$-6y + 9 = 5$

$-6y = -4$

$$y = \frac{2}{3}$$

$$x^2 + \left(\frac{2}{3}\right)^2 = 4$$

$$x^2 + \frac{4}{9} = 4$$

$$x^2 = \frac{32}{9}$$

$$x = \pm\sqrt{\frac{32}{9}}$$

$$x = \pm\frac{4\sqrt{2}}{3}$$

$$\left(\frac{4\sqrt{2}}{3}, \frac{2}{3}\right), \left(-\frac{4\sqrt{2}}{3}, \frac{2}{3}\right)$$

24. $xy = 5$

$2y = 2x + 8$

$y = x + 4$

$x(x + 4) = 5$

$x^2 + 4x = 5$

$x^2 + 4x - 5 = 0$

$(x + 5)(x - 1) = 0$

$x + 5 = 0$	or	$x - 1 = 0$
$x = -5$		$x = 1$
$y = -5 + 4 = -1$		$y = 1 + 4 = 5$

$(-5, -1), (1, 5)$

26. $xy = 1$

$3x + y - 6 = 0$

$y = 6 - 3x$

$x(6 - 3x) = 1$

$6x - 3x^2 = 1$

$0 = 3x^2 - 6x + 1$

$$x = \frac{-1(-6) \pm \sqrt{(-6)^2 - 4(3)(1)}}{2(3)}$$

$$= \frac{6 \pm \sqrt{24}}{6}$$

$$= \frac{6 \pm 2\sqrt{6}}{6}$$

$$= \frac{3 \pm \sqrt{6}}{3}$$

$x = \dfrac{3+\sqrt{6}}{3}$	or	$x = \dfrac{3-\sqrt{6}}{3}$
$y = 6 - 3\left(\dfrac{3+\sqrt{6}}{3}\right)$		$y = 6 - 3\left(\dfrac{3-\sqrt{6}}{3}\right)$
$= 6 - 3 - \sqrt{6}$		$= 6 - 3 + \sqrt{6}$
$= 3 - \sqrt{6}$		$= 3 + \sqrt{6}$

$$\left(\frac{3+\sqrt{6}}{3}, 3-\sqrt{6}\right), \left(\frac{3-\sqrt{6}}{3}, 3+\sqrt{6}\right)$$

28. $x^2 + y^2 = 0$

$x - y = 6$

$x = y + 6$

$(y + 6)^2 + y^2 = 0$

$y^2 + 12y + 36 + y^2 = 0$

$2y^2 + 12y + 36 = 0$

$y^2 + 6y + 18 = 0$

$$y = \frac{-6 \pm \sqrt{6^2 - 4(1)(18)}}{2(1)}$$

$$= \frac{-6 \pm \sqrt{-36}}{2}$$

No real solution

30. $2x^2 + 5.698y^2 = 39.768$

$3x^2 + 4.256y^2 = 34.087$

$-6x^2 - 17.094y^2 = -119.304$

$\underline{6x^2 + 8.512y^2 = 68.174}$

$-8.582y^2 = -51.13$

$y^2 = 5.95781869$

$y = \pm2.4409$

$2x^2 + 5.698(\pm2.4409)^2 = 39.768$

$2x^2 = 5.819356969$

$x^2 = 2.909678484$

$x = \pm1.7058$

$(1.71, \pm2.44), (-1.71, \pm2.44)$

32. $xy = 540$

$x^2 + y^2 = 39^2$

$$y = \frac{540}{x}$$

$$x^2 + \left(\frac{540}{x}\right)^2 = 1521$$

$$x^2 + \frac{291600}{x^2} = 1521$$

$$x^4 + 291600 = 1521x^2$$

$x^4 - 1521x^2 + 291600 = 0$

Let $u = x^2$

$u^2 - 1521u + 291600 = 0$

$(u - 1296)(u - 225) = 0$

$u - 1296 = 0$ or $u - 225 = 0$

$u = 1296$ $\qquad$ $u = 225$

$x^2 = 1296$ $\qquad$ $x^2 = 225$

$x = 36$ $\qquad$ $x = 15$

$y = \dfrac{540}{36} = 15$ $\qquad$ $y = \dfrac{540}{15} = 36$

Dimensions: 15 m by 36 m

Cumulative Review Problems

34.
$$3x+1 \overline{\smash{\big)}\,3x^3 - 8x^2 - 33x - 10}$$

quotient: $x^2 - 3x - 10$

$\underline{3x^3 + x^2}$

$\quad -9x^2 - 33x$

$\quad \underline{-9x^2 - 3x}$

$\qquad -30x - 10$

$\qquad \underline{-30x - 10}$

$\qquad\qquad 0$

36. $d = rt$, distance is equal

$55(5) = r(11)$

$25 = r$

The legal rate is 25 miles per hour.

Putting Your Skills to Work

2. $2\left(\sqrt{333.32}\right) = 36.5$

36.5 Au

4. $c^2 = a^2 - b^2$

$e = \dfrac{c}{a}$

$c = \sqrt{33,415.84 - 333.32} = 181.886$

$e = \dfrac{181.886}{\sqrt{33,415.84}} = 0.995$

Chapter 9 Review Problems

2. $d = \sqrt{(x_2 - x_1)^2 + (y_2 - y_1)^2}$

$= \sqrt{(10.5 - 7.5)^2 + [-6 - (-4)]^2}$

$= \sqrt{9 + 4}$

$= \sqrt{13}$

4. $(x-h)^2 + (y-k)^2 = r^2$

$[x - (-6)]^2 + (y-3)^2 = \left(\sqrt{15}\right)^2$

$(x+6)^2 + (y-3)^2 = 15$

6. $x^2 + y^2 - 10x + 12y + 52 = 0$

$x^2 - 10x + y^2 + 12y = -52$

$x^2 - 10x + 25 + y^2 + 12y + 36 = -52 + 25 + 36$

$(x-5)^2 + (y+6)^2 = 9$

$C(5, -6)$

$r = 3$

8. $y = -2(x+1)^2 - 3$

x	y
-2	-5
-1	-3
0	-5

Vertex: $(-1, -3)$

y-intercept: $(0, -5)$

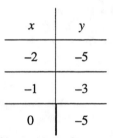

10. $x^2 + 6x = y - 4$

$x^2 + 6x + 4 = y$

$x^2 + 6x + 9 - 9 + 4 = y$

$(x+3)^2 - 5 = y$

Vertex: $(-3, -5)$

Opens upward since $a > 0$.

12. $\dfrac{x^2}{\frac{1}{4}} + \dfrac{y^2}{1} = 1$

$a^2 = \dfrac{1}{4}$ $\qquad$ $b^2 = 1$

$a = \dfrac{1}{2}$ $\qquad$ $b = 1$

Center $(0, 0)$

Intercepts: $\left(\dfrac{1}{2},\ 0\right), \left(-\dfrac{1}{2},\ 0\right),\ (0,\ 1),\ (0,\ -1)$

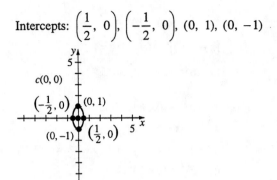

$c(0, 0)$

$\left(-\dfrac{1}{2}, 0\right)$ $(0, 1)$

$(0, -1)$ $\left(\dfrac{1}{2}, 0\right)$

14. $\dfrac{(x+1)^2}{9}+\dfrac{(y-2)^2}{16}=1$

Center $(-1, 2)$

$a^2 = 9 \qquad b^2 = 16$

$a = 3 \qquad\quad b = 4$

Vertices: $(-1\pm3,\ 2),\ (-1,\ 2\pm4)$

$= (2, 2), (-4, 2), (-1, 6), (-1, -2)$

16. $9y^2 - 25x^2 = 225$

$\dfrac{y^2}{25}-\dfrac{x^2}{9}=1$

Center $(0, 0)$

$b^2 = 25 \qquad\qquad a^2 = 9$

$b = 5 \qquad\qquad\quad a = 3$

Vertices: $(0, 5), (0, -5)$

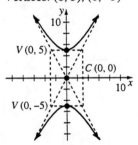

$V(0, 5)$

$C(0, 0)$

$V(0, -5)$

18. $\dfrac{(x-2)^2}{4}-\dfrac{(y+3)^2}{25}=1$

Center $(2, -3)$

$a^2 = 4$

$a = 2$

Vertices: $(2\pm2,\ -3) = (4, -3), (0, -3)$

20. $x^2 + y = 9$

$y - x = 3$

$x^2 + y = 9$

$\underline{x - y = -3}$

$x^2 + x = 6$

$x^2 + x - 6 = 0$

$(x+3)(x-2) = 0$

$x + 3 = 0 \qquad\text{or}\qquad x - 2 = 0$

$x = -3 \qquad\qquad\qquad x = 2$

$y - (-3) = 3 \qquad\qquad y - 2 = 3$

$y = 0 \qquad\qquad\qquad\quad y = 5$

$(-3, 0), (2, 5)$

22. $2x^2 + y^2 = 17$

$x^2 + 2y^2 = 22$

$2x^2 + y^2 = 17$

$\underline{-2x^2 - 4y^2 = -44}$

$-3y^2 = -27$

$y^2 = 9$

$y = \pm3$

$x^2 + 2(\pm3)^2 = 22$

$x^2 + 18 = 22$

$x^2 = 4$

$x = \pm2$

$(2, 3), (2, -3), (-2, 3), (-2, -3)$

24. $3x^2 - 4y^2 = 12$

$7x^2 - y^2 = 8$

$3x^2 - 4y^2 = 12$

$\underline{-28x^2 + 4y^2 = -32}$

$-25x^2 = -20$

$x^2 = \dfrac{4}{5}$

$x = \pm\dfrac{2}{\sqrt{5}}$

$= \pm\dfrac{2\sqrt{5}}{5}$

$7\left(\pm\dfrac{2}{\sqrt{5}}\right)^2 - y^2 = 8$

$\dfrac{28}{5} - y^2 = 8$

$-y^2 = \dfrac{12}{5}$

$y^2 = -\dfrac{12}{5}$

No real solution

26. $2x^2 + y^2 = 18$

$xy = 4$

$y = \dfrac{4}{x}$

$2x^2 + \left(\dfrac{4}{x}\right)^2 = 18$

$2x^2 + \dfrac{16}{x^2} = 18$

$2x^4 + 16 = 18x^2$

$2x^4 - 18x^2 + 16 = 0$

$x^4 - 9x^2 + 8 = 0$

Let $u = x^2$

$u^2 - 9u + 8 = 0$

$(u - 8)(u - 1) = 0$

$u - 8 = 0$	or	$u - 1 = 0$
$u = 8$		$u = 1$
$x^2 = 8$		$x^2 = 1$
$x = \pm\sqrt{8}$		$x = \pm 1$
$x = \pm 2\sqrt{2}$		$x = 1$

or $\qquad x = -1$

$x = 2\sqrt{2}$	or	$x = -2\sqrt{2}$

$y = \dfrac{4}{1} = 4 \qquad\qquad y = \dfrac{4}{-1} = -4$

$y = \dfrac{4}{2\sqrt{2}} = \sqrt{2} \qquad y = \dfrac{4}{-2\sqrt{2}} = -\sqrt{2}$

$\left(2\sqrt{2},\ \sqrt{2}\right),\ \left(-2\sqrt{2},\ -\sqrt{2}\right),\ (1,\ 4),\ (-1,\ -4)$

Chapter 9 Test

2. $x^2 + y^2 + 6x - 4y + 9 = 0$

$x^2 + 6x + y^2 - 4y = -9$

$x^2 + 6x + 9 + y^2 - 4y + 4 = -9 + 9 + 4$

$(x + 3)^2 + (y - 2)^2 = 4$

Circle

Center $(-3, 2)$

$r = 2$

Let $y = 0$:

$\left(x + 3^2\right) + (0 - 2)^2 = 4$

$(x + 3)^2 + 4 = 4$

$(x + 3)^2 = 0$

$x + 3 = 0$

$x = -3$

$(-3, 0)$

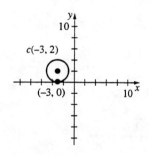

4. $\dfrac{x^2}{10} - \dfrac{y^2}{9} = 1$

Hyperbola

Center $(0, 0)$

$a^2 = 10 \qquad\qquad b^2 = 9$

$a = \sqrt{10} \qquad\qquad b = 3$

Vertices: $\left(\pm\sqrt{10},\ 0\right)$

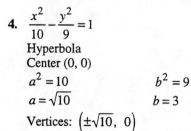

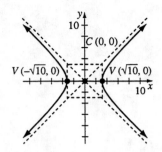

6. $y = -2(x+3)^2 + 4$
Parabola
Vertex: $(-3, 4)$
Let $x = 0$:
$y = -2(0+3)^2 + 4 = -14$
$(0, -14)$

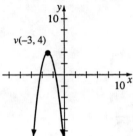

8. $7y^2 - 7x^2 = 28$

$\dfrac{y^2}{4} - \dfrac{x^2}{4} = 1$

Hyperbola
Center $(0, 0)$
$b^2 = 4$ $a^2 = 4$
$b = 2$ $a = 2$
Vertices: $(0, \pm 2)$

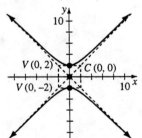

10. $x = a(y-k)^2 + h$
$x = a(y-3)^2 + (-7)$
$x = a(y-3)^2 - 7$
$2 = a(0-3)^2 - 7$
$2 = 9a - 7$
$9 = 9a$

$1 = a$
$x = (y-3)^2 - 7$

12. $b = \dfrac{|14-0|}{2} = 7$

$\dfrac{(y-k)^2}{b^2} - \dfrac{(x-h)^2}{a^2} = 1$

$\dfrac{(y-7)^2}{7^2} - \dfrac{(x-6)^2}{3^2} = 1$

$\dfrac{(y-7)^2}{49} - \dfrac{(x-6)^2}{9} = 1$

14. $-2x + y = 5$
$x^2 + y^2 - 25 = 0$
$y = 2x + 5$
$x^2 + (2x+5)^2 - 25 = 0$
$x^2 + 4x^2 + 20x + 25 - 25 = 0$
$5x^2 + 20x = 0$
$5x(x+4) = 0$

$5x = 0$ ⎯ or ⎯ $x + 4 = 0$
$x = 0$ — $x = -4$
$y = 2(0) + 5 = 5$ — $y = 2(-4) + 5 = -3$
$(0, 5), (-4, -3)$

16. $2x^2 + y^2 = 9$
$xy = -3$

$y = -\dfrac{3}{x}$

$2x^2 + \left(-\dfrac{3}{x}\right)^2 = 9$

$2x^2 + \dfrac{9}{x^2} = 9$

$2x^4 + 9 = 9x^2$
$2x^4 - 9x^2 + 9 = 0$
Let $u = x^2$
$2u^2 - 9u + 9 = 0$
$(2u-3)(u-3) = 0$

$2u - 3 = 0$ ⎯ or ⎯ $u - 3 = 0$
$2u = 3$ — $u = 3$

$u = \dfrac{3}{2}$ — $x^2 = 3$

$x^2 = \dfrac{3}{2}$

$x = \pm\sqrt{\dfrac{3}{2}}$

$$x = \frac{\sqrt{6}}{2} \quad \text{or} \quad x = -\frac{\sqrt{6}}{2}$$

$$y = \frac{-3}{\frac{\sqrt{6}}{2}} \qquad\qquad y = \frac{-3}{\frac{-\sqrt{6}}{2}}$$

$$= -\sqrt{6} \qquad\qquad\qquad = \sqrt{6}$$

$$x = \pm\sqrt{3}$$

$$x = \sqrt{3} \quad \text{or} \quad x = -\sqrt{3}$$

$$y = -\frac{3}{\sqrt{3}} \qquad\qquad y = \frac{-3}{-\sqrt{3}}$$

$$y = -\sqrt{3}$$

$$\left(\frac{\sqrt{6}}{2}, -\sqrt{6}\right), \left(-\frac{\sqrt{6}}{2}, \sqrt{6}\right), \left(\sqrt{3}, -\sqrt{3}\right),$$

$$\left(-\sqrt{3}, \sqrt{3}\right)$$

Cumulative Test for Chapters 1–9

2. $3(4-6)^3 + \sqrt{25}$

$$= 3(-2)^3 + 5$$
$$= 3(-8) + 5$$
$$= -24 + 5$$
$$= -19$$

4. $A = 3bt + prt$

$$A - 3bt = prt$$

$$\frac{A - 3bt}{rt} = p$$

6. $\dfrac{3}{x-4} + \dfrac{6}{x^2 - 16}$

$$= \frac{3}{x-4} + \frac{6}{(x+4)(x-4)}$$

$$= \frac{3(x+4)}{(x-4)(x+4)} + \frac{6}{(x+4)(x-4)}$$

$$= \frac{3(x+4) + 6}{(x-4)(x+4)}$$

$$= \frac{3x + 12 + 6}{(x-4)(x+4)}$$

$$= \frac{3x + 18}{(x-4)(x+4)}$$

8. $3x - 2y - 9z = 9$

$$x - y + z = 8$$
$$2x + 3y - z = -2$$

$$\begin{array}{ll}
3x - 2y - 9z = 9 & x - y + z = 8 \\
\underline{9x - 9y + 9z = 72} & \underline{2x + 3y - z = -2} \\
12x - 11y = 81 & 3x + 2y = 6
\end{array}$$

$$\begin{array}{l}
12x - 11y = 81 \\
\underline{-12x - 8y = -24} \\
-19y = 57 \\
y = -3
\end{array}$$

$$3x + 2(-3) = 6$$
$$3x - 6 = 6$$
$$3x = 12$$
$$x = 4$$

$$4 - (-3) + z = 8$$
$$7 + z = 8$$
$$z = 1$$
$$x = 4, \ y = -3, \ z = 1$$

10. $\left(\sqrt{2} + \sqrt{3}\right)\left(2\sqrt{6} - \sqrt{3}\right)$

$$= 2\sqrt{12} - \sqrt{6} + 2\sqrt{18} - 3$$
$$= 4\sqrt{3} - \sqrt{6} + 6\sqrt{2} - 3$$

12. $\dfrac{6(x-4)}{5} \geq \dfrac{3(x+2)}{4}$

$$24(x-4) \geq 15(x+2)$$
$$24x - 96 \geq 15x + 30$$
$$9x - 96 \geq 30$$
$$9x \geq 126$$
$$x \geq 14$$

14. $y = -\dfrac{1}{2}(x+2)^2 - 3$

Parabola

x	y
–4	–5
–2	–3
0	–5

Vertex: $(-2, -3)$
y-intercept: $(0, -5)$

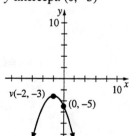

16. $16x^2 - 4y^2 = 64$

$\dfrac{x^2}{4} - \dfrac{y^2}{16} = 1$

Hyperbola

Center $(0, 0)$

$a^2 = 4 \qquad\qquad b^2 = 16$

$a = 2 \qquad\qquad b = 4$

Vertices: $(2, 0)$, $(-2, 0)$

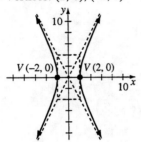

18. $y = 2x^2$

$y = 2x + 4$

$2x^2 = 2x + 4$

$2x^2 - 2x - 4 = 0$

$x^2 - x - 2 = 0$

$(x - 2)(x + 1) = 0$

$x - 2 = 0 \qquad$ or $\qquad x + 1 = 0$

$x = 2 \qquad\qquad\qquad\quad x = -1$

$y = 2(2)^2 = 8 \qquad\qquad y = 2(-1)^2 = 2$

$(2, 8)$, $(-1, 2)$

20. $xy = -15$

$4x + 3y = 3$

$y = -\dfrac{15}{x}$

$4x + 3\left(-\dfrac{15}{x}\right) = 3$

$4x - \dfrac{45}{x} = 3$

$4x^2 - 45 = 3x$

$4x^2 - 3x - 45 = 0$

$(4x - 15)(x + 3) = 0$

$4x - 15 = 0 \qquad$ or $\qquad x + 3 = 0$

$x = \dfrac{15}{4} \qquad\qquad\qquad x = -3$

$y = -\dfrac{15}{\frac{15}{4}} = -4 \qquad\qquad y = -\dfrac{15}{-3} = 5$

$\left(\dfrac{15}{4}, -4\right)$, $(-3, 5)$

Chapter 10

2. (a) $f(-2) = 5(-2)^2 + 2(-2) - 3$
$= 20 - 4 - 3$
$= 13$

(b) $f(a) = 5a^2 + 2a - 3$

(c) $f(a+1) = 5(a+1)^2 + 2(a+1) - 3$
$= 5(a^2 + 2a + 1) + 2a + 2 - 3$
$= 5a^2 + 10a + 5 + 2a - 1$
$= 5a^2 + 12a + 4$

4. Function; passes vertical line test

6. $f(x) = x^2$

x	$f(x)$
-2	4
-1	1
0	0
1	1
2	4

$h(x) = (x+2)^2 + 3$
Shift 2 units left and 3 units up.

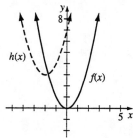

8. (a) $(f+g)(x) = (3x-4) + (-2x^3 - 6x + 3)$
$= -2x^3 - 3x - 1$

(b) $(f+g)(2) = -2(2)^3 - 3(2) - 1$
$= -16 - 6 - 1$
$= -23$

(c) $f[g(x)] = f[-2x^3 - 6x + 3]$
$= 3(-2x^3 - 6x + 3) - 4$
$= -6x^3 - 18x + 9 - 4$
$= -6x^3 - 18x + 5$

10. (a) $\left(\dfrac{f}{g}\right)(x) = \dfrac{6x^2 - 5x - 4}{3x - 4}$
$= \dfrac{(3x-4)(2x+1)}{3x-4}$
$= 2x + 1, \; 3x - 4 \neq 0$
$x \neq \dfrac{4}{3}$

(b) $\left(\dfrac{f}{g}\right)(-1) = 2(-1) + 1 = -1$

(c) $(f \circ g)(x) = f[g(x)]$
$= f[3x - 4]$
$= 6(3x-4)^2 - 5(3x-4) - 4$
$= 6(9x^2 - 24x + 16) - 15x + 20 - 4$
$= 54x^2 - 144x + 96 - 15x + 16$
$= 54x^2 - 159x + 112$

(d) $(g \circ f)(x) = g[f(x)]$
$= g[6x^2 - 5x - 4]$
$= 3(6x^2 - 5x - 4) - 4$
$= 18x^2 - 15x - 12 - 4$
$= 18x^2 - 15x - 16$

12. Not one-to-one; fails horizontal line test

14. $F^{-1} = \{(1, 7), (3, 6), (-1, 2), (5, -1)\}$

10.1 Exercises

2. $f(-4) = 3(-4) - 5 = -12 - 5 = -17$

4. $f(b) = 3b - 5$

6. $f(2a) = 3(2a) - 5 = 6a - 5$

8. $f(b + 3) = 3(b + 3) - 5 = 3b + 9 - 5 = 3b + 4$

10. $g(6) + g(b)$
$= \dfrac{1}{2}(6) - 3 + \left(\dfrac{1}{2}b - 3\right)$
$= 3 - 3 + \dfrac{1}{2}b - 3$
$= \dfrac{1}{2}b - 3$

12. $g(8b)$

$= \dfrac{1}{2}(8b) - 3$

$= 4b - 3$

14. $g(a - 4)$

$= \dfrac{1}{2}(a - 4) - 3$

$= \dfrac{1}{2}a - 2 - 3$

$= \dfrac{1}{2}a - 5$

16. $g(b^2) - g\left(\dfrac{4}{3}\right)$

$= \dfrac{1}{2}b^2 - 3 - \left[\dfrac{1}{2}\left(\dfrac{4}{3}\right) - 3\right]$

$= \dfrac{1}{2}b^2 - 3 - \dfrac{2}{3} + 3$

$= \dfrac{1}{2}b^2 - \dfrac{2}{3}$

18. $g(3b + 5)$

$= \dfrac{1}{2}(3b + 5) - 3$

$= \dfrac{3}{2}b + \dfrac{5}{2} - 3$

$= \dfrac{3}{2}b - \dfrac{1}{2}$

20. $g(2b) + g(5)$

$= \dfrac{1}{2}(2b) - 3 + \left[\dfrac{1}{2}(5) - 3\right]$

$= b - 3 + \dfrac{5}{2} - 3$

$= b - \dfrac{7}{2}$

22. $p(-3)$

$= 3(-3)^2 + 4(-3) - 2$

$= 27 - 12 - 2$

$= 13$

24. $p(b)$

$= 3b^2 + 4b - 2$

26. $p(b - 1)$

$= 3(b - 1)^2 + 4(b - 1) - 2$

$= 3(b^2 - 2b + 1) + 4b - 4 - 2$

$= 3b^2 - 6b + 3 + 4b - 6$

$= 3b^2 - 2b - 3$

28. $p(3a)$

$= 3(3a)^2 + 4(3a) - 2$

$= 3(9a^2) + 12a - 2$

$= 27a^2 + 12a - 2$

30. $p(3b) - p(b)$

$= 3(3b)^2 + 4(3b) - 2 - (3b^2 + 4b - 2)$

$= 3(9b^2) + 12b - 2 - 3b^2 - 4b + 2$

$= 27b^2 + 12b - 2 - 3b^2 - 4b + 2$

$= 24b^2 + 8b$

32. $p(b - 3) - p(3)$

$= 3(b - 3)^2 + 4(b - 3) - 2 - [3(3)^2 + 4(3) - 2]$

$= 3(b^2 - 6b + 9) + 4b - 12 - 2 - (27 + 12 - 2)$

$= 3b^2 - 18b + 27 + 4b - 14 - 37$

$= 3b^2 - 14b - 24$

34. $h(-4)$

$= \sqrt{-4 + 5}$

$= \sqrt{1}$

$= 1$

36. $h(23)$

$= \sqrt{23 + 5}$

$= \sqrt{28}$

$= 2\sqrt{7}$

38. $h(a - 3)$

$= \sqrt{a - 3 + 5}$

$= \sqrt{a + 2}$

40. $h(5a) = \sqrt{5a + 5}$

42. $h(4a + 3)$

$= \sqrt{4a + 3 + 5}$

$= \sqrt{4a + 8}$

$= \sqrt{4(a + 2)}$

$= 2\sqrt{a + 2}$

44. $h(9a + 4) - h(-4)$

$= \sqrt{9a + 4 + 5} - \sqrt{-4 + 5}$

$= \sqrt{9a + 9} - \sqrt{1}$

$= \sqrt{9(a + 1)} - 1$

$= 3\sqrt{a + 1} - 1$

46. $r(-1)$

$= \dfrac{7}{-1-3}$

$= -\dfrac{7}{4}$

48. $r(3.5)$

$= \dfrac{7}{3.5-3}$

$= \dfrac{7}{0.5}$

$= 14$

50. $r(3b^2) = \dfrac{7}{3b^2-3}$

52. $r(a-3)$

$= \dfrac{7}{a-3-3}$

$= \dfrac{7}{a-6}$

54. $r(a-3) - r(2a)$

$= \dfrac{7}{a-3-3} - \dfrac{7}{2a-3}$

$= \dfrac{7}{a-6} - \dfrac{7}{2a-3}$

$= \dfrac{7(2a-3)}{(a-6)(2a-3)} - \dfrac{7(a-6)}{(a-6)(2a-3)}$

$= \dfrac{7(2a-3)-7(a-6)}{(a-6)(2a-3)}$

$= \dfrac{14a-21-7a+42}{(a-6)(2a-3)}$

$= \dfrac{7a+21}{(a-6)(2a-3)}$ or $\dfrac{7(a+3)}{(a-6)(2a-3)}$

56. $r(b-1) + r(3b)$

$= \dfrac{7}{b-1-3} + \dfrac{7}{3b-3}$

$= \dfrac{7}{b-4} + \dfrac{7}{3(b-1)}$

$= \dfrac{7(3)(b-1)}{3(b-4)(b-1)} + \dfrac{7(b-4)}{3(b-4)(b-1)}$

$= \dfrac{21b-21+7b-28}{3(b-4)(b-1)}$

$= \dfrac{28b-49}{3(b-4)(b-1)}$ or $\dfrac{7(4b-7)}{3(b-4)(b-1)}$

58. $\dfrac{f(x+h)-f(x)}{h}$

$= \dfrac{2(x+h)-3-(2x-3)}{h}$

$= \dfrac{2x+2h-3-2x+3}{h}$

$= \dfrac{2h}{h}$

$= 2$

60. $\dfrac{f(x+h)-f(x)}{h}$

$= \dfrac{(x+h)^2-(x+h)-(x^2-x)}{h}$

$= \dfrac{x^2+2xh+h^2-x-h-x^2+x}{h}$

$= \dfrac{2xh+h^2-h}{h}$

$= \dfrac{h(2x+h-1)}{h}$

$= 2x+h-1$

62. **(a)** $P(w) = 2.5w^2$

(b) $P(20) = 2.5(20)^2 = 1000$
1000 kilowatts

(c) $P(20+e) = 2.5(20+e)^2$
$= 2.5(400+40e+e^2)$
$= 1000+100e+2.5e^2$
The expression for the power as a function
of error e is $1000+100e+2.5e^2$.

(d) $P'(2) = 1000+100(2)+2.5(2)^2$
$= 1000+200+10$
$= 1210$
1210 kilowatts

64. The percent level would be that for 2 years more
than x; $P(4+2) = P(6) \approx 20$
The percent is 20%.

66. $f(0.026a)$
$= 3(0.026a)^2 - 4.6(0.026a)+1.23$
$= 0.002a^2 - 0.120a + 1.23$

68. $f(a + 2.23)$

$= 3(a + 2.23)^2 - 4.6(a + 2.23) + 1.23$

$= 3(a^2 + 4.46a + 4.9729) - 4.6a - 10.258 + 1.23$

$= 3a^2 + 13.38a + 14.9187 - 4.6a - 10.258 + 1.23$

$= 3a^2 + 8.78a + 5.891$

70. smaller piece: x

longer piece: $20 - x$

Circumference of circle $= x$

$2\pi r = x$

$r = \dfrac{x}{2\pi}$

Perimeter of square $= 20 - x$

$4s = 20 - x$

$s = \dfrac{20 - x}{4}$

$A(x) = \pi\left(\dfrac{x}{2\pi}\right)^2 + \left(\dfrac{20 - x}{4}\right)^2$

$= \dfrac{\pi x^2}{4\pi^2} + \dfrac{400 - 40x + x^2}{16}$

$= \dfrac{x^2}{4\pi} + \dfrac{400 - 40x + x^2}{16}$

$\approx 0.0796x^2 + 25 - 2.5x + 0.0625x^2$

$\approx 0.1421x^2 - 2.5x + 25$

$A(3) = 0.1421(3)^2 - 2.5(3) + 25$

$= 18.78$

$A(9) = 0.1421(9)^2 - 2.5(9) + 25$

$= 14.01$

Cumulative Review Problems

72. $3 + \dfrac{2x + 7}{x + 6} = \dfrac{5}{2}$

$2(x + 6)(3) + 2(x + 6)\left(\dfrac{2x + 7}{x + 6}\right) = 2(x + 6)\left(\dfrac{5}{2}\right)$

$6x + 36 + 2(2x + 7) = 5(x + 6)$

$6x + 36 + 4x + 14 = 5x + 30$

$10x + 50 = 5x + 30$

$5x + 50 = 30$

$5x = -20$

$x = -4$

74. $\dfrac{5}{8} + \dfrac{3}{2x} = \dfrac{1}{4x}$

$8x\left(\dfrac{5}{8}\right) + 8x\left(\dfrac{3}{2x}\right) = 8x\left(\dfrac{1}{4x}\right)$

$5x + 12 = 2$

$5x = -10$

$x = -2$

10.2 Exercises

2. You can use the vertical line test to determine whether or not a relation is a function. If a vertical line intersects the graph more than once, then there are two different points that have the same first coordinate and the relation is not a function.

4. to the right

6. Function; passes vertical line test

8. Not a function; fails vertical line test

10. Function; passes vertical line test

12. Not a function: fails vertical line test

14. Not a function; fails vertical line test

16. Not a function; fails vertical line test

18. Not a function; fails vertical line test

In Exercises 20–24, make a table of values for $f(x) = x^2$:

x	$f(x)$
-2	4
-1	1
0	0
1	1
2	4

20. $f(x) = x^2$, $h(x) = x^2 + 4$

Shift 4 units up.

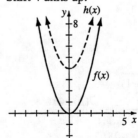

22. $f(x) = x^2$, $p(x) = (x+1)^2$
Shift 1 unit left.

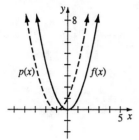

24. $f(x) = x^2$, $g(x) = (x+1)^2 - 2$
Shift 1 unit left and 2 units down.

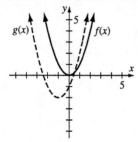

In Exercises 26–30, make a table of values for $f(x) = |x|$:

x	$f(x)$
–2	2
1	1
0	0
1	1
2	2

26. $f(x) = |x|$, $r(x) = |x| - 1$
Shift 1 unit down.

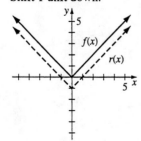

28. $f(x) = |x|$, $s(x) = |x+4|$
Shift 4 units left.

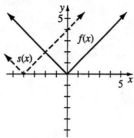

30. $f(x) = |x|$; $t(x) = |x+1| + 2$
Shift 1 unit left and 2 units up.

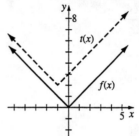

32. $f(x) = x^3$; $j(x) = (x-3)^3 + 3$
Shift 3 units right and 3 units up.

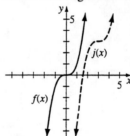

34. $f(x) = \dfrac{3}{x}$, $g(x) = \dfrac{3}{x} - 2$

x	$f(x)$
–2	$-\frac{3}{2}$
–1	–3
$-\frac{1}{2}$	–6
$\frac{1}{2}$	6
1	3
2	$\frac{3}{2}$

Shift 2 units down.

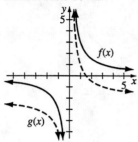

36. $f(x) = \dfrac{4}{x}$, $h(x) = \dfrac{4}{x-2} + 3$

x	$f(x)$
-2	-2
-1	-4
$-\frac{1}{2}$	-8
$\frac{1}{2}$	8
1	4
2	2

Shift 2 units right and 3 units up.

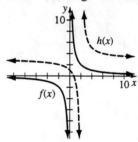

38. $f(x) = x^7$

$f(x) = (x + 1.3)^7 + 3.3$

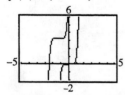

Cumulative Review Problems

40. $(\sqrt{3x} - \sqrt{y})^2$

$= (\sqrt{3x})^2 - 2\sqrt{3x}\sqrt{y} + (\sqrt{y})^2$

$= 3x - 2\sqrt{3xy} + y$

42. $620 - 315 - 120 = 185$

$\dfrac{185}{10} = 18.5$

He can eat $18\dfrac{1}{2}$ French fries.

10.3 Exercises

2. $f(x) = 3x + 4$, $g(x) = 1 - 2x$

(a) $(f + g)(x)$
$= (3x + 4) + (1 - 2x)$
$= x + 5$

(b) $(f - g)(x)$
$= (3x + 4) - (1 - 2x)$
$= 5x + 3$

(c) $(f + g)(2) = (2) + 5 = 7$

(d) $(f - g)(-1) = 5(-1) + 3 = -2$

4. (a) $(f + g)(x)$
$= (2 - x) + (x^2 + 3x - 1)$
$= x^2 + 2x + 1$

(b) $(f - g)(x)$
$= (2 - x) - (x^2 + 3x - 1)$
$= 2 - x - x^2 - 3x + 1$
$= -x^2 - 4x + 3$

(c) $(f + g)(2)$
$= 2^2 + 2(2) + 1$
$= 4 + 4 + 1$
$= 9$

(d) $(f - g)(-1)$
$= -(-1)^2 - 4(-1) + 3$
$= -1 + 4 + 3$
$= 6$

6. (a) $(f + g)(x)$
$= (2x^2 + x - 2) + (2x^3 - x)$
$= 2x^3 + 2x^2 - 2$

(b) $(f - g)(x)$
$= (2x^2 + x - 2) - (2x^3 - x)$
$= 2x^2 + x - 2 - 2x^3 + x$
$= -2x^3 + 2x^2 + 2x - 2$

(c) $(f+g)(2)$
$$= 2(2)^3 + 2(2)^2 - 2$$
$$= 16 + 8 - 2$$
$$= 22$$

(d) $(f-g)(-1)$
$$= -2(-1)^3 + 2(-1)^2 + 2(-1) - 2$$
$$= 2 + 2 - 2 - 2$$
$$= 0$$

8. (a) $(f+g)(x)$
$$= \frac{3}{x-3} + \frac{2}{x+1}$$
$$= \frac{3(x+1)}{(x-3)(x+1)} + \frac{2(x-3)}{(x-3)(x+1)}$$
$$= \frac{3(x+1) + 2(x-3)}{(x-3)(x+1)}$$
$$= \frac{3x+3+2x-6}{(x-3)(x+1)}$$
$$= \frac{5x-3}{(x-3)(x+1)}$$

(b) $(f-g)(x)$
$$= \frac{3}{x-3} - \frac{2}{x+1}$$
$$= \frac{3(x+1)}{(x-3)(x+1)} - \frac{2(x-3)}{(x+1)(x-3)}$$
$$= \frac{3(x+1) - 2(x-3)}{(x-3)(x+1)}$$
$$= \frac{3x+3-2x+6}{(x-3)(x+1)}$$
$$= \frac{x+9}{(x-3)(x+1)}$$

(c) $(f+g)(2)$
$$= \frac{5(2)-3}{(2-3)(2+1)} = \frac{7}{-3} = -\frac{7}{3}$$

(d) $(f-g)(-1) = \frac{-1+9}{(-1-3)(-1+1)} = \frac{8}{0}$
Not defined

10. (a) $(f+g)(x)$
$$= \sqrt{4x+4} + 3\sqrt{x+1}$$
$$= \sqrt{4(x+1)} + 3\sqrt{x+1}$$
$$= 2\sqrt{x+1} + 3\sqrt{x+1}$$
$$= 5\sqrt{x+1}$$

(b) $(f-g)(x)$
$$= \sqrt{4x+4} - 3\sqrt{x+1}$$
$$= \sqrt{4(x+1)} - 3\sqrt{x+1}$$
$$= 2\sqrt{x+1} - 3\sqrt{x+1}$$
$$= -\sqrt{x+1}$$

(c) $(f+g)(2) = 5\sqrt{2+1} = 5\sqrt{3}$

(d) $(f-g)(-1) = -\sqrt{-1+1} = -\sqrt{0} = 0$

12. (a) $(fg)(x) = (2x^2 - 1)(3x) = 6x^3 - 3x$

(b) $(fg)(-3)$
$$= 6(-3)^3 - 3(-3)$$
$$= -162 + 9 = -153$$

14. (a) $(fg)(x)$
$$= (2x-3)(-2x^2 - 3x + 1)$$
$$= -4x^3 - 6x^2 + 2x + 6x^2 + 9x - 3$$
$$= -4x^3 + 11x - 3$$

(b) $(fg)(-3)$
$$= -4(-3)^3 + 11(-3) - 3$$
$$= 108 - 33 - 3 = 72$$

16. (a) $(fg)(x)$
$$= (4x-1)\left(\frac{3}{x+5}\right)$$
$$= \frac{12x-3}{x+5}$$

(b) $(fg)(-3) = \frac{12(-3)-3}{-3+5} = -\frac{39}{2}$

18. (a) $(fg)(x) = 4x\sqrt{3x+10}$

(b) $(fg)(-3)$
$$= 4(-3)\sqrt{3(-3)+10}$$
$$= -12\sqrt{1} = -12$$

20. (a) $\left(\dfrac{f}{g}\right)(x) = \dfrac{x-6}{3x},$　　　$3x \neq 0$
　　　　　　　　　　　　　　　　$x \neq 0$

(b) $\left(\dfrac{f}{g}\right)(2) = \dfrac{2-6}{3(2)} = -\dfrac{4}{6} = -\dfrac{2}{3}$

22. (a) $\left(\dfrac{f}{g}\right)(x) = \dfrac{x^2+4}{3x+2},$ $3x+2 \neq 0$

$$x \neq -\dfrac{2}{3}$$

(b) $\left(\dfrac{f}{g}\right)(2) = \dfrac{2^2+4}{3(2)+2} = \dfrac{8}{8} = 1$

24. (a) $\left(\dfrac{f}{g}\right)(x) = \dfrac{4x^2+4x+1}{2x+1}$

$= \dfrac{(2x+1)(2x+1)}{2x+1}$

$= 2x+1,$ $2x+1 \neq 0$

$$x \neq -\dfrac{1}{2}$$

(b) $\left(\dfrac{f}{g}\right)(2) = 2(2)+1 = 5$

26. (a) $\left(\dfrac{f}{g}\right)(x)$

$= \dfrac{3x+2}{3x^2-x-2}$

$= \dfrac{3x+2}{(3x+2)(x-1)}$

$= \dfrac{1}{x-1},$

$3x+2 \neq 0$ $x-1 \neq 0$

$x \neq -\dfrac{2}{3}$ $x \neq 1$

(b) $\left(\dfrac{f}{g}\right)(2) = \dfrac{1}{2-1} = 1$

28. (a) $\left(\dfrac{f}{g}\right)(x)$

$\dfrac{2}{x-7} \div \dfrac{4}{x+1}$

$= \dfrac{2}{x-7} \cdot \dfrac{x+1}{4}$

$= \dfrac{x+1}{2(x-7)}$

$= \dfrac{x+1}{2x-14}$ $x-7 \neq 0, x+1 \neq 0$

$x \neq 7, x \neq -1$

(b) $\left(\dfrac{f}{g}\right)(2) = \dfrac{2+1}{2(2-7)} = \dfrac{3}{-10} = -\dfrac{3}{10}$

30. $(h+g)(x)$

$= \left(\dfrac{x-2}{3}\right) + \left(x^2-2x\right)$

$= \dfrac{1}{3}x - \dfrac{2}{3} + x^2 - 2x$

$= x^2 - \dfrac{5}{3}x - \dfrac{2}{3}$ or $\dfrac{3x^2-5x-2}{3}$

32. $(g-f)(x)$

$= (x^2-2x)-(3x+2)$

$= x^2-2x-3x-2$

$= x^2-5x-2$

34. $(gh)(x)$

$= (x^2-2x)\left(\dfrac{x-2}{3}\right)$

$= \dfrac{(x^2-2x)(x-2)}{3}$

$= \dfrac{x^3-2x^2-2x^2+4x}{3}$

$= \dfrac{x^3-4x^2+4x}{3}$ or $\dfrac{1}{3}x^3 - \dfrac{4}{3}x^2 + \dfrac{4}{3}x$

36. Using the function found in Exercise 34, $(gh)(3)$

$= \dfrac{3^3-4(3)^2+4(3)}{3}$

$= \dfrac{27-36+12}{3} = \dfrac{3}{3} = 1$

38. $\left(\dfrac{g}{f}\right)(x) = \dfrac{x^2-2x}{3x+2},$ $3x+2 \neq 0$

$$x \neq -\dfrac{2}{3}$$

40. Using the function found in Exercise 38, $\left(\dfrac{g}{f}\right)(-1)$

$= \dfrac{(-1)^2-2(-1)}{3(-1)+2}$

$= \dfrac{1+2}{-3+2} = \dfrac{3}{-1} = -3$

42. $f[g(x)] = f(4x-1) = 3(4x-1)+2 = 12x-1$

44. $f[g(x)] = f[x-2]$

$= (x-2)^2 + 3$

$$= x^2 - 4x + 4 + 3$$
$$= x^2 - 4x + 7$$

46. $f[g(x)] = f[3x^2 + x - 1]$
$$= 1 - 2(3x^2 + x - 1)$$
$$= 1 - 6x^2 - 2x + 2$$
$$= -6x^2 - 2x + 3$$

48. $f[g(x)] = f[4x + 1]$
$$= \frac{4}{(4x+1) - 3}$$
$$= \frac{4}{4x - 2}$$
$$= \frac{4}{2(2x-1)}$$
$$= \frac{2}{2x-1}, \qquad 2x - 1 \neq 0$$
$$x \neq \frac{1}{2}$$

50. $f[g(x)] = f[2x - 1]$
$$= \sqrt{(2x-1) + 4}$$
$$= \sqrt{2x + 3}, \qquad 2x + 3 \geq 0$$
$$x \geq -\frac{3}{2}$$

52. $g[h(x)] = g\left[\dfrac{1}{x}\right]$
$$= 3\left(\frac{1}{x}\right) + 5$$
$$= \frac{3}{x} + 5 \text{ or } \frac{3 + 5x}{x}, x \neq 0$$

54. $h[g(x)] = h[3x + 5]$
$$= \frac{1}{3x + 5}, \qquad 3x + 5 \neq 0$$
$$x \neq -\frac{5}{3}$$

56. Using the function found in Exercise 54,
$$h[g(2)] = \frac{1}{3(2) + 5} = \frac{1}{11}$$

58. $(f \circ h)(x) = f[h(x)] = f\left[\dfrac{1}{x}\right]$
$$= \left(\frac{1}{x}\right)^2 + 2$$
$$= \frac{1}{x^2} + 2 \text{ or } \frac{1 + 2x^2}{x^2}, x \neq 0$$

60. $(f \circ p)(x) = f[p(x)] = f\left[\sqrt{x - 1}\right]$
$$= \left(\sqrt{x-1}\right)^2 + 2$$
$$= x - 1 + 2$$
$$= x + 1, \qquad x - 1 \geq 0$$
$$x \geq 1$$

62. Using the function found in Exercise 60,
$$(f \circ p)(10) = 10 + 1 = 11$$

64. $(h \circ h)(x) = h[h(x)] = h\left[\dfrac{1}{x}\right]$
$$= \frac{1}{\frac{1}{x}} = 1 \div \frac{1}{x} = 1 \cdot \frac{x}{1} = x, x \neq 0$$

66. $p[g(126.9)] = \sqrt{3(126.9) + 5} - 1 = 19.61377067$

68. $c[n(x)] = 5(3x) + 4 = 15x + 4$

70. $v[r(h)] = v[3.5h]$
$$= 31.4(3.5h)^2$$
$$= 31.4(12.25h^2)$$
$$= 384.65h^2$$
$$v[r(8)] = 384.65(8)^2 = 24{,}617.6$$
$$24{,}617.6 \text{ ft}^3$$

Cumulative Review Problems

72. $36x^2 - 12x + 1$
$$= (6x)^2 - 2(6x)(1) + 1^2$$
$$= (6x - 1)^2$$

74. $x^4 - 10x^2 + 9$
Let $u = x^2$
$$u^2 - 10u + 9$$
$$= (u - 9)(u - 1)$$
$$= (x^2 - 9)(x^2 - 1)$$
$$= (x + 3)(x - 3)(x + 1)(x - 1)$$

10.4 Exercises

2. It is not one to one.

4. No, only those functions that are one-to-one functions

6. No; 0 is used twice as a second coordinate

8. Yes

10. Yes

12. No; it fails the horizontal line test.

14. Yes; it passes the horizontal line test.

16. No; it fails the horizontal line test.

18. No, it does not pass the vertical line test. No, it is not a one-to-one function because it is not a function at all.

20. $G^{-1} = \{(0, -1), (8, 5)\}$

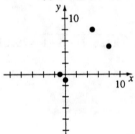

22. $J^{-1} = \{(2, 8), (1, 1), (0, 0), (-2, -8)\}$

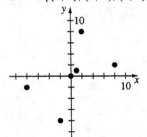

24. $M^{-1} = \{(0, 0), (1, -1), (-1, 1), (8, 2)\}$

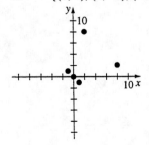

26. $f(x) = \dfrac{5}{7}x + \dfrac{1}{2}$

$$y = \frac{5}{7}x + \frac{1}{2}$$

$$x = \frac{5}{7}y + \frac{1}{2}$$

$$x - \frac{1}{2} = \frac{5}{7}y$$

$$\frac{7}{5}\left(x - \frac{1}{2}\right) = \frac{7}{5}\left(\frac{5}{7}y\right)$$

$$\frac{7}{5}x - \frac{7}{10} = y$$

$$f^{-1}(x) = \frac{7}{5}x - \frac{7}{10} \ \text{ or } \ \frac{14x - 7}{10}$$

28. $f(x) = \dfrac{2 - 4x}{3}$

$$y = \frac{2 - 4x}{3}$$

$$x = \frac{2 - 4y}{3}$$

$$3x = 2 - 4y$$

$$4y = 2 - 3x$$

$$y = \frac{2 - 3x}{4}$$

$$f^{-1}(x) = \frac{2 - 3x}{4} \ \text{ or } \ \frac{1}{2} - \frac{3}{4}x$$

30. $f(x) = \dfrac{3}{x}$

$$y = \frac{3}{x}$$

$$x = \frac{3}{y}$$

$$y = \frac{3}{x}$$

$$f^{-1}(x) = \frac{3}{x}$$

32. $f(x) = \dfrac{2}{x + 4}$

$$y = \frac{2}{x + 4}$$

$$x = \frac{2}{y + 4}$$

$$x(y + 4) = 2$$

$$y + 4 = \frac{2}{x}$$

$$y = \frac{2}{x} - 4$$

$$f^{-1}(x) = \frac{2}{x} - 4 \text{ or } \frac{2 - 4x}{x}$$

34. No, $f(x)$ is not one-to-one.

36. $g(x) = 2x + 5$
$y = 2x + 5$
$x = 2y + 5$
$x - 5 = 2y$
$$\frac{x - 5}{2} = y$$
$$g^{-1}(x) = \frac{x - 5}{2}$$

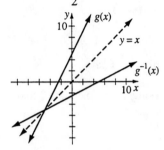

38. $h(x) = \frac{1}{2}x - 2$

$$y = \frac{1}{2}x - 2$$

$$x = \frac{1}{2}y - 2$$

$$x + 2 = \frac{1}{2}y$$

$$y = 2x + 4$$

$$h^{-1}(x) = 2x + 4$$

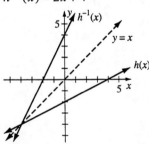

40. $r(x) = -3x - 1$
$y = -3x - 1$
$x = -3y - 1$
$x + 1 = -3y$
$$\frac{x + 1}{-3} = y$$
$$y = -\frac{x + 1}{3}$$

$$r^{-1}(x) = -\frac{x + 1}{3}$$

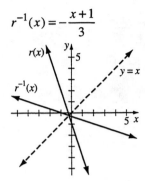

42. $t(x) = 1 - \frac{2}{3}x$

$$y = 1 - \frac{2}{3}x$$

$$x = 1 - \frac{2}{3}y$$

$$\frac{2}{3}y = 1 - x$$

$$y = \frac{3}{2}(1 - x)$$

$$y = \frac{3 - 3x}{2}$$

$$t^{-1}(x) = \frac{3 - 3x}{2}$$

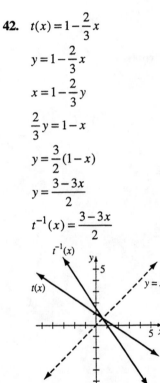

44. $y = 1.437x - 4$
$x = 1.437y - 4$
$x + 4 = 1.437y$
$$\frac{x + 4}{1.437} = y$$
$$f^{-1}(x) = \frac{x + 4}{1.437}$$
The inverse function would tell Sean the number of Irish pounds given by the bank for x dollars if the bank paid Sean $4.00 to make the transaction. No, because the bank will charge (not pay) Sean for the transaction.

46. $f\left[f^{-1}(x)\right] = f\left[\dfrac{-x-10}{3}\right]$

$= -3\left(\dfrac{-x-10}{3}\right) - 10$

$= x + 10 - 10 = x$

$f^{-1}\left[f(x)\right] = f^{-1}\left[-3x - 10\right]$

$= \dfrac{-(-3x-10)-10}{3}$

$= \dfrac{3x+10-10}{3}$

$= \dfrac{3x}{3} = x$

Cumulative Review Problems

48. $x = \sqrt{15 - 2x}$

$x^2 = \left(\sqrt{15 - 2x}\right)^2$

$x^2 = 15 - 2x$

$x^2 + 2x - 15 = 0$

$(x + 5)(x - 3) = 0$

$x + 5 = 0$ or $x - 3 = 0$

$x = -5$ $x = 3$

Check: $x = -5$

$-5 \overset{?}{=} \sqrt{15 - 2(-5)}$

$-5 \overset{?}{=} \sqrt{25}$

$-5 \neq 5$

Extraneous

Check: $x = 3$

$3 \overset{?}{=} \sqrt{15 - 2(3)}$

$3 \overset{?}{=} \sqrt{9}$

$3 = 3$

$x = 3$

50. Let x = number of overtime hours

$17(40) + 17(1.5)x = 1011.50$

$680 + 25.5x = 1011.5$

$25.5x = 331.5$

$x = 13$

She worked 13 overtime hours.

Putting Your Skills to Work

2. It would raise the graph 10 units higher.

$G(x) = -0.4(x - 23)^2 + 110$

4. $F = 1.8C + 32$

$F - 32 = 1.8C$

$C = \dfrac{F - 32}{1.8}$

$G(x) = -0.4(x - 23)^2 + 100$

$G(F) = -0.4\left(\dfrac{F - 32}{1.8} - 23\right)^2 + 100$

6. Temperature of maximum growth $= \dfrac{9 + 41}{2} = 25$

$20.4 = a(41 - 25)^2 + 110$

$20.4 = a(16)^2 + 110$

$a = \dfrac{20.4 - 110}{16^2}$

$a = -0.35$

$G(x) = -0.35(x - 25)^2 + 110$

Chapter 10 Review Problems

2. $f(-2) = 7 - 2(-2) = 11$

4. $f(3b) = 7 - 2(3b) = 7 - 6b$

6. Using the results from Exercises 2 and 4,

$f(3b) + f(-2)$

$= 7 - 6b + 11$

$= 18 - 6b$

8. $f(a + 2)$

$= \dfrac{1}{2}(a + 2) + 3$

$= \dfrac{1}{2}a + 1 + 3$

$= \dfrac{1}{2}a + 4$

10. $f(a + 2) - f(a)$

$= \dfrac{1}{2}(a + 2) + 3 - \left(\dfrac{1}{2}a + 3\right)$

$= \dfrac{1}{2}a + 1 + 3 - \dfrac{1}{2}a - 3 = 1 = 1$

12. $f(2a - 3)$

$= \dfrac{1}{2}(2a - 3) + 3$

$= a - \dfrac{3}{2} + 3$

$= a + \dfrac{3}{2}$

14. $p(3) = -2(3)^2 + 3(3) - 1 = -18 + 9 - 1 = -10$

16. Using the result from Exericse 14,

$p(3a) + p(3)$

$= -2(3a)^2 + 3(3a) - 1 + (-10)$

$= -18a^2 + 9a - 1 - 10$

$= -18a^2 + 9a - 11$

18. $p(a-3)$

$= -2(a-3)^2 + 3(a-3) - 1$

$= -2(a^2 - 6a + 9) + 3a - 9 - 1$

$= -2a^2 + 12a - 18 + 3a - 10$

$= -2a^2 + 15a - 28$

20. $h(7a) = |2(7a) - 1| = |14a - 1|$

22. $h\left(\dfrac{1}{2}a\right) = \left|2\left(\dfrac{1}{2}a - 1\right)\right| = |a - 1|$

24. $h(a+4)$

$= |2(a+4) - 1|$

$= |2a + 8 - 1|$

$= |2a + 7|$

26. $r(-2) = \dfrac{3(-2)}{-2+4} = \dfrac{-6}{2} = -3$

28. $r(a-2) = \dfrac{3(a-2)}{a-2+4} = \dfrac{3a-6}{a+2}$

30. Using the result from Exercise 26,

$r(a) + r(-2)$

$= \dfrac{3a}{a+4} - 3$

$= \dfrac{3a}{a+4} - \dfrac{3(a+4)}{a+4}$

$= \dfrac{3a - 3(a+4)}{a+4}$

$= \dfrac{3a - 3a - 12}{a+4}$

$= -\dfrac{12}{a+4}$

32. $\dfrac{f(x+h) - f(x)}{h}$

$= \dfrac{6(x+h) - 5 - (6x - 5)}{h}$

$= \dfrac{6x + 6h - 5 - 6x + 5}{h}$

$= \dfrac{6h}{h} = 6$

34. $\dfrac{f(x+h) - f(x)}{h}$

$= \dfrac{\frac{1}{4}(x+h) + 1 - \left(\frac{1}{4}x + 1\right)}{h}$

$= \dfrac{\frac{1}{4}x + \frac{1}{4}h + 1 - \frac{1}{4}x - 1}{h}$

$= \dfrac{\frac{1}{4}h}{h} = \dfrac{1}{4}$

36. $\dfrac{f(x+h) - f(x)}{h}$

$= \dfrac{2(x+h) - 3(x+h)^2 - (2x - 3x^2)}{h}$

$= \dfrac{2x + 2h - 3(x^2 + 2xh + h^2) - 2x + 3x^2}{h}$

$= \dfrac{2x + 2h - 3x^2 - 6xh - 3h^2 - 2x + 3x^2}{h}$

$= \dfrac{2h - 6xh - 3h^2}{h}$

$= \dfrac{h(2 - 6x - 3h)}{h}$

$= 2 - 6x - 3h$

38. **(a)** No; it fails the vertical line test.

(b) No; it is not a function.

40. **(a)** Yes; it passes the vertical line test.

(b) No; it fails the horizontal line test.

42. **(a)** Yes; it passes the vertical line test.

(b) Yes; it passes the horizontal line test.

44. **(a)** No; it fails the vertical line test.

(b) No; it is not a function.

46. $f(x) = x^2$

x	y
-2	4
-1	1
0	0
1	1
2	4

$g(x) = (x+1)^2 - 3$
Shift 1 unit left and 3 units down

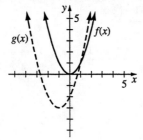

48. $f(x) = |x|$

x	y
-2	2
-1	1
0	0
1	1
2	2

$g(x) = |x+3|$
Shift 3 units left.

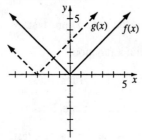

50. Using the table from Exercise 48,
$f(x) = |x|$
$h(x) = |x| - 2$
Shift 2 units down.

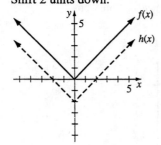

52. $f(x) = x^3$

x	y
-2	-8
-1	-1
0	0
1	1
2	8

$r(x) = (x+3)^3 + 1$
Shift 3 units left and 1 unit up

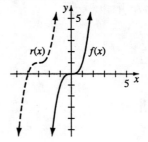

54. $f(x) = \dfrac{4}{x}, x \neq 0$

x	y
-2	-2
-1	-4
$-\frac{1}{2}$	-8
$\frac{1}{2}$	8
1	4
2	2

$r(x) = \dfrac{4}{x+2}, x \neq -2$
Shift 2 units left

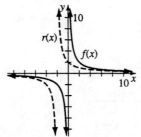

56. $(f+p)(x)$
$= (3x+5) + (2x^2 - 3x + 4)$
$= 2x^2 + 9$

58. $(t - f)(x)$

$= \left(-\dfrac{1}{2}x - 3\right) - (3x + 5)$

$= -\dfrac{1}{2}x - 3 - 3x - 5$

$= -\dfrac{7}{2}x - 8$

60. Using the result from Exercise 58,
$(t - f)(-3)$

$= -\dfrac{7}{2}(-3) - 8$

$= \dfrac{21}{2} - 8 = \dfrac{5}{2}$

62. $(fg)(x)$

$= (3x + 5)\left(\dfrac{2}{x}\right)$

$= 6 + \dfrac{10}{x}, x \neq 0$

or $\dfrac{6x + 10}{x}, x \neq 0$

64. $\left(\dfrac{g}{h}\right)(x) = \dfrac{\frac{2}{x}}{\frac{x+1}{x-4}}$

$= \dfrac{2}{x} \div \dfrac{x+1}{x-4}$

$= \dfrac{2}{x} \cdot \dfrac{x-4}{x+1}$

$= \dfrac{2(x-4)}{x(x+1)}$

$= \dfrac{2x-8}{x^2+x}, x \neq 0, x \neq -1, x \neq 4$

66. Using the result from Exercise 64,
$\left(\dfrac{g}{h}\right)(-2) = \dfrac{2(-2)-8}{(-2)^2+(-2)} = \dfrac{-12}{2} = -6$

68. $h[f(x)] = h[3x+5]$

$= \dfrac{3x+5+1}{3x+5-4}$

$= \dfrac{3x+6}{3x+1}$ $3x+1 \neq 0$

$x \neq -\dfrac{1}{3}$

70. $s[p(x)]$

$= s[2x^2 - 3x + 4]$

$= \sqrt{2x^2 - 3x + 4 - 2}$

$= \sqrt{2x^2 - 3x + 2}$

72. Using the result from Exercise 70,
$s[p(2)]$

$= \sqrt{2(2)^2 - 3(2) + 2}$

$= \sqrt{8 - 6 + 2}$

$= \sqrt{4} = 2$

74. $(g \circ h)(x) = g[h(x)]$

$= g\left[\dfrac{x+1}{x-4}\right]$

$= \dfrac{2}{\frac{x+1}{x-4}}$

$= \dfrac{2(x-4)}{x+1}$

$= \dfrac{2x-8}{x+1}, x \neq 4, x \neq -1$

76. $f[f(x)] = f[3x+5]$
$= 3(3x+5) + 5$
$= 9x + 15 + 5$
$= 9x + 20$

78. $f[g(x)] = f\left[\dfrac{2}{x}\right]$

$= 3\left(\dfrac{2}{x}\right) + 5$

$= \dfrac{6}{x} + 5$

$= \dfrac{6+5x}{x}$

$g[f(x)] = g[3x+5]$

$= \dfrac{2}{3x+5}$

$\dfrac{6+5x}{x} \neq \dfrac{2}{3x+5}$

$f[g(x)] \neq g[f(x)]$

80. (a) $D = \{100, 200, 300, 400\}$

(b) $R = \{10, 20, 30\}$

(c) Yes

(d) No, 10 is used twice as a second coordinate.

82. (a) $D = \{12, 0, -6\}$

(b) $R = \{-12, -1, 6\}$

(c) No, 0 is used twice as a first coordinate.

(d) No; it is not a function.

84. (a) $D = \{-1, 0, 1, 2\}$

(b) $R = \{-2, 1, 2, 9\}$

(c) Yes

(d) Yes

86. $\left\{\left(\dfrac{1}{3}, 3\right), \left(-\dfrac{1}{2}, -2\right), \left(-\dfrac{1}{4}, -4\right), \left(\dfrac{1}{5}, 5\right)\right\}$

88. $f(x) = -\dfrac{2}{3}x + 4$

$y = -\dfrac{2}{3}x + 4$

$x = -\dfrac{2}{3}y + 4$

$x - 4 = -\dfrac{2}{3}y$

$-\dfrac{3}{2}(x - 4) = y$

$-\dfrac{3}{2}x + 6 = y$

$f^{-1}(x) = -\dfrac{3}{2}x + 6$

90. $h(x) = \dfrac{x+2}{3}$

$y = \dfrac{x+2}{3}$

$x = \dfrac{y+2}{3}$

$3x = y + 2$

$3x - 2 = y$

$h^{-1}(x) = 3x - 2$

92. $p(x) = \sqrt[3]{x+1}$

$y = \sqrt[3]{x+1}$

$x = \sqrt[3]{y+1}$

$x^3 = \left(\sqrt[3]{y+1}\right)^3$

$x^3 = y + 1$

$x^3 - 1 = y$

$p^{-1}(x) = x^3 - 1$

94. $f(x) = -\dfrac{3}{4}x + 1$

$y = -\dfrac{3}{4}x + 1$

$x = -\dfrac{3}{4}y + 1$

$\dfrac{3}{4}y = 1 - x$

$y = \dfrac{4}{3}(1 - x)$

$y = \dfrac{4}{3} - \dfrac{4}{3}x$

$f^{-1}(x) = \dfrac{4}{3} - \dfrac{4}{3}x$

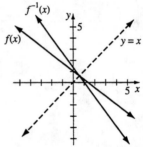

96. $f\left[f^{-1}(x)\right] = f\left[\dfrac{4x+3}{2}\right]$

$= \dfrac{1}{2}\left(\dfrac{4x+3}{2}\right) - \dfrac{3}{4}$

$= \dfrac{4x+3}{4} - \dfrac{3}{4}$

$= \dfrac{4x+3-3}{4}$

$= \dfrac{4x}{4} = x$

$f^{-1}[f(x)] = f^{-1}\left[\dfrac{1}{2}x - \dfrac{3}{4}\right]$

$= \dfrac{4\left(\frac{1}{2}x - \frac{3}{4}\right) + 3}{2}$

$= \dfrac{2x - 3 + 3}{2} = \dfrac{2x}{2} = x$

Chapter 10 Test

2. $f(2a) = \dfrac{3}{4}(2a) - 2 = \dfrac{3}{2}a - 2$

4. $f(3) = 3(3)^2 - 2(3) + 4 = 27 - 6 + 4 = 25$

6. $f(a) + f(1)$

$= 3a^2 - 2a + 4 + 3(1)^2 - 2(1) + 4$

$= 3a^2 - 2a + 4 + 3 - 2 + 4$

$= 3a^2 - 2a + 9$

8. (a) Yes; it passes the vertical line test.

(b) No; it fails the horizontal line test.

10. $f(x) = x^2$

x	y
-2	4
-1	1
0	0
1	1
2	4

$g(x) = (x-1)^2 + 3$

Shift 1 unit right and 3 units up

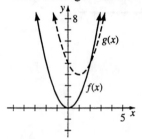

12. (a) $(f+g)(x)$

$= (3x^2 - x - 6) + (-2x^2 + 5x + 7)$

$= x^2 + 4x + 1$

(b) $(f-g)(x)$

$= (3x^2 - x - 6) - (-2x^2 + 5x + 7)$

$= 3x^2 - x - 6 + 2x^2 - 5x - 7$

$= 5x^2 - 6x - 13$

(c) $(f-g)(-2)$

$= 5(-2)^2 - 6(-2) - 13$

$= 20 + 12 - 13 = 19$

14. (a) $(f \circ g)(x) = f[g(x)] = f[4x + 5]$

$= \frac{1}{2}(4x + 5) - 3 = 2x + \frac{5}{2} - 3 = 2x - \frac{1}{2}$

(b) $(g \circ f)(x) = g[f(x)] = g\left[\frac{1}{2}x - 3\right]$

$= 4\left(\frac{1}{2}x - 3\right) + 5 = 2x - 12 + 5 = 2x - 7$

(c) $f[f(x)] = f\left[\frac{1}{2}x - 3\right]$

$= \frac{1}{2}\left(\frac{1}{2}x - 3\right) - 3$

$= \frac{1}{4}x - \frac{3}{2} - 3$

$= \frac{1}{4}x - \frac{9}{2}$

16. (a) Yes

(b) $B^{-1} = \{(8, 1), (1, 8), (10, 9), (9, -10)\}$

18. $f(x) = -3x + 2$

$y = -3x + 2$

$x = -3y + 2$

$3y = 2 - x$

$y = \frac{2 - x}{3}$

$f^{-1}(x) = \frac{2 - x}{3} = \frac{2}{3} - \frac{1}{3}x$

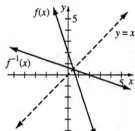

Cumulative Test for Chapters 1–10

2. $3(4 - 6)^3 + \sqrt{25}$

$= 3(-2)^3 + 5$

$= 3(-8) + 5$

$= -24 + 5 = -19$

4. $A = 3bt + prt$

$A - 3bt = prt$

$\frac{A - 3bt}{rt} = p$

6. $\dfrac{3}{x-4}+\dfrac{6}{x^2-16}$

$=\dfrac{3}{x-4}+\dfrac{6}{(x-4)(x+4)}$

$=\dfrac{3(x+4)}{(x-4)(x+4)}+\dfrac{6}{(x-4)(x+4)}$

$=\dfrac{3(x+4)+6}{(x-4)(x+4)}$

$=\dfrac{3x+12+6}{(x-4)(x+4)}$

$=\dfrac{3x+18}{(x-4)(x+4)}$

8. $\begin{array}{r} 3x-2y-9z=\ 9 \\ x-\ y+\ z=\ 8 \\ 2x+3y-\ z=-2 \end{array}$

$\begin{array}{r} 3x-2y-9z=\ 9 \\ 9x-9y+9z=72 \\ \hline 12x-11y\ \ \ \ \ \ =81 \end{array}$

$\begin{array}{r} x-\ y+z=\ 8 \\ 2x+3y-z=-2 \\ \hline 3x+2y\ \ \ \ =\ 6 \end{array}$

$\begin{array}{r} 12x-11y=\ 81 \\ -12x-\ 8y=-24 \\ \hline -19y=\ 57 \\ y=-3 \end{array}$

$3x+2(-3)=6$
$3x=12$
$x=4$

$4-(-3)+z=8$
$7+z=8$
$z=1$

$x=4,\ y=-3,\ z=1$

10. $\left(\sqrt{2}+\sqrt{3}\right)\left(2\sqrt{6}-\sqrt{3}\right)$

$=2\sqrt{12}-\sqrt{6}+2\sqrt{18}-3$

$=4\sqrt{3}-\sqrt{6}+6\sqrt{2}-3$

12. $12x^2-11x+2$

$=12x^2-8x-3x+2$

$=4x(3x-2)-1(3x-2)$

$=(3x-2)(4x-1)$

14. $(x-h)^2+(y-k)^2=r^2$

$[x-(-3)]^2+(y-6)^2=14^2$

$(x+3)^2+(y-6)^2=196$

16. $f(x)=x^3$

x	y
-2	-8
-1	-1
0	0
1	1
2	8

$g(x)=(x+2)^3+4$

Shift 2 units left and 4 units up

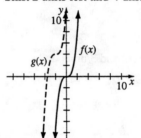

18. **(a)** Yes

(b) Yes

(c) $A^{-1}=\{(6,3),(8,1),(7,2),(4,4)\}$

20. **(a)** $f(2)=5(2)^3-3(2)^2-6=40-12-6=22$

(b) $f(-3)=5(-3)^3-3(-3)^2-6$
$=-135-27-6=-168$

(c) $f(2a)=5(2a)^3-3(2a)^2-6$
$=40a^3-12a^2-6$

22. $f\left[f^{-1}(x)\right]=f\left[-\dfrac{3}{2}x+3\right]$

$=-\dfrac{2}{3}\left(-\dfrac{3}{2}x+3\right)+2$

$=x-2+2=x$

Chapter 11

2. $3^{2x-1} = 27$

$3^{2x-1} = 3^3$

$2x - 1 = 3$

$2x = 4$

$x = 2$

4. $\dfrac{1}{36} = 6^{-2}$

$\log_6 \dfrac{1}{36} = -2$

6. $\log_{10}(10,000) = x$

$10^x = 10,000$

$10^x = 10^4$

$x = 4$

8. $\dfrac{1}{2}\log_4 x - 3\log_4 w$

$= \log_4 x^{1/2} - \log_4 w^3$

$= \log_4 \dfrac{x^{1/2}}{w^3}$ or $\log_4 \dfrac{\sqrt{x}}{w^3}$

10. $\log x = 3.9170$

$10^{3.9170} = x$

$x = 8260.3795$

12. $\log_6 5.02 = \dfrac{\log 5.02}{\log 6} = 0.9005$

14. $\ln x = 22.976$

$x = \text{antilog}_e 22.976$

$x = 9.5137 \times 10^9$

16. $4^{2x+1} = 9$

$\log 4^{2x+1} = \log 9$

$(2x + 1)\log 4 = \log 9$

$2x + 1 = \dfrac{\log 9}{\log 4}$

$2x = \dfrac{\log 9}{\log 4} - 1$

$2x = \dfrac{\log 9 - \log 4}{\log 4}$

$x = \dfrac{\log 9 - \log 4}{2\log 4}$

$x = 0.2925$

11.1 Exercises

2. 2.7183

4. $f(x) = 3^x$

x	y
-1	$\frac{1}{3}$
0	1
1	3
2	9

6. $f(x) = 5^x$

x	y
-2	$\frac{1}{25}$
-1	$\frac{1}{5}$
0	1
1	5
2	25

8. $f(x) = \left(\dfrac{1}{3}\right)^x$

x	y
-2	9
-1	3
0	1
1	$\frac{1}{3}$

10. $f(x) = 3^{-x}$

x	y
-2	9
-1	3
0	1
1	$\frac{1}{3}$
2	$\frac{1}{9}$

12. $f(x) = 4^{-x}$

x	y
-2	16
-1	4
0	1
1	$\frac{1}{4}$
2	$\frac{1}{16}$

14. $f(x) = 2^{x+5}$

x	y
-6	$\frac{1}{2}$
-5	1
-4	2
-3	4
-2	8

16. $f(x) = 3^{x-4}$

x	y
3	$\frac{1}{3}$
4	1
5	3
6	9

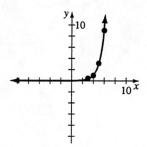

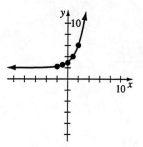

18. $f(x) = \left(\dfrac{2}{3}\right)^x$

x	y
−2	$\frac{9}{4}$
−1	$\frac{3}{2}$
0	1
1	$\frac{2}{3}$
2	$\frac{4}{9}$

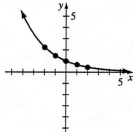

22. $f(x) = e^{x-1}$

x	y
−1	0.1
0	0.4
1	1
2	2.7
3	7.4

20. $f(x) = 2^x + 2$

x	y
−2	$\frac{9}{4}$
−1	$\frac{5}{2}$
0	3
1	4
2	6

24. $f(x) = 3e^x$

x	y
−2	0.4
−1	1.1
0	3
1	8.2
2	22.2

26. $f(x) = e^{1-x}$

x	y
-1	7.4
0	2.7
1	1
2	0.4

28. $2^x = 8$
$2^x = 2^3$
$x = 3$

30. $2^x = 2$
$2^x = 2^1$
$x = 1$

32. $2^x = \dfrac{1}{16}$
$2^x = \dfrac{1}{2^4}$
$2^x = 2^{-4}$
$x = -4$

34. $3^x = 27$
$3^x = 3^3$
$x = 3$

36. $3^x = 729$
$3^x = 3^6$
$x = 6$

38. $3^{-x} = \dfrac{1}{3}$
$3^{-x} = 3^{-1}$
$-x = -1$
$x = 1$

40. $4^{-x} = \dfrac{1}{16}$
$4^{-x} = \dfrac{1}{4^2}$
$4^{-x} = 4^{-2}$
$-x = -2$
$x = 2$

42. $6^{2x} = 36$
$6^{2x} = 6^2$
$2x = 2$
$x = 1$

44. $5^{2x+3} = 25$
$5^{2x+3} = 5^2$
$2x + 3 = 2$
$2x = -1$
$x = -\dfrac{1}{2}$

46. $10^{x+6} = 0.01$
$10^{x+6} = \dfrac{1}{100}$
$10^{x+6} = \dfrac{1}{10^2}$
$10^{x+6} = 10^{-2}$
$x + 6 = -2$
$x = -8$

48. $A = P\left(1 + \dfrac{r}{n}\right)^{nt}$
$= 6000\left(1 + \dfrac{0.15}{1}\right)^{(1)(4)}$
$= 6000(1.15)^4$
$\approx 10{,}494.04$
$\$10{,}494.04$

50. $A = P\left(1 + \dfrac{r}{n}\right)^{nt}$
$= 8000\left(1 + \dfrac{0.17}{4}\right)^{(4)(2)}$
$\approx 8000(1.0425)^8$
$\approx 11{,}160.88$
$\$11{,}160.88$

$$A = P\left(1+\frac{r}{n}\right)^{nt}$$

$$= 8000\left(1+\frac{0.17}{12}\right)^{(12)(2)}$$

$$\approx 8000(1.0142)^{24}$$

$$\approx 11{,}212.80$$

$$\$11{,}212.80$$

52. $A = P\left(1+\frac{r}{n}\right)^{nt}$

$$= 9000\left(1+\frac{0.08}{26}\right)^{(26)(3)}$$

$$= 9000(1.003076923)^{78}$$

$$\approx 11{,}437.03$$

$$\$11{,}437.03$$

54. 3 hours: $B(3) = 4000(2^3)$

$$= 4000(8)$$

$$= 32{,}000$$

9 hours: $B(9) = 4000(2^9)$

$$= 4000(512)$$

$$= 2{,}048{,}000$$

56. $f(t) = (1-0.08)^t$

$$f(5) = (0.92)^5$$

$$f(5) \approx 0.659$$

65.9% still using septic tanks in 5 years

$$f(25) = (0.92)^{25}$$

$$f(25) = 0.12$$

The goal will not be achieved in 25 years.

58. $A = Ce^{-0.1813t}$

$$A = 1.5e^{-0.1813t}$$

$$= 1.5e^{-0.1813(-10)}$$

$$= 1.5e^{1.813}$$

$$\approx 9.19$$

9.19 mg

60. $P = 14.7e^{-0.21d}$

$$= 14.7e^{-0.21(10)}$$

$$= 14.7e^{-2.1}$$

$$\approx 1.80$$

1.80 lb/sq. in.

62. 1.6 billion people would be the estimated population.

64. $7(1.014) = 7.1$

7.1 billion people in year 2010.

66. $g(x) = \dfrac{e^x - e^{-x}}{2}$

x	y
-2	3.63
-1	-1.18
-0.5	-0.52
0	0
0.5	0.52
1	1.18
1.5	2.13
2	3.63

Cumulative Review Problems

68. $\dfrac{1}{2}x - 5 = \dfrac{2}{3}x - 3 - \dfrac{5}{6}x$

$$6\left(\frac{1}{2}x\right) - 6(5) = 6\left(\frac{2}{3}x\right) - 6(3) - 6\left(\frac{5}{6}x\right)$$

$$3x - 30 = 4x - 18 - 5x$$

$$3x - 30 = -x - 18$$

$$4x - 30 = -18$$

$$4x = 12$$

$$x = 3$$

70. $2[5 - 3(2 - x)] = 3x$

$$2(5 - 6 + 3x) = 3x$$

$$2(-1 + 3x) = 3x$$

$$-2 + 6x = 3x$$

$$-2 = -3x$$

$$\frac{2}{3} = x$$

11.2 Exercises

2. base

4. $b > 0,\ b \neq 1$

6. $125 = 5^3$

$$\log_5 125 = 3$$

8. $100 = 10^2$
$\log_{10} 100 = 2$

10. $0.01 = 10^{-2}$
$\log_{10} 0.01 = -2$

12. $\dfrac{1}{64} = 2^{-6}$
$\log_2 \dfrac{1}{64} = -6$

14. $y = e^{-4}$
$\log_e y = -4$

16. $10^{0.6990} = 5$
$\log_{10} 5 = 0.6990$

18. $e^{-6} = 0.0025$
$\log_e 0.0025 = -6$

20. $2 = \log_2 4$
$2^2 = 4$

22. $4 = \log_3 81$
$3^4 = 81$

24. $2 = \log_{10} 100$
$10^2 = 100$

26. $-3 = \log_{10}(0.001)$
$10^{-3} = 0.001$

28. $-5 = \log_2\left(\dfrac{1}{32}\right)$
$2^{-5} = \dfrac{1}{32}$

30. $6 = \log_e x$
$e^6 = x$

32. $\log_{10} 6 = 0.7782$
$10^{0.7782} = 6$

34. $\log_e 0.4 = -0.9163$
$e^{-0.9163} = 0.4$

36. $\log_2 x = 6$
$2^6 = x$
$64 = x$

38. $\log_{10} x = -2$
$10^{-2} = x$
$\dfrac{1}{100} = x$

40. $\log_6 216 = y$
$6^y = 216$
$6^y = 6^3$
$y = 3$

42. $\log_4\left(\dfrac{1}{64}\right) = y$
$4^y = \dfrac{1}{64}$
$4^y = 4^{-3}$
$y = -3$

44. $\log_a 81 = 4$
$a^4 = 81$
$a^4 = 3^4$
$a = 3$

46. $\log_a 100 = 2$
$a^2 = 100$
$a^2 = 10^2$
$a = 10$

48. $\log_8 2 = w$
$8^w = 2$
$2^{3w} = 2^1$
$3w = 1$
$w = \dfrac{1}{3}$

50. $\log_{12} 1 = w$
$12^w = 1$
$12^w = 12^0$
$w = 0$

52. $\log_{10} w = -3$
$10^{-3} = w$
$\dfrac{1}{1000} = w$ or $w = 0.001$

54. $\log_w 64 = -6$

$w^{-6} = 64$

$w^{-6} = 2^6$

$w^{-6} = \left(\dfrac{1}{2}\right)^{-6}$

$w = \dfrac{1}{2}$

56. $\log_e w = 7$

$e^7 = w$

58. $\log_{81} x = \dfrac{1}{4}$

$81^{1/4} = x$

$(3^4)^{1/4} = x$

$3 = x$

60. $\log_{10} 100 = x$

$10^x = 100$

$10^x = 10^2$

$x = 2$

62. $\log_{10}(0.0001) = x$

$10^x = 0.0001$

$10^x = 10^{-4}$

$x = -4$

64. $\log_3 27 = x$

$3^x = 27$

$3^x = 3^3$

$x = 3$

66. $\log_5 125 = x$

$5^x = 125$

$5^x = 5^3$

$x = 3$

68. $\log_7 \sqrt{7} = x$

$7^x = \sqrt{7}$

$7^x = 7^{1/2}$

$x = \dfrac{1}{2}$

70. $\log_2 16 = x$

$2^x = 16$

$2^x = 2^4$

$x = 4$

72. $\log_e 1 = x$

$e^x = 1$

$e^x = e^0$

$x = 0$

74. $\log_4 x = y$

$4^y = x$

x	y
$\frac{1}{16}$	-2
$\frac{1}{4}$	-1
1	0
4	1
16	2

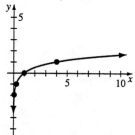

76. $\log_{1/4} x = y$

$\left(\dfrac{1}{4}\right)^y = x$

$4^{-y} = x$

$-y = \log_4 x$

$y = -\log_4 x$

x	y
4	-1
1	0
$\frac{1}{4}$	1
$\frac{1}{16}$	2

78. $\log_8 x = y$

$8^y = x$

x	y
$\frac{1}{64}$	-2
$\frac{1}{8}$	-1
1	0
8	1
64	2

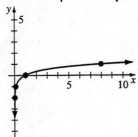

80. $f(x) = \log_4 x, \quad f^{-1}(x) = 4^x$

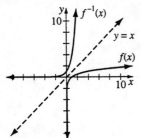

82. $pH = -\log_{10}[H^+]$

$pH = -\log_{10} 10^{-2.5}$

$-pH = \log_{10} 10^{-2.5}$

$10^{-pH} = 10^{-2.5}$

$-pH = -2.5$

$pH = 2.5$

84. $pH = -\log_{10}[H^+]$

$9 = -\log_{10}[H^+]$

$-9 = \log_{10}[H^+]$

$10^{-9} = [H^+]$

86. $pH = -\log_{10}[H^+]$

$pH = -\log_{10}(1.103 \times 10^{-3})$

$pH = -(-2.957)$

$pH = 2.957$

88. $N = 1200 + (2500)(\log_{10} d)$

$N = 1200 + (2500)(\log_{10} 100,000)$

$N = 1200 + 12,500$

$N = 13,700$

13,700 sets of software

90. $18,700 = 1200 + (2500)(\log_{10} d)$

$17,500 = 2500 \log_{10} d$

$7 = \log_{10} d$

$10^7 = d$

$10,000,000 = d$

$\$10,000,000$ on advertising

92. $\log_2 \sqrt[4]{2} = x$

$2^x = \sqrt[4]{2}$

$2^x = 2^{1/4}$

$x = \frac{1}{4}$

Cumulative Review Problems

94. $6x + 3y = -6$

x	y
-1	0
0	-2
1	-4

96. $y = -\frac{2}{3}x + 4$

$m = -\frac{2}{3}$

$m_\perp = \frac{3}{2}$

$y - y_1 = m_\perp(x - x_1)$

$y - 1 = \frac{3}{2}[x - (-4)]$

$y - 1 = \frac{3}{2}(x + 4)$

$$y - 1 = \frac{3}{2}x + 6$$

$$y = \frac{3}{2}x + 7$$

98. (a) $C(t) = P(1.04)^t$

$C(5) = 4400(1.04)^5$

$C(5) \approx 5353.27$

$5353.27

(b) $C(t) = P(1.04)^t$

$C(10) = 16,500(1.04)^{10}$

$C(10) \approx 24,424.03$

$24,424.03

11.3 Exercises

2. $\log_4 CD = \log_4 C + \log_4 D$

4. $\log_6(13 \cdot 5) = \log_6 13 + \log_6 5$

6. $\log_b 5d = \log_b 5 + \log_b d$

8. $\log_2\left(\frac{17}{3}\right) = \log_2 17 - \log_2 3$

10. $\log_b\left(\frac{H}{10}\right) = \log_b H - \log_b 10$

12. $\log_6\left(\frac{8}{M}\right) = \log_6 8 - \log_6 M$

14. $\log_5 y^6 = 6\log_5 y$

16. $\log_a B^{-5} = -5\log_a B$

18. $\log_6 \sqrt{z} = \log_6 z^{1/2} = \frac{1}{2}\log_6 z$

20. $\log_3 x^4 \sqrt{y}$

$= \log_3 x^4 + \log_3 \sqrt{y}$

$= 4\log_3 x + \log_3 y^{1/2}$

$= 4\log_3 x + \frac{1}{2}\log_3 y$

22. $\log_8\left(\frac{3y}{x^2}\right)$

$= \log_8 3y - \log_8 x^2$

$= \log_8 3 + \log_8 y - 2\log_8 x$

24. $\log_5\left(\frac{3x^5 \sqrt[3]{y}}{z^4}\right)$

$= \log_5 3x^5 y^{1/3} - \log_5 z^4$

$= \log_5 3 + \log_5 x^5 + \log_5 y^{1/3} - \log_5 z^4$

$= \log_5 3 + 5\log_5 x + \frac{1}{3}\log_5 y - 4\log_5 z$

26. $\log_b \sqrt[4]{\frac{z}{x^2 y^3}}$

$= \log_b\left(\frac{z}{x^2 y^3}\right)^{1/4}$

$= \frac{1}{4}\log_b \frac{z}{x^2 y^3}$

$= \frac{1}{4}[\log_b z - \log_b(x^2 y^3)]$

$= \frac{1}{4}[\log_b z - (\log_b x^2 + \log_b y^3)]$

$= \frac{1}{4}(\log_b z - \log_b x^2 - \log_b y^3)$

$= \frac{1}{4}(\log_b z - 2\log_b x - 3\log_b y)$

$= \frac{1}{4}\log_b z - \frac{1}{2}\log_b x - \frac{3}{4}\log_b y$

28. $\log_e e^{-4} y^3 z$

$= \log_e e^{-4} + \log_e y^3 + \log_e z$

$= -4 + 3\log_e y + \log_e z$

30. $\log_5 7 + \log_5 11 + \log_5 y$

$= \log_5(7)(11)(y) = \log_5 77y$

32. $3\log_8 5 - \log_8 z$

$= \log_8 5^3 - \log_8 z$

$= \log_8 \frac{5^3}{z} = \log_8 \frac{125}{z}$

34. $\frac{3}{4}\log_b x + 2\log_b y - \frac{1}{2}\log_b z$

$= \log_b x^{3/4} + \log_b y^2 - \log_b z^{1/2}$

$= \log_b\left(\frac{x^{3/4} y^2}{z^{1/2}}\right)$

$= \log_b\left(\frac{\sqrt[4]{x^3} y^2}{\sqrt{z}}\right)$

36. $\frac{1}{3}(\log_4 x - \log_4 2 - \log_4 z^2)$

$= \frac{1}{3}\left(\log_4 \frac{x}{2} - \log_4 z^2\right)$

$= \frac{1}{3}\log_4 \frac{\frac{x}{2}}{z^2}$

$= \frac{1}{3}\log_4 \frac{x}{2z^2}$

$= \log_4 \sqrt[3]{\frac{x}{2z^2}}$

38. $\log_7 7 = 1$

40. $\log_{10} 10 = 1$

42. $\log_e 1 = 0$

44. $\log_6 6 + \log_6 1 = 1 + 0 = 1$

46. $\log_9 x = \log_9 5$
$x = 5$

48. $\log_5 8 = \log_5(2x+1)$
$8 = 2x + 1$
$7 = 2x$
$3.5 = x$

50. $\log_8 1 = x$
$8^x = 1$
$8^x = 8^0$
$x = 0$

52. $\log_5 5 = x$
$1 = x$

54. $\log_{10} 10^{-4} = x$
$-4 \log_{10} 10 = x$
$-4 = x$

56. $\log_e e^8 = x$
$8 \log_e e = x$
$8 = x$

58. $\log_{10} x + \log_{10} 5 = 1$
$\log_{10} 5x = 1$
$10^1 = 5x$
$2 = x$

60. $\log_5 1 = \log_5 x - \log_5 8$
$\log_5 1 = \log_5\left(\frac{x}{8}\right)$
$1 = \frac{x}{8}$
$8 = x$

62. $\frac{1}{2}\log_3 x = \log_3 4$
$\log_3 x^{1/2} = \log_3 4$
$x^{1/2} = 4$
$x^{1/2} = 16^{1/2}$
$x = 16$

64. $\log_e x + \log_e 3 = 1$
$\log_e 3x = 1$
$e^1 = 3x$
$\frac{e}{3} = x$

66. $\log_4(x+2) - \log_4(x-2) = 2$
$\log_4 \frac{x+2}{x-2} = 2$
$4^2 = \frac{x+2}{x-2}$
$16 = \frac{x+2}{x-2}$
$16(x-2) = x+2$
$16x - 32 = x + 2$
$15x - 32 = 2$
$15x = 34$
$x = \frac{34}{15}$

68. $\log_{10} A = \log_{10}(1000)(1.12)^x$
$\log_{10} A = \log_{10} 1000 + \log_{10} 1.12^x$
$\log_{10} A = \log_{10} 10^3 + x \log_{10} 1.12$
$\log_{10} A = 3 + x \log_{10} 1.12$
$\log_{10} A - 3 = x \log_{10} 1.12$
$\frac{\log_{10} A - 3}{\log_{10} 1.12} = x$

70. $\log_7 \sqrt[4]{7} + \log_6 \sqrt[12]{6}$

$= \log_7 7^{1/4} + \log_6 6^{1/12}$

$= \dfrac{1}{4} + \dfrac{1}{12}$

$= \dfrac{4}{12}$

$= \dfrac{1}{3}$

72. Let $\log_b M = x$.

Then $b^x = M$.

$(b^x)^p = M^p$

$b^{px} = M^p$

$\log_b M^p = px$

$\log_b M^p = p \log_b M$

74. Let $\log_b b = y$.

Then $b^y = b$.

$b^y = b^1$

$y = 1$

$\log_b b = 1$

Cumulative Review Problems

76. $V = \pi r^2 h$

$\approx (3.14)(2)^2(5)$

$= 62.8$

62.8 m^3

78. $2x - y + z = 3$
$x + 2y + 2z = 1$
$4x + y + 2z = 0$

$\begin{array}{rcl} 4x - 2y + 2z = 6 \\ x + 2y + 2z = 1 \\ \hline 5x \qquad + 4z = 7 \end{array}$ $\qquad$ $\begin{array}{rcl} 2x - y \ + z = 3 \\ 4x + y + 2z = 0 \\ \hline 6x \qquad + 3z = 3 \end{array}$

$\begin{array}{rcl} -15x - 12z = -21 \\ 24x + 12z = \ \ 12 \\ \hline 9x \qquad\ \ = -9 \\ x \qquad\ \ = -1 \end{array}$

$5(-1) + 4z = 7$
$4z = 12$
$z = 3$

$4(-1) + y + 2(3) = 0$
$-4 + y + 6 = 0$
$y + 2 = 0$
$y = -2$
$x = -1, \ y = -2, \ z = 3$
$(-1, -2, 3)$

80. $2.594 \times 10^{12} = 9.36 \times 10^{11}(1 + r)$

$\dfrac{2.594 \times 10^{12}}{9.36 \times 10^{11}} = 1 + r$

$2.771 \approx 1 + r$

$1.771 \approx r$

There was approximately a 177.1% increase for the 14-year period.

Yearly Average Increase:

$2.594 \times 10^{12} = 9.36 \times 10^{11}(1 + r)^{14}$

$\dfrac{2.594 \times 10^{12}}{9.36 \times 10^{11}} = (1 + r)^{14}$

$\left(\dfrac{2.594 \times 10^{12}}{9.36 \times 10^{11}} \right)^{1/14} = 1 + r$

$1.076 \approx 1 + r$

$0.076 \approx r$

$A = 9.36 \times 10^{11}(1 + 0.076)^{20}$

$A \approx 4.051 \times 10^{12}$

The estimated value of the gross national product of Japan in the year 2000 is 4.051×10^{12}.

82. $\dfrac{45}{5} = 9$ miles per second

$\dfrac{65}{9} = 7.\overline{2}$

It will take approximately 7.22 seconds to reach 65 mph from a standstill.

Average speed while braking $= \dfrac{65 + 0}{2} = 32.5$

Distance while braking

$= \dfrac{32.5 \text{ miles}}{\text{hour}} \cdot \dfrac{5280 \text{ ft}}{\text{mile}} \cdot \dfrac{\text{hour}}{3600 \text{ sec}} \cdot 14 \text{ sec}$

$= 667\dfrac{1}{3}$ feet

11.4 Exercises

2. $\log 2.19 \approx 0.340444115$

4. $\log 83.8 \approx 1.923244019$

6. $\log 896 \approx 2.95230801$

8. $\log 78{,}500 \approx 4.894869657$

10. $\log 0.567 \approx -0.246416941$

12. $\log 0.00045 \approx -3.346787486$

14. Error. You cannot take the log of a negative number.

16. $\log x = 0.2480$
$x \approx 1.770108958$

18. $\log x = 0.5922$
$x \approx 3.910209261$

20. $\log x = 1.7896$
$x \approx 61.60273583$

22. $\log x = 3.9576$
$x \approx 9069.847815$

24. $\log x = 5.6274$
$x \approx 424{,}033.3354$

26. $\log x = 0.9974 - 3$
$\log x = -2.0026$
$x \approx 0.009940312$

28. $\log x = -4.0458$
$x \approx 0.000089991$

30. $\log x = 2.1034$
$x \approx 126.8819954$

32. antilog $(4.3894) \approx 24{,}513.19952$

34. antilog $(-2.1773) \approx 0.006648138$

36. $\ln 8.81 \approx 2.17588744$

38. $\ln 88.1 \approx 4.478472533$

40. $\ln 129{,}000 \approx 11.76756768$

42. $\ln 0.0362 \approx -3.31869616$

44. $\ln 1.01 \approx 0.009950331$

46. $\ln x = 0.55$
$x \approx 1.733253018$

48. $\ln x = 4.4$
$x \approx 81.45086867$

50. $\ln x = 12$
$x \approx 162{,}754.7914$

52. $\ln x = -0.18$
$x \approx 0.835270211$

54. $\ln x = -3.8$
$x \approx 0.022370772$

56. $\text{antilog}_e (2.4294) \approx 11.35206879$

58. $\text{antilog}_e (-3.3712) \approx 0.0343483945$

60. $\log_2 6.13 = \dfrac{\log 6.13}{\log 2}$
≈ 2.615887074

62. $\log_8 7.98 = \dfrac{\log 7.98}{\log 8}$
≈ 0.998796249

64. $\log_5 0.173 = \dfrac{\log 0.173}{\log 5}$
≈ -1.090109579

66. $\log_{15} 243 = \dfrac{\log 243}{\log 15}$
≈ 2.028419355

68. $\log_7 0.004462 = \dfrac{\ln 0.004462}{\ln 7}$
≈ -2.7812991

70. $\log_{12} 8534 = \dfrac{\ln 8534}{\ln 12} \approx 3.6427177$

72. $\ln 1537 \approx 7.3375877$

74. $\text{antilog}_e (-1.874) \approx 0.1535084$

76. $\ln x = 7.9631$
$e^{7.9631} = x$
$2872.9654 \approx x$

78. $\log_3 x = 0.5649$
$x = 3^{0.5649}$
$x \approx 1.860055$

80. $y = \log_4 x$

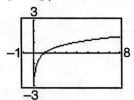

82. $R = \log 56{,}000$
$R \approx 4.75$

84. $6.6 = \log x$
$x = 10^{6.6}$
$\approx 3{,}981{,}000$

Cumulative Review Problems

86. $17x^2 - 7x = 0$
$x(17x - 7) = 0$
$x = 0$ or $17x - 7 = 0$
$$x = \frac{7}{17}$$

88. $2y^2 + 4y - 3 = 0$
$a = 2, b = 4, c = -3$
$$y = \frac{-4 \pm \sqrt{16 - 4(2)(-3)}}{2(2)}$$
$$= \frac{-4 \pm \sqrt{40}}{4}$$
$$= \frac{-4 \pm \sqrt{4}\sqrt{10}}{4}$$
$$= \frac{-4 \pm 2\sqrt{10}}{4} = \frac{-2 \pm \sqrt{10}}{2}$$
$$y = \frac{-2 + \sqrt{10}}{2} \text{ or } y = \frac{-2 - \sqrt{10}}{2}$$

11.5 Exercises

In Exercises 2–24, checks are left to the instructor.

2. $\log_4(x + 2) + \log_4 3 = 2$
$\log_4(x + 2)(3) = 2$
$4^2 = 3(x + 2)$
$16 = 3x + 6$
$10 = 3x$
$$\frac{10}{3} = x$$

4. $\log_2 4 + \log_2(x - 1) = 5$
$\log_2 4(x - 1) = 5$
$2^5 = 4(x - 1)$
$32 = 4x - 4$
$36 = 4x$
$9 = x$

6. $\log_5(3x + 1) = 1 - \log_5 2$
$\log_5(3x + 1) + \log_5 2 = 1$
$\log_5(3x + 1)(2) = 1$
$5^1 = 2(3x + 1)$
$5 = 6x + 2$
$3 = 6x$
$$\frac{1}{2} = x$$

8. $1 + \log x = \log(9x + 1)$
$1 = \log(9x + 1) - \log x$
$$1 = \log\left(\frac{9x + 1}{x}\right)$$
$$10^1 = \frac{9x + 1}{x}$$
$10x = 9x + 1$
$x = 1$

10. $\log_2 x = \log_2(x + 5) - 1$
$\log_2 x - \log_2(x + 5) = -1$
$$\log_2\left(\frac{x}{x + 5}\right) = -1$$
$$2^{-1} = \frac{x}{x + 5}$$
$$\frac{1}{2} = \frac{x}{x + 5}$$
$x + 5 = 2x$
$5 = x$

12. $\log_3(x + 6) + \log_3 x = 3$
$\log_3(x + 6)(x) = 3$
$3^3 = x(x + 6)$
$27 = x^2 + 6x$
$0 = x^2 + 6x - 27$
$0 = (x + 9)(x - 3)$
$x + 9 = 0$ or $x - 3 = 0$
$x = -9$ or $x = 3$
$x = -9$ leads to the log of a negative number, so the only solution is $x = 3$.

14. $\log_4(x - 3) + \log_4(x + 3) = 2$
$\log_4(x - 3)(x + 3) = 2$
$4^2 = (x - 3)(x + 3)$
$16 = x^2 - 9$
$25 = x^2$
$x = 5$ or $x = -5$
$x = -5$ leads to the log of a negative number, so the only solution is $x = 5$.

16. $\log_5(2x) - \log_5(x - 3) = 3\log_5 2$
$$\log_5\left(\frac{2x}{x - 3}\right) = \log_5 2^3$$
$$\frac{2x}{x - 3} = 8$$
$2x = 8x - 24$
$-6x = -24$
$x = 4$

18. $\log_3(x-1)-3=\log_3(2x+1)$

$-3=\log_3(2x+1)-\log_3(x-1)$

$-3=\log_3\dfrac{2x+1}{x-1}$

$3^{-3}=\dfrac{2x+1}{x-1}$

$\dfrac{1}{27}=\dfrac{2x+1}{x-1}$

$x-1=27(2x+1)$

$x-1=54x+27$

$-1=53x+27$

$-28=53x$

$x=-\dfrac{28}{53}$ leads to the log of a negative number.

No solution.

20. $\log x+\log(x-1)=\log 12$

$\log x(x-1)=\log 12$

$x(x-1)=12$

$x^2-x=12$

$x^2-x-12=0$

$(x-4)(x+3)=0$

$x-4=0$ or $x+3=0$

$x=4$ or $x=-3$

$x=-3$ leads to the log of a negative number, so the only solution is $x=4$.

22. $\log_7(2x-1)=\log_7(x+2)+\log_7(x-2)$

$\log_7(2x-1)=\log_7(x+2)(x-2)$

$2x-1=(x+2)(x-2)$

$2x-1=x^2-4$

$0=x^2-2x-3$

$0=(x-3)(x+1)$

$x-3=0$ or $x+1=0$

$x=3$ or $x=-1$

$x=-1$ leads to the log of a negative number, so the only solution is $x=3$.

24. $\log(x-3)=\log(3x-8)-\log x$

$\log(x-3)=\log\dfrac{3x-8}{x}$

$x-3=\dfrac{3x-8}{x}$

$x^2-3x=3x-8$

$x^2-6x+8=0$

$(x-4)(x-2)=0$

$x-4=0$ or $x-2=0$

$x=4$ or $x=2$

$x=2$ leads to the log of a negative number, so the only solution is $x=4$.

26. $9^x=11$

$\log 9^x=\log 11$

$x\log 9=\log 11$

$x=\dfrac{\log 11}{\log 9}$

28. $4^{x+2}=7$

$\log 4^{x+2}=\log 7$

$(x+2)\log 4=\log 7$

$x+2=\dfrac{\log 7}{\log 4}$

$x=\dfrac{\log 7}{\log 4}-2$ or $\dfrac{\log 7-2\log 4}{\log 4}$

30. $5^{2x-1}=11$

$\log 5^{2x-1}=\log 11$

$(2x-1)\log 5=\log 11$

$2x-1=\dfrac{\log 11}{\log 5}$

$2x=\dfrac{\log 11}{\log 5}+1$

$2x=\dfrac{\log 11+\log 5}{\log 5}$

$x=\dfrac{\log 11+\log 5}{2\log 5}$

32. $e^{3x}=55$

$\ln e^{3x}=\ln 55$

$3x\ln e=\ln 55$

$3x=\ln 55$

$x=\dfrac{\ln 55}{3}$

34. $8^{3x+1}=26$

$\log 8^{3x+1}=\log 26$

$(3x+1)\log 8=\log 26$

$3x+1=\dfrac{\log 26}{\log 8}$

$3x=\dfrac{\log 26}{\log 8}-1$

$3x=\dfrac{\log 26-\log 8}{\log 8}$

$x=\dfrac{\log 26-\log 8}{3\log 8}$

$x\approx 0.189$

36. $3^x = 2^{x+3}$

$\log 3^x = \log 2^{x+3}$

$x \log 3 = (x+3) \log 2$

$x \log 3 = x \log 2 + 3 \log 2$

$x \log 3 - x \log 2 = 3 \log 2$

$x(\log 3 - \log 2) = 3 \log 2$

$x = \dfrac{3 \log 2}{\log 3 - \log 2}$

≈ 5.129

38. $9^x = 7^{x+3}$

$\log 9^x = \log 7^{x+3}$

$x \log 9 = (x+3) \log 7$

$x \log 9 = x \log 7 + 3 \log 7$

$x \log 9 - x \log 7 = 3 \log 7$

$x(\log 9 - \log 7) = 3 \log 7$

$x = \dfrac{3 \log 7}{\log 9 - \log 7}$

$x \approx 23.229$

40. $e^{x+1} = 17$

$\ln(e^{x+1}) = \ln 17$

$(x+1) \ln e = \ln 17$

$x + 1 = \ln 17$

$x = \ln 17 - 1$

$x \approx 1.833$

42. $e^{-x} = 0.18$

$\ln e^{-x} = \ln 0.18$

$-x \ln e = \ln 0.18$

$-x = \ln 0.18$

$x = -\ln 0.18$

$x \approx 1.715$

44. $37 = e^{3x-2}$

$\ln 37 = \ln e^{3x-2}$

$\ln 37 = (3x - 2) \ln e$

$\ln 37 = 3x - 2$

$(\ln 37) + 2 = 3x$

$\dfrac{(\ln 37) + 2}{3} = x$

$x \approx 1.870$

46. $5000 = 1500(1 + 0.08)^t$

$\dfrac{10}{3} = (1.08)^t$

$\log \dfrac{10}{3} = \log 1.08^t$

$\log \dfrac{10}{3} = t \log 1.08$

$\dfrac{\log 10 - \log 3}{\log 1.08} = t$

$16 \approx t$

16 years

48. $3P = P(1 + 0.06)^t$

$3 = (1.06)^t$

$\log 3 = \log (1.06)^t$

$\log 3 = t \log (1.06)$

$t = \dfrac{\log 3}{\log (1.06)}$

$t \approx 19$

19 years

50. $3600 = 3000(1 + r)^3$

$1.2 = (1 + r)^3$

$\log 1.2 = \log (1 + r)^3$

$\log 1.2 = 3 \log (1 + r)$

$\dfrac{\log 1.2}{3} = \log (1 + r)$

$10^{\frac{\log 1.2}{3}} = 1 + r$

$0.0263937 \approx \log (1 + r)$

$10^{0.0263937} \approx \log (1 + r)$

$1.0626586 \approx 1 + r$

$0.0626586 \approx r$

6.3%

52. $A = A_0 e^{rt}$

$9 = 6e^{(0.02)t}$

$\dfrac{3}{2} = e^{(0.02)t}$

$\ln\left(\dfrac{3}{2}\right) = \ln e^{(0.02)t}$

$\ln 3 - \ln 2 = (0.02)t$

$t = \dfrac{\ln 3 - \ln 2}{0.02}$

$t \approx 20$

20 years

54. $A = A_0 e^{rt}$

$4A_0 = A_0 e^{0.02t}$

$4 = e^{0.02t}$

$\ln 4 = \ln e^{0.02t}$

$\ln 4 = 0.02t$

$\dfrac{\ln 4}{0.02} = t$

$69 \approx t$

69 years

56. $A = A_0 e^{rt}$

$2A_0 = A_0 e^{0.03t}$

$2 = e^{0.03t}$

$\ln 2 = \ln e^{0.03t}$

$\ln 2 = 0.03t$

$\dfrac{\ln 2}{0.03} = t$

$23 \approx t$

23 years

58. $A = A_0 e^{rt}$

$120,000 = 80,000 e^{0.015t}$

$1.5 = e^{0.015t}$

$\ln 1.5 = \ln e^{0.015t}$

$\ln 1.5 = 0.015t$

$\dfrac{\ln 1.5}{0.015} = t$

$27 \approx t$

27 years

60. $A = A_0 e^{rt}$

$4.5 = 3.5 e^{0.015t}$

$\dfrac{9}{7} = e^{0.015t}$

$\ln \dfrac{9}{7} = \ln e^{0.015t}$

$\ln 9 - \ln 7 = 0.015t$

$\dfrac{\ln 9 - \ln 7}{0.015} = t$

$17 \approx t$

17 years

62. $A = A_0 e^{rt}$

$2.0 = 1.3 e^{0.075t}$

$\dfrac{2.0}{1.3} = e^{0.075t}$

$\ln\left(\dfrac{2.0}{1.3}\right) = \ln e^{0.075t}$

$\ln 2.0 - \ln 1.3 = 0.075t$

$\dfrac{\ln 2.0 - \ln 1.3}{0.075} = t \quad 5.7 \approx t$

Approximately 6 years

64. $7.1 = \log\left(\dfrac{I_U}{I_O}\right) \qquad 8.2 = \log\left(\dfrac{I_{JR}}{I_O}\right)$

$7.1 - 8.2 = \log\left(\dfrac{I_U}{I_O}\right) - \log\left(\dfrac{I_{JR}}{I_O}\right)$

$-1.1 = \log\left(\dfrac{\frac{I_U}{I_O}}{\frac{I_{JR}}{I_O}}\right)$

$-1.1 = \log \dfrac{I_U}{I_{JR}}$

$10^{-1.1} = \dfrac{I_u}{I_{JR}}$

$I_{JR} = \dfrac{I_U}{10^{-1.1}}$

$I_{JR} \approx 12.6 I_U$

It was approximately 12.6 times greater.

66. $8.9 = \log\left(\dfrac{I_J}{I_O}\right) \qquad 6.7 = \log\left(\dfrac{I_T}{I_O}\right)$

$8.9 - 6.7 = \log\left(\dfrac{I_J}{I_O}\right) - \log\left(\dfrac{I_T}{I_O}\right)$

$2.2 = \log \dfrac{\frac{I_J}{I_O}}{\frac{I_T}{I_O}}$

$2.2 = \log \dfrac{I_J}{I_T}$

$10^{2.2} = \dfrac{I_J}{I_T}$

$158 \approx \dfrac{I_J}{I_T}$

$I_J \approx 158 I_T$

I_J is approximately 158 times greater than I_T.

68. $y_1 = 300e^{0.12x}$
$y_2 = 750 + 100x$

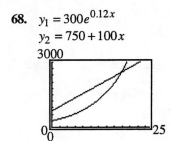

The intersection of the two graphs is at about $x = 17.8$, $y = 2525.3$. The two populations will become equal in approximately 17.8 years.

Cumulative Review Problems

70. $\sqrt[3]{81x^6y^9} = \sqrt[3]{27x^6y^9 \cdot 3}$
$= 3x^2y^3\sqrt[3]{3}$

72. $2\sqrt{50x} + 3\sqrt{72x} - 4\sqrt{128x}$
$= 10\sqrt{2x} + 18\sqrt{2x} - 32\sqrt{2x}$
$= -4\sqrt{2x}$

Putting Your Skills to Work

2. $P = P_0e^{rt}$
$P = P_0e^{0.0277t}$

4. $y = 3000e^{0.0277x}$

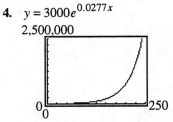

6. $t = 2(60) = 120$
$P = 2,313,700e^{0.003851(120)}$
$P \approx 3,672,800$
Approximately 3,672,800 bacteria

8. $3000 = 3,672,800(0.80)^x$
$$\frac{3000}{3,672,800} = 0.80^x$$
$$\ln\frac{3000}{3,672,800} = x\ln 0.80$$
$$x = \frac{\ln 3000 - \ln 3,672,800}{\ln 0.80}$$
$x \approx 32$
$32 + 6 = 38$
It will approximately 38 hours since the patient was admitted.

Chapter 11 Review Problems

2. $f(x) = e^{x-3}$

x	y
0	0.05
2	0.4
3	1
4	2.7
5	7.4

4. $\dfrac{1}{32} = 2^{-5}$
$$\log_2\frac{1}{32} = -5$$

6. $\log_3 x = -2$
$3^{-2} = x$
$$\frac{1}{9} = x$$

8. $\log_7 w = -1$
$7^{-1} = w$
$$\frac{1}{7} = w$$

10. $\log_w 27 = 3$
$w^3 = 27$
$w^3 = 3^3$
$w = 3$

12. $\log_{10} 1000 = x$
$10^x = 1000$
$10^x = 10^3$
$x = 3$

14. $\log_2\left(\dfrac{1}{4}\right) = x$
$$2^x = \frac{1}{4}$$

$$2^x = \frac{1}{2^2}$$
$$2^x = 2^{-2}$$
$$x = -2$$

16. $\log_3 x = y$
$$3^y = x$$

x	y
$\frac{1}{9}$	-2
$\frac{1}{3}$	-1
1	0
3	1
9	2

18. $\log_2\left(\dfrac{5x}{\sqrt{w}}\right) = \log_2 5x - \log_2 w^{1/2}$

$$= \log_2 5 + \log_2 x - \frac{1}{2}\log_2 w$$

20. $4\log_8 w - \dfrac{1}{3}\log_8 z$

$$= \log_8 w^4 - \log_8 z^{1/3}$$

$$= \log_8 \frac{w^4}{z^{1/3}}$$

$$= \log_8 \frac{w^4}{\sqrt[3]{z}}$$

22. $\log_8 x + \log_8 3 = \log_8 75$
$$\log_8 3x = \log_8 75$$
$$3x = 75$$
$$x = 25$$

24. $\log 23.8 = 1.376576957$

26. $\ln 3.92 = 1.366091654$

28. $\log n = 1.1367$
$$n = \text{antilog } 1.1367$$
$$n = 13.69935122$$

30. $\log_8 2.81 = \dfrac{\log 2.81}{\log 8} = 0.49685671$

For Exercises 32–38, checks are left to the instructor.

32. $\log_3(2x+3) = \log_3(2) - 3$
$$\log_3(2x+3) - \log_3 2 = -3$$
$$\log_3 \frac{2x+3}{2} = -3$$
$$3^{-3} = \frac{2x+3}{2}$$
$$\frac{1}{27} = \frac{2x+3}{2}$$
$$2 = 27(2x+3)$$
$$2 = 54x + 81$$
$$-79 = 54x$$
$$-\frac{79}{54} = x$$

34. $\log_5(x+1) - \log_5 8 = \log_5 x$
$$\log_5 \frac{x+1}{8} = \log_5 x$$
$$\frac{x+1}{8} = x$$
$$x + 1 = 8x$$
$$1 = 7x$$
$$\frac{1}{7} = x$$

36. $\log_2(x-2) + \log_2(x+5) = 3$
$$\log_2(x-2)(x+5) = 3$$
$$2^3 = (x-2)(x+5)$$
$$8 = x^2 + 3x - 10$$
$$0 = x^2 + 3x - 18$$
$$0 = (x+6)(x-3)$$
$$x + 6 = 0 \text{ or } x - 3 = 0$$
$$x = -6 \text{ or } x = 3$$
$x = -6$ leads to the log of a negative number, so the only solution is $x = 3$.

38. $\log(2t+4) - \log(3t+1) = \log 6$
$$\log \frac{2t+4}{3t+1} = \log 6$$
$$\frac{2t+4}{3t+1} = 6$$
$$2t + 4 = 6(3t+1)$$
$$2t + 4 = 18t + 6$$
$$4 = 16t + 6$$
$$-2 = 16t$$
$$-\frac{1}{8} = t$$

40. $5^x = 4^{x+2}$

$\log 5^x = \log 4^{x+2}$

$x \log 5 = (x+2) \log 4$

$x \log 5 = x \log 4 + 2 \log 4$

$x \log 5 - x \log 4 = 2 \log 4$

$x(\log 5 - \log 4) = 2 \log 4$

$x = \dfrac{2 \log 4}{\log 5 - \log 4}$

42. $16e^{x+1} = 56$

$e^{x+1} = 3.5$

$\ln e^{x+1} = \ln 3.5$

$x + 1 = \ln 3.5$

$x = -1 + \ln 3.5$

44. $3^{x+1} = 7$

$\log 3^{x+1} = \log 7$

$(x+1) \log 3 = \log 7$

$x + 1 = \dfrac{\log 7}{\log 3}$

$x = \dfrac{\log 7}{\log 3} - 1$

$x \approx 0.7712$

46. $(1.03)^x = 20$

$\log(1.03)^x = \log 20$

$x \log 1.03 = \log 20$

$x = \dfrac{\log 20}{\log 1.03}$

$x \approx 101.3482$

48. $A = P(1+r)^t$

$2P = P(1+0.08)^t$

$2 = (1.08)^t$

$\log 2 = \log(1.08)^t$

$\log 2 = t \log 1.08$

$\dfrac{\log 2}{\log 1.08} = t$

$9 \approx t$

9 years

50. $A_R = 3500(1+0.05)^t$

$A_B = 3500(1+0.06)^t$

$A_R = A_B - 500$

$3500(1.05)^t = 3500(1.06)^t - 500$

$(1.05)^t = (1.06)^t - \dfrac{1}{7}$

Use guess and check method.

$t \approx 9$

9 years

52. $A = A_0 e^{rt}$

$10 = 6e^{0.02t}$

$\dfrac{5}{3} = e^{0.02t}$

$\ln \dfrac{5}{3} = \ln e^{0.02t}$

$\ln \dfrac{5}{3} = 0.02t$

$\dfrac{\ln 5 - \ln 3}{0.02} = t$

$26 \approx t$

26 years

54. $A = A_0 e^{rt}$

$2600 = 2000e^{0.03t}$

$1.3 = e^{0.03t}$

$\ln 1.3 = 0.03t$

$\dfrac{\ln 1.3}{0.03} = t$

$9 \approx t$

9 years

56. **(a)** $W = p_0 V_0 \ln\left(\dfrac{V_1}{V_0}\right)$

    $= 40(15) \ln\left(\dfrac{24}{15}\right)$

    ≈ 282

  (b) $100 = p_0(8) \ln\left(\dfrac{40}{8}\right)$

    $100 = p_0(8 \ln 5)$

    $\dfrac{100}{8 \ln 5} = p_0$

    $7.77 \approx p_0$

Chapter 11 Test

2. $4^{x+3} = 64$

  $4^{x+3} = 4^3$

  $x + 3 = 3$

  $x = 0$

4. $\log_w 125 = 3$

  $w^3 = 125$

  $w^3 = 5^3$

  $w = 5$

6. $\log 23.6 \approx 1.3729$

8. $\log_3 1.62 = \dfrac{\log 1.62}{\log 3}$

≈ 0.4391

10. $\ln x = 0.14$
$x = \text{antilog}_e \, 0.14$
$x = 1.150273799$

12. $\log_8 (x+3) - \log_8 2x = \log_8 4$

$\log_8 \dfrac{x+3}{2x} = \log_8 4$

$\dfrac{x+3}{2x} = 4$

$x + 3 = 8x$
$3 = 7x$
$\dfrac{3}{7} = x$

Check is left to the instructor.

14. $5^{3x+6} = 17$

$\log 5^{3x+6} = \log 17$

$(3x+6) \log 5 = \log 17$

$3x + 6 = \dfrac{\log 17}{\log 5}$

$3x = \dfrac{\log 17}{\log 5} - 6$

$3x = \dfrac{\log 17 - 6 \log 5}{\log 5}$

$x = \dfrac{\log 17 - 6 \log 5}{3 \log 5}$

$x \approx -1.4132$

16. $A = P_0 (1+r)^t$

$2P_0 = P_0 (1 + 0.05)^t$

$2 = (1.05)^t$

$\log 2 = \log (1.05)^t$

$\log 2 = t \log 1.05$

$\dfrac{\log 2}{\log 1.05} = t$

$14 \approx t$
14 years

Cumulative Test for Chapters 1–11

2. $H = 3bx - 2ay$
$H + 2ay = 3bx$
$\dfrac{H + 2ay}{3b} = x$

4. $5ax + 5ay - 7wx - 7wy$
$= 5a(x+y) - 7w(x+y)$
$= (x+y)(5a - 7w)$

6. $(5\sqrt{2} + \sqrt{3})(\sqrt{5} - 2\sqrt{6})$
$= 5\sqrt{10} - 10\sqrt{12} + \sqrt{15} - 2\sqrt{18}$
$= 5\sqrt{10} - 20\sqrt{3} + \sqrt{15} - 6\sqrt{2}$

8. $2x - y = 4$
$4x - y^2 = 0$
$-4x + 2y = -8$
$\underline{4x - y^2 = 0}$
$-y^2 + 2y = -8$
$0 = y^2 - 2y - 8$
$0 = (y-4)(y+2)$
$y - 4 = 0 \text{ or } y + 2 = 0$
$y = 4 \text{ or } y = -2$

$2x - 4 = 4$	or	$2x - (-2) = 4$
$2x = 8$	or	$2x = 2$
$x = 4,$		$x = 1$

$x = 4, \, y = 4; \, x = 1, \, y = -2$

10. $\dfrac{5}{\sqrt[3]{2xy^2}} = \dfrac{5}{\sqrt[3]{2xy^2}} \cdot \dfrac{\sqrt[3]{2^2 x^2 y}}{\sqrt[3]{2^2 x^2 y}}$

$= \dfrac{5\sqrt[3]{4x^2 y}}{2xy}$

12. $5^{2x-1} = 25$
$5^{2x-1} = 5^2$
$2x - 1 = 2$
$2x = 3$
$x = \dfrac{3}{2}$

14. $\log 2.53 = 0.403120521$

16. $\log_3 7 = \dfrac{\log 7}{\log 3}$
$= 1.771243749$

18.
$$\log_9 x = 1 - \log_9(x-8)$$
$$\log_9 x + \log_9(x-8) = 1$$
$$\log_9 x(x-8) = 1$$
$$9^1 = x(x-8)$$
$$9 = x^2 - 8x$$
$$0 = x^2 - 8x - 9$$
$$0 = (x-9)(x+1)$$
$$x - 9 = 0 \text{ or } x + 1 = 0$$
$$x = 9, \; x = -1$$
$x = -1$ leads to the log of a negative number, so the only solution is $x = 9$.

20.
$$3^{x+2} = 5$$
$$\log 3^{x+2} = \log 5$$
$$(x+2)\log 3 = \log 5$$
$$x + 2 = \frac{\log 5}{\log 3}$$
$$x = \frac{\log 5}{\log 3} - 2$$
$$x \approx -0.535$$

22.
$$A = P_0(1+r)^t$$
$$= 3000(1 + 0.09)^4$$
$$= 3000(1.09)^4$$
$$\approx 4234.74$$
$$\$4234.74$$

Practice Final Examination

2.
$$\left(\frac{2x^3 y^{-2}}{3x^4 y^{-3}}\right)^{-2} = \frac{2^{-2} x^{-6} y^4}{3^{-2} x^{-8} y^6}$$
$$= \frac{3^2 x^8}{2^2 x^6 y^2}$$
$$= \frac{9x^2}{4y^2}$$

4.
$$3[2x - 5(x+y)] = 3(2x - 5x - 5y)$$
$$= 3(-3x - 5y)$$
$$= -9x - 15y$$

6.
$$\frac{1}{3}y - 4 = \frac{1}{2}y + 1$$
$$6\left(\frac{1}{3}y\right) - 6(4) = 6\left(\frac{1}{2}y\right) + 6(1)$$
$$2y - 24 = 3y + 6$$
$$-24 = y + 6$$
$$-30 = y$$

8.
$$\left|\frac{2}{3}x - 4\right| = 2$$
$$\frac{2}{3}x - 4 = 2 \text{ or } \frac{2}{3}x - 4 = -2$$
$$\frac{2}{3}x = 6 \quad \text{or} \quad \frac{2}{3}x = 2$$
$$x = 9 \quad \text{or} \quad x = 3$$

10. width: x
length: $2x - 200$

$$2(x) + 2(2x - 200) = 1760$$
$$2x + 4x - 400 = 1760$$
$$6x - 400 = 1760$$
$$6x = 2160$$
$$x = 360$$
$$2x - 200 = 2(360) - 200 = 520$$
Length = 520 m; width = 360 m

12.
$$x + 5 \le -4 \text{ or } 2 - 7x \le 16$$
$$x \le -9 \text{ or } -7x \le 14$$
$$x \ge -2$$
$$x \le -9 \text{ or } x \ge -2$$

14. $7x - 2y = -14$

x	y
0	7
-2	0

16. $m = \dfrac{5 - (-3)}{1 - (-2)} = \dfrac{8}{3}$

18.
$$f(x) = 3x^2 - 4x - 3$$
$$f(3) = 3(3)^2 - 4(3) - 3$$
$$= 27 - 12 - 3$$
$$= 12$$

20. $f(x) = |2x - 2|$

x	$f(x)$
-1	4
0	2
1	0
2	2
3	4

22. $4x - 3y = 12$
$3x - 4y = 2$

$12x - 9y = 36$
$\underline{-12x + 16y = -8}$
$7y = 28$
$y = 4$

$3x - 4(4) = 2$
$3x - 16 = 2$
$3x = 18$
$x = 6$

$x = 6,\ y = 4$

24. $y + z = 2$
$x + z = 5$
$x + y = 5$

$-x - z = -5$
$\underline{x + y = \ \ 5}$
$y - z = \ \ 0$

$y - z = 0$
$\underline{y + z = 2}$
$2y = 2$
$y = 1$

$1 + z = 2$
$z = 1$

$x + 1 = 5$
$x = 4$

$x = 4,\ y = 1,\ z = 1$

26. $3y \geq 8x - 12$
$2x + 3y \leq -6$

28.

$$5x + 1 \overline{)\ 25x^3 + 0x^2 + 9x + 2\ } \quad \frac{5x^2 - x + 2}{}$$

$$\underline{25x^3 + 5x^2}$$
$$-5x^2 + 9x$$
$$\underline{-5x^2 - \ x}$$
$$10x + 2$$
$$\underline{10x + 2}$$
$$0$$

$(25x^3 + 9x + 2) \div (5x + 1) = 5x^2 - x + 2$

30. $x^3 + 2x^2 - 4x - 8$
$= x^2(x + 2) - 4(x + 2)$
$= (x + 2)(x^2 - 4)$
$= (x + 2)(x - 2)(x + 2)$

32. $x^2 + 15x + 54 = 0$
$(x + 9)(x + 6) = 0$
$x + 9 = 0$ or $x + 6 = 0$
$x = -9,\ x = -6$

34. $\dfrac{x^2 - 9}{2x^2 + 7x + 3} \div \dfrac{x^2 - 3x}{2x^2 + 11x + 5}$

$= \dfrac{x^2 - 9}{2x^2 + 7x + 3} \cdot \dfrac{2x^2 + 11x + 5}{x^2 - 3x}$

$= \dfrac{(x + 3)(x - 3)}{(2x + 1)(x + 3)} \cdot \dfrac{(2x + 1)(x + 5)}{x(x - 3)}$

$= \dfrac{x + 5}{x}$

36. $\dfrac{\frac{3}{2x+1}+2}{1-\frac{2}{4x^2-1}}$

$= \dfrac{\frac{3}{2x+1}+2}{1-\frac{2}{(2x+1)(2x-1)}}$

$= \dfrac{\frac{3}{2x+1}+2}{1-\frac{2}{(2x+1)(2x-1)}} \cdot \dfrac{(2x+1)(2x-1)}{(2x+1)(2x-1)}$

$= \dfrac{3(2x-1)+2(2x+1)(2x-1)}{1(2x+1)(2x-1)-2}$

$= \dfrac{6x-3+2(4x^2-1)}{4x^2-1-2}$

$= \dfrac{6x-3+8x^2-2}{4x^2-3}$

$= \dfrac{8x^2+6x-5}{4x^2-3}$

38. $\dfrac{5x^{-4}y^{-2}}{15x^{-1/2}y^3}$

$= \dfrac{1}{3}x^{-4-(-1/2)}y^{-2-3}$

$= \dfrac{1}{3}x^{-7/2}y^{-5}$

$= \dfrac{1}{3x^{7/2}y^5}$

40. $5\sqrt{2}-3\sqrt{50}+4\sqrt{98}$

$= 5\sqrt{2}-3\sqrt{25\cdot2}+4\sqrt{49\cdot2}$

$= 5\sqrt{2}-15\sqrt{2}+28\sqrt{2}$

$= 18\sqrt{2}$

42. $i^3+\sqrt{-25}+\sqrt{-16}$

$= -i+5i+4i$

$= 8i$

44. $y = kx^2$

$15 = k(2)^2$

$15 = 4k$

$\dfrac{15}{4} = k$

$y = \dfrac{15}{4}x^2$

$= \dfrac{15}{4}(3)^2$

$= \dfrac{135}{4}$ or 33.75

46. $5x^2-9x = -12x$

$5x^2+3x = 0$

$x(5x+3) = 0$

$x = 0$ or $5x+3 = 0$

                         $5x = -3$

                         $x = -\dfrac{3}{5}$

48. width: x

length: $3x+1$

$x(3x+1) = 52$

$3x^2+x = 52$

$3x^2+x-52 = 0$

$(3x+13)(x-4) = 0$

$3x+13 = 0$ or $x-4 = 0$

$3x = -13$ $x = 4$

$x = -\dfrac{13}{3}$

Since $x > 0$, $x = 4$ and $3x+1 = 3(4)+1 = 13$.

Length = 13 cm; width = 4 cm

50. $3x^2-11x-4 \geq 0$

$3x^2-11x-4 = 0$

$(3x+1)(x-4) = 0$

$3x+1 = 0$ or $x-4 = 0$

$3x = -1$ $x = 4$

$x = -\dfrac{1}{3}$

Region I: Test $x = -1$

$3(-1)^2-11(-1)-4 = 10 > 0$

Region II: Test $x = 0$

$3(0)^2-11(0)-4 = -4 < 0$

Region III: Test $x = 5$

$3(5)^2-11(5)-4 = 16 > 0$

$x \leq -\dfrac{1}{3}$ or $x \geq 4$

52. $\dfrac{x^2}{16}+\dfrac{y^2}{25} = 1$

$a^2 = 16$ $b^2 = 25$

$a = 4$ $b = 5$

Ellipse, center (0, 0)

54. $x = (y-3)^2 + 5$

Parabola opening right, vertex (5, 3)

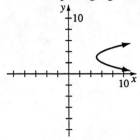

56. $f(x) = 3x^2 - 2x + 5$

(a) $f(-1) = 3(-1)^2 - 2(-1) + 5 = 3 + 2 + 5 = 10$

(b) $f(a) = 3a^2 - 2a + 5$

(c) $f(a+2)$
$= 3(a+2)^2 - 2(a+2) + 5$
$= 3(a^2 + 4a + 4) - 2a - 4 + 5$
$= 3a^2 + 12a + 12 - 2a + 1$
$= 3a^2 + 10a + 13$

58. $f(x) = \dfrac{1}{2}x - 7$

$y = \dfrac{1}{2}x - 7$

Inverse:

$x = \dfrac{1}{2}y - 7$

$x + 7 = \dfrac{1}{2}y$

$2(x + 7) = y$

$y = 2x + 14$

$f^{-1}(x) = 2x + 14$

60. $f(x) = 2^{1-x}$

x	$f(x)$
-1	4
0	2
1	1

62. $\log_4(3x + 1) = 3$
$4^3 = 3x + 1$
$64 = 3x + 1$
$63 = 3x$
$21 = x$

64. $\log_2 6 + \log_2 x = 4 + \log_2(x - 5)$
$\log_2 6x - \log_2(x - 5) = 4$

$\log_2 \dfrac{6x}{x - 5} = 4$

$2^4 = \dfrac{6x}{x - 5}$

$16(x - 5) = 6x$
$16x - 80 = 6x$
$-80 = -10x$
$8 = x$